Control of Manu

LEVEL 3

DAVID EVANS, BA, DipM, AInstM, MISM
Senior Lecturer in Management Studies

and

ROY FORD, CEng, MIMechE, MRAeS, Cert. Ed.
Lecturer in Aero and Mechanical Engineering

West Oxfordshire Technical College

HOLT, RINEHART AND WINSTON
LONDON · NEW YORK · SYDNEY · TORONTO

Holt, Rinehart and Winston Ltd: 1 St Anne's Road,
Eastbourne, East Sussex BN21 3UN

British Library Cataloguing in Publication Data

Evans, David
Control of manufacture.—(Holt technician
texts) Level 3
1. Engineering—Management
I. Title   II. Ford, Roy
620′.0068   TA190

ISBN 0-03-910424-9

Typeset by Photo-Graphics, Honiton, Devon.
Printed in Great Britain by Mackays of Chatham Ltd.

Last digit is print number: 9 8 7 6 5 4 3 2 1

Contents

About This Book and How to Use It

The book

This book has several significant features:

1. It follows closely the order and sequence of topics set out in the BTEC Standard Unit Control of Manufacture Level 3.
2. Its scope is broad enough to apply to those working in a wide range of manufacturing concerns.
3. Examples are drawn from situations likely to be readily understood by most students.

How to use it

Students

1. Each chapter should be studied until the content has been understood. Any points which raise queries should be discussed with your lecturer or tutor.
2. You should then tackle the questions and exercises at the end of each chapter, as set by your lecturer or tutor.

Lecturers

1. The questions at the conclusion of each chapter can be discussed orally, either by asking individual students to reply or in small groups, or even by the class as a whole. Where time permits, one or more discussion topics can be considered.
2. The case studies can also be used in various ways. Set as individual assignments, a written 'homework' answer can be required, or one or more case studies could be included in a progress test. By discussing the cases in small groups, or even considering the cases in class, social and communication skills can be developed, especially by ensuring that each group elects a chairperson, a secretary and a group spokesperson for report-back sessions.

Preface

The various sections in this book aim to cover the list of topic areas included in the recently revised BTEC's Standard Unit Control of Manufacture Level 3. The overall objectives of the unit (and hence of this book) are basically to give students an awareness of the management structure and the organisation of the production and planning functions in a manufacturing concern. Implicit in such an appreciation is some understanding of the constraints and problems which could be faced by the managers of a planning and manufacturing process.

This BTEC unit, as laid out, combines both theory and practice. This dual approach is reflected in the layout of the chapters in the book: first, individual concepts are defined, explained and analysed in the text, followed (after summaries and review questions) by a series of practical, work-related activities, assignments and case studies. Rather less use is made in this text of discussion topics than in general management texts, as with only 60 contact hours allowed for the unit, there will be less time available to make use of them. Nevertheless, where appropriate, a few have been included.

Both authors have had long connections with engineering/manufacturing industries. They bring with them an intimate knowledge of the planning and production aspects outlined in the book.

The co-operation of the publishers is acknowledged in permitting certain material (albeit somewhat modified and revised) to be included from *Supervisory Management* by David Evans, first published in 1981.

DAVID EVANS
ROY FORD

Acknowledgements

We express our grateful thanks to all who provided encouragement, help and criticism during the preparation of this book. In particular we thank Bryn Hitchings of Gloucester College of Art and Technology for advice, Bernard Caswell of Oxford Polytechnic for references to work study, production planning and control, the publishers' reviewers and their staff, especially Simon Lake and Chris Coyer.

The British Standards Institution were kind enough to permit us to quote from their publications, and Compton (Headdress and Gloves) Ltd of Witney gave us facilities to study their production processes.

Finally we acknowledge the support of our families, and especially of our wives Wendy and Barbara, who helped with the typing.

1
The Functions of Management

1.1 Introduction

In this section is a detailed examination of the structure of organisations and the various divisions/sections/departments/functions into which organisations can be split. After an overview of *all* the functions likely to be found in a manufacturing concern, there follows a discussion on the production/manufacturing function, which will have to be carefully defined.

Inevitably we shall tend to concentrate on the medium- to large-sized enterprise, because in the main it is only in such enterprises that the division into separate sub-functions (such as quality control as a distinct department) can be found, or indeed afforded. However, we must not lose sight of the fact that many large and flourishing concerns started life as very small family, or even one-person, businesses. Thus in the earlier years of the business the owner was not only the decision-maker but also sales representative, accountant and operative all rolled into one.

Gradually, however, the different functions became too much for one person to cope with and others had to be brought into the firm; jobs were then *delegated* or handed over to the new employees. In time, due to the increased need for *specialisation*, different activities became separate *departments* or divisions. Later still, they became even more complex, necessitating splitting into further sub-divisions as the technology advanced and techniques for information-handling improved. What were previously the activities of the owner/manager were now split up among separate departments, each emphasising one or more of these basic functions.

To achieve a better understanding of the role and function of the different elements of the production function it will be necessary first to examine closely the functions of managers and supervisors.

1.2 Fayol's five managerial activities

Henri Fayol (1841–1925) was an engineer who worked with a French mining and metal-producing firm, and after working his way up the managerial ladder became (and remained for 30 years) its managing director. We shall discuss some of his 14 principles of management later, but here we are more interested in his concern with the *process of management*, that is, what he imagined the job of a manager to be. Drawing upon his years of experience as a managing director, he suggested that there are *five elements of management* which are universal to all managers of all organisations. In his words, 'to manage is to forecast and plan, to organise, to command, to co-ordinate and to control'.

To forecast and plan (prévoyance)

The French word *prévoyance* means 'foresight' or 'forethought'. Managing, then, means looking ahead, assessing the future and planning for it. Most contemporary organisations have taken this idea to heart (even though some may not be very successful in its practical application) and have both long-term and short-term plans on a company basis, expecting individual managers and supervisors to do their own planning to fit in with the overall planning.

To organise

By this Fayol meant the division of the material and human resources of the organisation. This includes not only the purchasing process for material and the recruitment procedure for personnel, but also the task of dividing up the work (specialisation) among the employees, determining the sphere of action of each person or group, and giving the appropriate training. All these lead to the best use of resources.

The unities of command and direction (discussed in Chapter 2) must be present and responsibilities clearly defined.

To command

Fayol was conscious of the need to keep everyone on his or her toes, to keep the organisation in an active, rather than a passive, state.

Commanding implies knowing the staff well and the business thoroughly, and issuing instructions in such a way that a high level of activity by the staff is maintained. By using leadership skills the manager gets the best possible performance from his or her subordinates.

To co-ordinate

The underlying theme here is *harmony*. Managers' efforts must dovetail with those of others, and they must keep their departments in line with the total, overall objectives of the organisation. Regular exchanges of information (including meetings) are necessary for the 'binding together, unifying, and harmonising (of) all activity and effort'.

To control

When all the activity has been put into motion, then it is essential that everything being done is in conformity with the plan. To use modern terminology, we want a *control system*, or inspection organisation to set standards, monitor performance and take corrective action if it is needed. Inspection must be impartial, so departments responsible for checking, inspection or quality control must be independent of production departments.

1.3   Modern views of management functions

Many definitions exist today of what a manager's job consists of, but all can be traced back to Fayol's ideas. Table 1.1 lists some of the most common versions of management functions. Fayol's list is on the extreme left.

Table 1.1   *Five summaries of the manager's role.*

To	To	To	To	To
Forecast and plan	Plan	Plan	Set objectives	Create
Organise	Organise (including staffing)	Organise staff	Organise	Plan
Command	Direct	Direct	Motivate	Organise
Co-ordinate	Control (including co-ordinating)	Co-ordinate	Communicate	Motivate
Control		Report	Measure performance	Communicate
		Budget	Develop subordinates	Control

There can be no *complete* agreement about precisely what a manager's job is, but it could be said that even apparently very different jobs call for *all* of these activities, but with vastly different emphases. Production supervisors give instructions, direct. control and measure performance most of the time, but at other times will need to plan their work, report back to superiors and motivate their staff; technical supervisors would probably be more concerned with organising, setting objectives, measuring performance and communicating, but they too will need to plan ahead, be creative and motivate at particular times.

It will be seen that there is a degree of overlap between the terms used. Of all the lists, the final one seems closest to a complete survey: creating, planning, organising, motivating, communicating and controlling.

Creating

It used to be thought that most people were not 'creative'. We even used the term 'creative people' to describe artists, authors and advertising staff; there are 'ideas people' in large organisations; and the government has a 'think-tank'. The notion that creativity belonged to a small, special group was dispelled by, among others, Douglas McGregor,[1] who concluded that 'the capacity to exercise a relatively high degree of imagination, ingenuity and creativity in the solution of organizational problems is widely, not narrowly, distributed in the population'.

Creativity can include innovation, synthesis and development. *Innovation* is where we find an absolutely new way of thinking about, or doing, something. Examples are the hovercraft principle and prefabricating buildings — innovations at the time they were revealed to the world. It is one thing, however, to have plenty of time to think about something new, another to improvise quickly on the shop floor; but when a supervisor makes 'bricks without straw', uses an alternative material for a job in an emergency, finds a quicker way round a job, works out a new procedure, then he or she is being innovative or creative.

Synthesis is where we take ideas from two distinct sources — for example the computer and the typewriter — and combine them, in this case to produce a word processor.

Development occurs when we take a basic idea and extend it. For example, the original idea of the car has been altered out of all recognition, its use extended to freight carriage (lorries), warfare (motorised guns, half-tracks), medical use (ambulances), and so on.

The department within the production function which performs most of its creative activity is variously known as the design department, research or research and development (R & D), design and development, projects department, or even new products department.

Product design and development. We live in an exciting era of ever-accelerating change: every day new techniques and new uses for existing techniques, materials and skills are discovered and old ones discarded. Fashions in technologies, techniques and materials change, and companies cannot hope to survive, never mind prosper, without reviewing their product lines regularly.

This could entail product replacement, that is, an entirely new model, or, more usually, significant modifications to existing models. In some industries innovations of this order are incorporated in production as a result of some research breakthrough or arise in the research and development department, but it must not be overlooked that ideas do come from customers, from looking at the product ranges offered by competitive organisations, or from suggestions from employees, especially those working in the sales/marketing function. (Often the marketing department has its own product research teams.) Whatever the source, it will normally be the production function's research and development department which will have the tasks of analysing and developing the idea and vetting it thoroughly. It is important to ensure that an idea has at least a reasonable chance of being translated into a useful and

---

[1] McGregor, D. (1960) *The Human Side of Enterprise*. New York: McGraw Hill.

saleable product before beginning an expensive design/development/production programme.

The product life-cycle. Ever since the Industrial Revolution dramatically increased
the number of manufactured products it has become apparent not only that products
have a 'life', with stages very similar to those in the human life, but that they
eventually 'die', that is they become obsolete, outmoded or of no further use as
progress has passed them by. This process can be expressed diagrammatically as in
Figure 1.1. However, what is more significant is that the demand for the product will
vary over time, as shown in Figure 1.2.

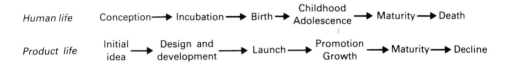

Figure 1.1 *Comparison of human and product life-cycle.*

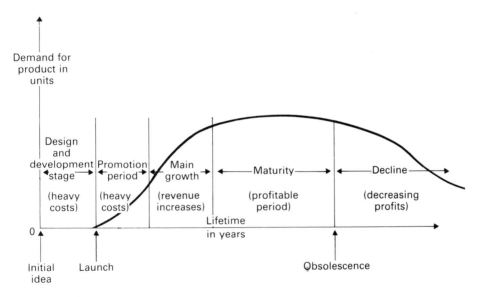

Figure 1.2 *Typical product life-cycle.*

Just because a successful product has been launched, it does not mean that the
innovation process is over. Eventually the product will become obsolescent and will
contribute less and less revenue to the business. The time to develop the next product
is therefore well before the maturity period of an existing product ends. A company's
success depends on a continuous product replacement programme, as outlined in
Figure 1.3.

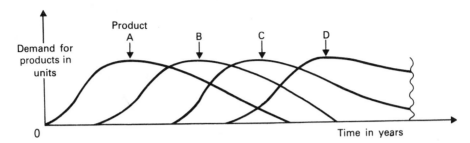

Figure 1.3 *Product replacement programme.*

Finally, we should note two recent and very significant trends in production demand within advanced Western nations and Japan. First, there is a trend towards shorter and shorter life-cycles. Products, particularly in fast-developing fields like electronics, word processors, and information systems technology, are becoming obsolete within a few years of launch. Compare this with the nineteenth-century steam engines which often had lives exceeding 50 years.

The second trend is one away from long-run totally standardised mass production towards shorter-run, more sophisticated products. The days have gone when Henry Ford I was able to say that customers could have any colour of car they liked, as long as it was black! Now, for example in military aircraft, weaponry and motor vehicles, there are numerous 'versions', which provide a greater flexibility in use as well as a larger potential market; and again, in 'customised' cars we can see variations round a common theme.[2]

Planning and forecasting

Forecasting means looking into the future, while planning means making decisions about what course of action should be adopted to meet the challenge of the future.

No one can plan in the abstract. Planning implies having precise aims or objectives and working out how to achieve them. Thus planning is involved in:

(a)   setting goals;
(b)   deciding on the means by which the goals will be achieved.

At company level this could mean:

(a)   setting a target-line, for example a £7 million turnover next year;
(b)   deciding to sell abroad as well as to the home market, as a way of achieving this (higher) target.

Forecasting is an art, not a science, and no one can predict the state of the economy or an organisation's probable situation in ten years' time with a great degree of accuracy, but the better the forecasting, the better the plans can be.

---

[2] Students who would like to read a full and well-argued account of this trend are recommended to consult Toffler, A. (1980) *The Third Wave*, pp. 189–196, 239–242. London: Pan/Collins.

Planning at different levels. All levels of management are involved in planning, but as the plans of lower levels depend on those of the higher, then higher-level plans must:

(a)   be developed first;
(b)   be more long-term;
(c)   be more flexible.

Top managers should therefore concentrate on overall *strategies* and *long-term* plans; what the organisation's goals should be two, four, five or even ten years ahead.

Middle management should concentrate on *tactics*, or how the overall strategies are to be achieved. This often entails devising and operating short-term plans, from six months to two years ahead.

Supervisors should plan work activities such as how to meet this month's production quota, and decide what each member of the workforce will be doing at any given time. Such plan time-scales can vary from a few minutes ahead to a year or even longer.

Production planning departments. Before looking at specific departments concerned with planning in the production process, it must be realised that not all planning is carried on in these departments. For example, selecting the factory site and the most appropriate type of building, planning the shop layouts, and deciding on the type of labour to be recruited and the appropriate training for that labour are all tasks that could be carried out by individual senior managers, or groups of them. However, this section concentrates on planning carried on immediately prior to production.

The main aims of production are:

(a)   to produce goods, articles or products which, as far as is practicable, comply with the specifications, quality, quantity and delivery requirements laid down by the customers;
(b)   to produce these goods, articles or products in such a way as to make the best possible use of the resources of the organisation — workers, money, machines, materials — at least possible cost;
(c)   to produce these goods, articles or products in a balanced, continuous programme as far as is practicable, and to minimise excessive fluctuations in the rate of production.

Although these three major objectives are not in themselves incompatible, it must be recognised that in attaining the first, and main, objective (unless the planning departments are extremely efficient and flexible in approach, and luck runs one's way) the other two objectives may have to be sacrificed to a greater or lesser degree. Too often it happens that, in an endeavour to get repeat business by supplying goods on time, excessive overtime is worked, materials are ordered at higher prices, work is put out to competitors and quality control standards are less strictly applied. All these things are done to overcome some deficiencies in the system, such as insufficient material stocks, inadequate maintenance programmes, or even lack of communication between departments.

To attempt to meet the three major objectives, we need to make decisions about a wide variety of activities, the most important of which are:

(a)   the allocation of suitable types of labour to the various departments;
(b)   the precise sequence of operations to be followed in executing a customer's order;
(c)   the precise deployment of labour in any given department involved in the production sequence (often with the aid of such techniques as network analysis and method and work study) where jobs are continuous or routine;
(d)   the purchase and storage policies in respect of raw materials and bought-out components;
(e)   the provision of suitable space for finished goods;
(f)   the establishment of an adequate information-gathering system to record all production activities in such a way as to assist their control.

How these activities are allocated in any given manufacturing organisation will depend on a whole host of factors. Basically, however, once the R & D department has decided on the product's design and specification, the *materials control* department will be involved in the purchase and availability of the raw materials and their storage, and the *production planning* department will be involved in establishing layouts, production methods, operations sequences and job timings; this department could also be involved in the scheduling and loading of individual orders, but often this is the work of *production control*. Once the order is in hand it passes out of the planning stage and is dealt with by a *progress department*, but if there are production difficulties, problems are referred back to production planning for further guidance and amendment as required.

Organising

Organising is the next stage after planning. Organising can be broken down into:

(a)   working out the actual jobs needing to be done to fulfil the plans agreed on;
(b)   grouping activities into a pattern or structure;
(c)   giving specific people in the organisation specific jobs to achieve the agreed objectives.

Thus if a cricket test team is selected to tour Australia, a plan is worked out to win the series. It might be, for example, to use the fast bowlers in spells of eight overs each, with spinners held back until later in the match, in which case organising would involve drawing up details of the bowlers to be used and the type of field to be used. In the light of the way play develops, decisions can be taken on the order of the bowlers and the setting of appropriate fields. (The hallmark of a good sports team is the way in which they function apparently without orders, though obviously everything has been planned and organised in advance.)

   The *organisation chart* (see Chapter 2) is a picture of the formal organisational relations within the organisation.

Co-ordination.   If there is a series of plans covering not only all departments in the organisation, but also each individual in each department, it is essential to ensure that all their efforts move together in the same direction. Co-ordination is, then, an essential part of organising, rather than a function in itself.

Bureaucracy. The organisation's role and purpose were explained by Max Weber. In his *Theory of Bureaucracy*, organising had a central position; specialisation, hierarchy of authority, rules, and trained managers in precisely defined jobs — all these are facets of organising.

Summary. Organisation is a method of ensuring that:

(a) the work required to fulfil plans is broken down into parts and given out to various individuals in the organisation;
(b) there is neither duplication nor 'underlap' of work;
(c) all efforts are harnessed to a common goal.

Organising is essentially an activity carried out in the production function by the various *managers* and *supervisors*, who make decisions on a day-to-day (even minute-to-minute) basis about the allocation of work to particular machines or the use of particular members of the workforce — all in the cause of fulfilling the objectives and plans already laid down. (It is essential, however, that these managers and supervisors are fully aware of the plans, predetermined layouts, task sequences, chosen materials and job methods before the jobs arrive in their departments.)

Thus for the manager organising would include ordering materials needed for the production schedules, ordering tools and other equipment needed in the department (large, expensive items might need authorisation at a higher level), and ensuring that the best use of the available labour is being made.

In short, organising is making *all* the arrangements for production.

Motivating

The importance of motivation of *all* staff in an organisation has in recent years at last begun to be recognised. The problem of finding ways to motivate staff employed in the production function is possibly greater than in other departments, probably because of the nature of the tasks which production workers are called on to do. Certainly, production workers are more likely to strike than administrative, office or managerial workers; because of this, the control of manufacture is all the more difficult an operation.

D. Katz[3] said that there are three basic types of behaviour essential for an organisation to function properly and effectively:

1. People must be induced to enter and remain within the system: labour turnover and absenteeism can be costly and unproductive if allowed to get out of control. However, physical attendance is not enough.
2. People must do their appointed jobs in a dependable fashion: organisations, if they are to function at all, have to rely on a continuous, fairly stable pattern of relationships over time.
3. People must on occasion (and depending on the job) be innovative and exhibit spontaneous activity in achieving organisational objectives which go beyond those which are laid down for them.

---

[3] The motivational basis of organizational behavior (1964), *Behavioral Science,* **19**, pp. 131–146.

A great deal of work has been done in trying to find the 'magic formula' which would ensure that all these three types of behaviour were always present in all organisations. A discussion of all the various theories and the ideas and research on which the theories are based would be out of place in a book such as this,[4] but we might think the following propositions worthy of consideration:

1. Human beings like working in groups, and many of them prefer to identify with a group.
2. Many people like to be consulted about the work they are to do, and to feel they have a say in how their work is to be carried out.
3. Certain people are underemployed (i.e. not enough use is made of their talents), and this is a cause of dissatisfaction.
4. Repetitive assembly work is likely to be less attractive in the long run (and more conflict is likely to be generated in such surroundings) than work demanding the use of skills and decision-making. Playing about with the job surroundings rather than trying to make the job more interesting is likely to have little effect.
5. Money is not the only motivation, but it can be regarded as a levy exacted in a society which asks some workers to work at repetitive tasks.
6. People want status and a superior position in relation to others, and very often the need for a certain status is a strong motivator. (For example, in pay claims there is often talk about 'relativities'.)
7. It is up to the supervisor to try to find what motivates his or her group most, and to convince each subordinate to want to do what he or she has been assigned or asked to do.

It can be seen that there are no 'motivating departments' in the sense that specific departments exist to carry out tasks such as creating, researching, planning, marketing or producing. Motivating the workforce is the task of all managers and supervisors, an 'across-the-board' activity. While the basic motivating 'package' (pay structures, fringe benefits, welfare provision, etc.) and management attitudes are decided at board level, it is up to individual managers and supervisors to work out how best to lead their own work groups, to identify which management style is best for them.

It is true to say, however, that these managers and supervisors will need to rely heavily on the assistance, advice and often training provided by the *personnel department*, in acquiring the skills of group management, such as team building.

Communicating

As with motivating, this fifth function of management is not confined to one department, but is again the task of every manager. A subject like 'communication' is so large and complex that it requires fuller treatment. However, we should clearly identify what is involved.

By 'communicating' we mean the transfer of an idea from my mind to yours in such a way that it is understood. Good communication occurs when a useful or appropriate idea is transferred efficiently. Bad communication has many causes, but it results in either the non-arrival of a message or the arrival of a distorted or inappropriate

---

[4] See Evans, D. (1981) *Supervisory Management: Principles and Practice*, pp. 90–94, 130–134, 170–174. Eastbourne: Holt, Rinehart and Winston.

message. A useful analogy of the communication process is the transmission of a message by radio from the source to the receiver (see Figure 1.4).

Note that in this model the journey of idea X from A to B could be subject to *interference* (distraction such as noise or movement; or distance fading the message; or anything which prevents the message from getting through). In radio transmission this is usually 'crackling' or 'static'. In communication at work, the noise of machinery, the worries on the receiver's mind and the inability of the receiver to decode the message accurately are all *interference*.

It should also be noted that there is a need for the sender to *encode* the message: in radio terms this means to convert sound into a 'signal', or a series of electrical impulses. For communicators at work, this means converting ideas into a recognisable set of symbols — written, spoken, or in the form of gestures. We can establish a few general rules for good communication:

1. Source-senders of messages should ensure that their facts are accurate and that their language is clear, concise and readily understood by receivers.
2. Unless it is appropriate, source-senders should keep their own prejudices, emotions and attitudes out of messages, especially if the messages are supposed to be factual.
3. Source-senders should introduce a feedback system into their communications. Not only does this give receivers a chance to become senders, but it helps the original senders to check that their communications were received, understood and acted upon.
4. Source-senders should therefore become *listeners/receivers* when feedback responses arrive. They should pay as much attention to the return messages as they would expect from those receiving their messages.
5. In a formal situation, communications should be sent up or down the chain of command. (Beware of the 'line bypass' (see Chapter 2): people tend to get upset if they are left out.)
6. A source-sender should choose the most appropriate channel for each communication: verbal for interviews, meetings and giving orders; written for giving orders, messages over a long distance, very important matters and matters which involve a lot of detail.

Informal communications. Besides the formal communication network (which will be examined in Chapter 2 under the general heading 'organisation charts'), there exists in any organisation a complex system of *informal* communications, often quite unsuspected.

The most significant network of informal communication, and the one that is most distrusted by management, is the *grapevine*, that mysterious mixture of rumour and truth, surmise and gossip, which circulates at all levels within the organisation. It only needs one member of an informal group within the organisation to receive an interesting piece of information (an extra day's holiday at Christmas, for example) and to circulate the message quickly round his or her group; most of the group members will inevitably belong to other small, informal groups of people, and in turn they will pass the message on to them. If a message is interesting enough it will be passed on very quickly: it is estimated that 95 per cent of the citizens of the USA living in towns knew of President Kennedy's assassination within 90 minutes of the event.

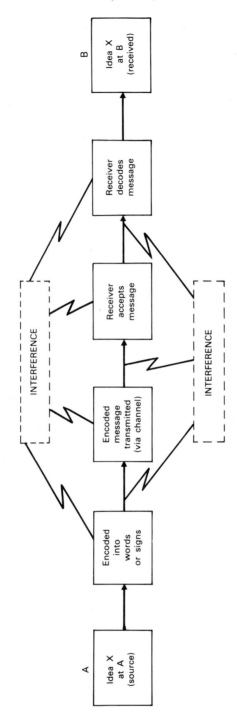

Figure 1.4 *The communication process. From Evans, D. (1981) Supervisory Management. Eastbourne: Holt, Rinehart and Winston. Reproduced with permission.*

Management tends to dislike, and possibly fear, the grapevine, because information that management would like to keep to itself becomes common knowledge, often in distorted form. Through the grapevine the possibility of a temporary cutback in production becomes threatened redundancies, the possibility of some redundancies becomes a plant shut-down, and so on.

The only way to counter the grapevine (and help it wither) is for management always to keep the workforce as fully informed as possible about the company's present fortunes and future prospects. In any case, legislation encouraging the publication of this type of information is already in existence, and without doubt will be reinforced in the future.

Controlling

Controlling is the essential process of seeing that what was planned to happen actually *does* happen. As this function is of primary importance we shall explore the idea of controlling in some detail, but first we need to consider the notion of 'feedback' (which we encountered briefly in the last section).

Feedback.   The notion of feedback features in general systems theory (GST), which attempts to establish general laws to describe and to make predictions about *all* systems, of which manufacturing organisations are but one special case. The idea of feedback, however, is not a new one.

James Watt included in his engines a device for keeping a steam engine working at a reasonably constant speed, whatever the load and whatever the steam pressure. Whenever the engine started to speed up, weights on a revolving shaft linked to a steam valve were flung outwards, partly shutting the valve: the amount of steam admitted to the driving mechanism was reduced, and the engine slowed down. Conversely, if the engine slowed down more than was desired, the reverse took place. The weights fell inwards and the steam valve opened wide to admit greater quantities of steam. Of course this was a rather crude device: the speed of the engine fluctuated around a 'mean' speed within rather wide limits. Nevertheless, we can say that the system was self-correcting: it controlled itself.

We call any example of a self-correcting control mechanism 'feedback': a thermostat (very similar in concept to James Watt's device) is a feedback mechanism. Now, the notion of feedback is essential in understanding how we can keep a system in a steady state, or equilibrium. Through the process of feedback the system continually receives information from its environment which helps it to make the appropriate adjustment.

This helps us to gain an insight into what lies behind *every* successful control system. Taking, for example, the thermostat, we can set it at a predetermined temperature (say 22°C) which we want to prevail in a given environment. The thermostat constantly monitors the *ambient* temperature (the temperature of the surrounding air). If this temperature drops by a significant amount (say 1°C), the thermostat immediately switches on the heating system to provide more heat. As the temperature rises the thermostat continues to monitor the environment, and as soon as the desired temperature is reached it cuts the heat source out again.

In this example feedback has been explained in terms of *automatic* control. It must be stressed that feedback is *any* process which ensures that information about what is going on at any particular stage is fed back to an earlier stage, so that a measure of control can be exercised on the process. Human beings can be part of this monitoring and reporting system, as well as the takers of appropriate corrective action.

An example of human involvement could be where a departmental inspector finds that parts produced on a machine are dangerously close to the tolerance limits which have been laid down, and advises the shop supervisor, who in turn checks the machine, finds tool wear, and changes the tool.

Thus to *control* we must first have targets, ideals or standards to go by. These could be room temperatures, material specifications, quality or quantity standards, rates of flow, levels of expenditure, mandatory safety procedures, and so on. We then measure exactly what is going on and compare these results with our predetermined standards. Our measurement techniques and equipment should be sufficiently accurate to spot significant variations between the expected and actual results.

We can then investigate these deviations (sometimes called 'variances') to discover reasons for them, so that we can modify our output until it begins to correspond more closely to the chosen standards.

Thus controlling involves the following activities:

(a) setting objectives or standards of work;
(b) devising ways of measuring performance;
(c) measuring performance against the objectives or standards;
(d) evaluating what deviations there are from the planned results and why they occurred;
(e) taking corrective action where this is possible, to restore the position.

In essence, control is the 'checking up' part of a supervisor's or manager's job. Of course it implies planning: the setting of the original targets, objectives and standards is absolutely essential, as well as the planning of the checking or inspection process.

We shall now take two illustrations from budgetary control to explore the idea of control further.

Budgets. A budget is a statement (usually in *financial* but sometimes in *volume* terms) of what is planned, or of what is expected to happen. The Chancellor of the Exchequer is responsible each April (at least!) for reviewing the state of economy publicly and estimating government income and expenditure over the following twelve months.

Such an overall budget is made up of many smaller budgets, and it is the same with the firm or organisation. As an example, let us take a company called Winnits Ltd, making parts for the motor industry. The firm start by working out total income and expenditure budgets for the year. Included in the expenditure is the item 'oil for heating'. If we consider this in detail we shall get a clearer picture of the process.

Constructing a budget. Budgeting requires careful record keeping: if this has not been done in the past, then the first time a budget is prepared difficulties may be encountered. In the case of our oil heating budget, however, we shall have available last year's total consumption figures (from the oil company, even if we have not recorded this total) of, for example, 5500 litres. Now it is obvious that we cannot simply divide the yearly total by twelve and say that our monthly consumption is about 450 litres, since consumption will be high in mid-winter and very low in the summer. We must also take into account considerations such as lengths of the months (February being shorter than the others) and holidays, including perhaps complete shut-downs in July or August, or a whole week at Christmas and New Year.

We could eventually come up with a budget like the one in Table 1.2. We could compare the *actual* consumption through an appropriate flow meter, month by month.

Table 1.2 *Winnits Ltd: heating oil budget (litres).*

Jan.	Feb.	Mar.	Apr.	May	Jun.	Jul.	Aug.	Sept.	Oct.	Nov.	Dec.
1000	900	850	500	250	100	50	50	200	350	500	750

Variances. Any differences recorded between what was originally budgeted and what was actually consumed are called *variances*. In any control system we must be able to spot variances and try to find explanations for them. Our investigations can then result in corrective action to bring us back on course (or can sometimes mean resetting the objectives or standards, though this should not be done without careful thought).

Suppose we obtained the actual results during a given year as shown in Table 1.3. Now during the year taken as a whole we have consumed exactly what we anticipated, but in any good control system we should want explanations for each of the monthly variances: perhaps there was a very cold spell in January and the thermostat was turned up too high; a warm spell in March, which reduced consumption; boiler trouble in November and December, resulting in a not very efficient oil/energy ratio; and so on. We must pinpoint every significant variance and explain it.

Table 1.3 *Winnits Ltd: heating oil budget (litres).*

	Jan.	Feb.	Mar.	Apr.	May	Jun.	Jul.	Aug.	Sept.	Oct.	Nov.	Dec.	Total
Budget	1000	900	850	500	250	100	50	50	200	350	500	750	5500
Actual	1100	950	750	400	300	50	50	50	200	250	600	800	5500
Variance	+100	+50	−100	−100	+50	−50	−	−	−	−100	+100	+50	

Production budgets. We can now take the idea a stage further by considering an example of a production budget. In such a budget there is not only a budgeted volume output for a period (say a month) but budgets for material used in manufacture and a budgeted cost per item (usually called a *standard* cost). We must then look for variances in each of these.

In this second example (Table 1.4) the manager of the assembly department has been given a budget of £30 000 for production in January, and is pleased to note he has underspent by £750 when the results are circulated in February. The works superintendent is not so pleased, and if you look at Table 1.4 perhaps you can see why.

Table 1.4 *Winnit Assembly Department: performance January 19—.*

	Output	Sets of components used	Cost per Winnit (£)	Total Winnit costs (£)
Budget	5000	5000	6.00	30 000
Actual (at budget cost)	4250	4500	6.00	27 000
Actual (at actual cost)	4250	4500	6.50	29 250

Analysing the variances. The superintendent would look at the following:

1. Output. Why were only 4500 units started? Was it lack of orders? Shortage of operatives? Industrial relations problems? Lack of usable machines? Why were only 4250 units completed? The scrap rate was about 5½ per cent. Is this in line with normal scrap rates? If not, was this due to poor working methods? Over-zealous inspection? Mistakes in other departments? Inadequate machinery?
2. Costs. Why did the actual cost rise 50p above the budget (standard) figure? Was this caused by material price increases, labour cost increases, or inefficiency in the department? (Here the superintendent would want to look at overtime figures.)
3. Remedies. Depending on the findings, remedies would have to be sought, for example inadequate machinery repaired or replaced, workers recruited or trained, or consideration given to making the job cheaper by using alternative materials.

Analysis of a budget. Many avenues of investigation present themselves in a small set of figures. With experience, solutions to many of the questions would soon be found and appropriate action would be taken to correct imbalances. Of course, variances cannot always be corrected: material price increases or wage increases cannot be reversed, cold spells avoided, or economic recessions ignored.

Variances do show where to direct the scarcest of management resources — time — in maintaining a dynamic steady state or equilibrium in the organisation.

Controlling departments. Any manager or supervisor of any department in an organisation (including production departments) is normally the controller of that department's outputs. However, especially in the production function, there are particular departments whose major task is to control the manufacturing process.

First, *production planning* (and *production control* where these departments are separate) controls the use of plant on an overall basis, some individual decisions being made on the spot by management; it often controls the sequence of operations and the progress of individual orders. Cost accounts (part of the accounts function) will provide data on the cost of production, which will include the scrutiny of variances, to enable costs to be controlled as far as it is possible to control them. These two departments of necessity have a close relationship.

Material (or stock) control has the job of ensuring that the optimum stock levels are maintained; that is, in conjunction with the accounting function, it ensures that stock varieties are as comprehensive and plentiful as the money available for stocks can provide.

Quality control — whether as a central department (in a dairy, for example), as a decentralised function (inspectors in every department, roving and patrol inspectors; or frequent inspection during the process), as a once-and-for-all check at the end of the line, or as a combination of any or all of these methods — is perhaps the one example of a control function of which most people are aware.

Summary

1. Henri Fayol suggested there were *five elements of management*:
   (a) to forecast and plan;
   (b) to organise;
   (c) to command;
   (d) to co-ordinate;
   (e) to control.
2. Modern views, though different from Fayol's list, are still based upon it.
3. Various lists exist, but the one which seems to provide the best possible picture of a manager's role includes the following functions:
   (a) *Creating*, which includes innovation, synthesis and development. In an era of ever accelerating change the need to be innovative and to adapt to change quickly is essential to organisational survival. The research and development department plays an important role in creating in the production function. Products need to be replaced and updated well in advance of their obsolescence and there is an increasing emphasis on variety, smaller runs and 'customised' products.
   (b) *Planning and forecasting*, which means making realistic assessments of the future and making decisions about which courses of action to take, assuming the future *does* conform to our expectations.
      The aims of production planning are to produce goods, articles or products as close as possible to customers' needs and requirements, using the firm's

resources in the most effective way, to ensure a balanced, continuous steady production flow.

To achieve these aims, careful planning of labour allocation, operations sequences, use of network analysis, method and work study, provision of suitable stores space, and an adequate information system will be required.

Research and development, materials control and production planning (and control) are involved in planning in the production function.

(c) *Organising* is the next stage after planning. It involves sorting out the jobs to be done to fulfil the agreed objectives, grouping activities and allocating workers to particular jobs.

Essentially a job for every manager or supervisor, organising is making *all* the arrangements for production.

(d) *Motivating*, which is the process of giving workers an incentive to work. We need to be able to recruit workers who will attend regularly and work responsibly and dependably over a period of time.

The promotion of viable groups, proper consultation with the workforce about the work they are to do, jobs which make use of people's abilities and talents and contain an element of personal choice and decision-making, and recognition of the status of individual workers — all these, besides money and similar benefits, can help motivation and morale.

While the personnel department can play an important supporting role in motivating the workforce, it is primarily the job of managers and supervisors to establish the best way to motivate their own work groups.

(e) *Communication* is again the 'task' of individual managers rather than of a specific department, and is basically the task of transferring (without any loss of meaning) an idea, whether simple or complex, from one person to another. A checking, feedback loop in the communication system will help the communicator/sender to ensure that his or her objectives are achieved.

As well as a formal communication system (and a series of rules about who speaks to whom) as illustrated in a firm's organisation chart, informal communication systems exist. The most important of these is the 'grapevine', the hidden network of rumour and half-truths. The only sure way to counter it is to tell the truth, the whole truth and nothing but the truth to the workforce.

(f) *Controlling*, which is the essential process of ensuring that what was planned to happen actually does happen. All control systems are basically feedback loops involving:
(i) setting standards;
(ii) devising systems to measure performance;
(iii) measuring that performance;
(iv) noting any differences between the standards and actual performance;
(v) investigating the reasons for these differences or deviations;
(vi) taking corrective action to ensure that future performance conforms to the predetermined standards.

A special version of a control system is a budget, and the technique of controlling expenditure is called budgetary control. Departments with a specific control task include production planning and control, cost accounts, material stock control and quality control.

Questions

Review questions

1.1 What did Fayol say were the five elements of management?

1.2 What are the six functions that summarise a modern view of the manager's job? How do these functions differ from Fayol's list?

1.3 Suggest (by taking particular aspects of the job in question and relating them to particular functions of management) how the six functions would be performed by:
    (a) a works manager of a manufacturing company;
    (b) the manager of a local supermarket;
    (c) a football team manager;
    (d) a lecturer in charge of a class.

1.4 Take all the lists of managerial functions mentioned in the early part of this chapter, compare them, and decide which list *you* think is the best summary.

1.5 Why do you think planning is necessary? What would happen to an organisation without any future plans?

1.6 What is the purpose of organising?

1.7 What are the basic principles of any control system?

1.8 Explain the purpose and importance of budgeting.

Discussion topics

1.9 What would happen to an organisation if, next Monday morning, all the managers ceased to perform the six functions?

1.10 Discuss how best to motivate:
    (a) sales representatives;
    (b) works managers;
    (c) assembly-line workers;
    (d) students.

1.11 Discuss the view that there is no need for managers to control the quality of the work of their departments if there is an inspection team or quality control department.

1.12 Discuss the methods by which teachers can control the work of their classes. How can they check individuals' performances? Which is better: continuous assessment or periodic tests?

Assignments

1.13 Students who are not yet supervisors or managers should ask a practising supervisor or manager exactly what he or she does, making a list of the functions performed, allocating jobs to each function, and suggesting the total time spent each week on each separate function.

1.14 Review the department in which you normally work (or one in which you have recently worked). How could quality, output levels and use of materials be better controlled? Investigate *one* area of waste and suggest how savings could be made.

1.15 Part of the process of organising entails ensuring that there is no duplication of effort or overlap of function or jobs. Take an example from an organisation with which you are familiar (work organisation or college) where such duplication has occurred, and suggest how improvements could be made.

1.16   Imagine your course is to hold a residential weekend towards the end of the course to do practical work and exercises, and you are course tutor. Plan the weekend, paying attention to:

    (a)   selection of accommodation and the facilities you would require;

    (b)   cost of the accommodation (who would be paying — firms, individuals, etc.);

    (c)   a balance of activities throughout the weekend, including some 'free' time. Work out a budget, to include *two* visiting speakers (1½ hours each) at £12 per hour including expenses, which will cover the cost per student for the whole weekend.

Case studies

1.17   Bill Shepherd, works manager of Marinecraft Ltd, summoned all his managers to an emergency meeting last week. 'It's amazing,' he told them. 'The Boat show was many times more successful than we could have possibly imagined: the Velocity class was in great demand. The plain fact is, with new orders coming in every day, we must start increasing production now, the target being at least 50 per cent up this time next week. I'll leave it up to each of you to decide how to cope.'

    Shepherd dismissed his staff, and Kim Newman, the recently promoted supervisor in the marine engine shop, was keen to show her mettle. Within minutes she was in Personnel: 'I'll be needing another ten fitters at once,' she said eagerly. 'There should be plenty around now Johnson's are closing down.' Within three days Kim's section was augmented, but she was having problems finding enough work for everyone to do, as parts were slow in coming from other departments.

    Percy Hull, on the other hand, opted to get his staff to work overtime and for several days his targets were easily met and passed. At the end of the week, however, he was surprised to find that there was a slight increase in absenteeism, and that Harry had cut his hand again. At lunch time on Monday, Percy confided to Kim Newman that he wondered how he was going to cope. Kim shifted uneasily in her seat. 'I've got a problem too,' she said. 'My staff are jealous of all the overtime your staff are getting.'

    (a)   What problems are there at Marinecraft Ltd? How did they arise?

    (b)   What should be done to put matters right, and who should do it? What solutions can you offer to the problems of the supervisors?

1.18   After the revolution in Ruritania, Commissioner Brown issued Industrial Proclamation No 1. This read as follows:

Ruritanian Government Proclamation
Workers' Control

With immediate effect workers will assume control of the factories they work in. The jobs of all directors, managers and supervisors are hereby abolished; ex-managers will join the workforce as producers forthwith.

    In future, factory policy decisions will be taken by mass meetings of workers, and shop production problems will be handled by the individual work groups concerned.

    (a)   What do you think would be the immediate consequences of such an order, including the consequences to production?

    (b)   What are likely to be the longer-term consequences?

2
The Structure of the Organisation

The kinds of organisations to be examined in this chapter are those likely to be encountered by those whose career will be in production-oriented businesses. However, it should be noted that many 'non-productive' (i.e. service) industries have features in common with the productive enterprises.

As mentioned in Chapter 1, before this century most organisations were smaller and simpler than those of today, so small and simple that the unifying power of one person — the owner manager — was such that he or she alone made decisions, and the success (or failure) of the whole enterprise depended upon him or her. Today, even small firms have more than one manager; power is shared and decisions are decentralised. The primary objectives and the tasks undertaken decide the form of the organisation: a change in the market-place or a different kind of raw material (substituting plastics for metal for making car heaters, for example) can dictate a change in the organisation's form.

Thus, most organisations have developed structures (consciously or unconsciously) to cope with the problems that they face. We must look, therefore, at such structures in more detail, including the use of job descriptions.

2.1 The use of models

Models aid understanding. Sometimes the purpose of a model is to *remind* ourselves of something with which we are familiar e.g. a model railway locomotive; sometimes to *assist discovery* — a model aeroplane in a wind tunnel can be used to test various theories about the behaviour of a full-scale aeroplane in flight; and finally sometimes as an *explanation*, to make an idea clearer. When information is turned into a working model the relationship of certain factors with time (and perhaps space) becomes much easier to grasp. We say we can 'see' the connections, or the relationships, at once.

While it is possible to make *exact* copies of things, models are usually less than exact and are less complicated than the original. This loss of detail is often irrelevant, as the usual purpose of the model is to highlight certain, selected aspects of a situation rather than *all* of them.

Diagrams and maps are also models, except they are only two-dimensional. As with all models, maps sacrifice complexity to concentrate on a particular aspect; relief maps describe the hills and valleys, road maps concentrate on the road communication networks, and weather maps show fronts, wind speeds and areas of high or low pressure. When we look at organisation structure maps,[1] we must realise that these, too, are two-dimensional models and do not illustrate the real factory. On a visit to the factory, you will see people who are moving around performing tasks in different buildings. Organisation structure maps do not attempt to reproduce every nook and cranny of the buildings, or the appearance and activities of the workers, but rather concentrate upon the formal power structure of the organisation: the *relationships* between different levels of management and the workers.

So, although the 'structure map' — we usually call this an 'organisation chart' — is very different from the factory's personnel, it does help us to 'see' the whole, and how it fits together, more clearly. From one point of view, it could be said the structure exists *apart* from the people, for while a particular employee may leave and be replaced, the job or position in the structure remains. Indeed, even if jobs remain unfilled, the organisation may well go on functioning.

2.2 Organisation charts

Organisation charts are very similar to the maps we use to plan holiday journeys. Just as maps concentrate mainly on the road network, organisation charts concentrate on only a few aspects of the network of communication which exists between various managers and officials in the organisation. They often have 'keys', 'legends' or 'conventions' (explanations of the symbols used). Both, of course, are two-dimensional representations of three-dimensional situations.

Maps also come in all sorts of shapes and sizes, and have different scales, signs and symbols. So it is with organisations charts. Contrary to popular belief, the 'family tree' type of organisation chart is not the only kind of chart to be used.

Types of organisation charts

As we aim normally to model (or map) only the formal structure of the organisation, a chart can be seen as a network. It can be described in spatial terms, with important people at the top of the chart, or in the centre, with those seemingly less important at the bottom, or on the periphery.

The examples of different types of organisation charts which follow are all based on either an up–down or a left–right relationship, with the exception of the circle charts. All use a spatial relationship (i.e. a *distance* between) to illustrate differences in rank, power, authority or status.

Basic.   The basic relationship is that between superior and subordinate, and usually this is shown vertically, as illustrated in Figure 2.1.

---

[1] Or 'organograms' as used in BS 3138.

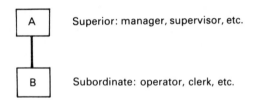

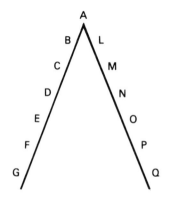

Figure 2.1 *Superior/subordinate relationship.*

Scalar chain. Most organisations that a manager or supervisor is likely to encounter will have more than two members. Henri Fayol (mentioned in Chapter 1) produced what he called the 'scalar chain' or 'chain of grades or steps', and his chart looked like a triangle without a connecting base line (see Figure 2.2).

Figure 2.2 *Henri Fayol's scalar chain.*

   This chart looks odd to our eyes, as we have seen we do not often meet a situation where nearly every employee (i.e. F, E, D, C, B, L, M, N, O, P) has only one subordinate. However it would appear that Fayol's chart was even more abstract than the type of charts we commonly use today. It does help to understand that:

(a)   authority and power flow from the top (A) downwards,
(b)   accountability flows upwards.

Authority is the right or power to make decisions which are binding on others, or to give instructions or orders. *Accountability* is the obligation to give an account to one's superior of the way in which any delegated authority has been used. Superiors are in turn accountable to *their* superiors. This reporting or accounting chain is what Fayol refers to as the 'scalar chain', and some contemporary writers as the 'job task pyramid'.

The 'T' chart.   The job task pyramid idea becomes a little clearer if we use a 'T' chart, the most widely used and understood map of the organisation.

In its most basic form it consists of a series of inverted letter 'T's (see Figure 2.3). (Taking a ruler, we can quite quickly draw a pyramid shape around the chart.)

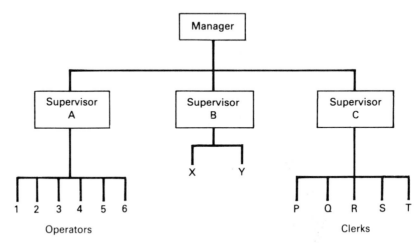

Figure 2.3 *Basic 'T' chart or job task pyramid.*

Of course, we will get a result like this only if the three supervisors are of almost equal status and the numbers of staff that each control are similar. Even in Figure 2.3, there is some doubt about the perfect pyramid, and if we transferred supervisor B to the outside, to replace either A or C, the 'pyramid' shape would become somewhat distorted.

Wheel charts.   Sometimes it is more useful to indicate, in addition to a superior/ subordinate relationship, a geographical one. Consider a firm with a head office in Birmingham and factories in London, Bristol, Liverpool, Glasgow, Newcastle and Ipswich. We could envisage such an organisation as a *wheel* with the group production director (A) in the centre, and the factories at the ends of the various spokes.

The form of the wheel would not be exactly geographical (the well-known map of the London Underground is neither strictly 'geographical' nor to scale), but would represent the 'structure' in a very appropriate way (see Figure 2.4.).

Modified 'T' charts.   There are many different ways of setting out relationships, and we are at liberty to combine 'T' charts with wheel charts (or any other variety) (see Figure 2.5).

The implication here is that London, Liverpool, Newcastle and Glasgow *do not* communicate with each other: had they been expressed as illustrated in Figure 2.6 then we might feel that London, Liverpool, etc. *do* communicate.

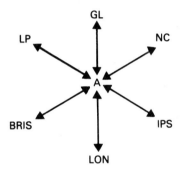

Figure 2.4 *Wheel chart.*

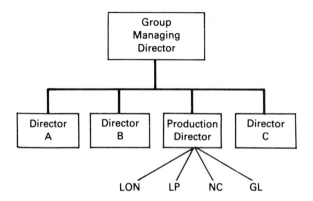

Figure 2.5 *Modified 'T' chart (1).*

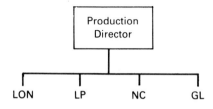

Figure 2.6 *Modified 'T' chart (2).*

Circular (concentric) charts. Finally, in this brief survey, we come to the *circular* chart, a slightly different idea from the wheel or circle chart (Figure 2.7). Here we place the top person in the centre, and jobs at different levels are shown in concentric circles surrounding the central job.

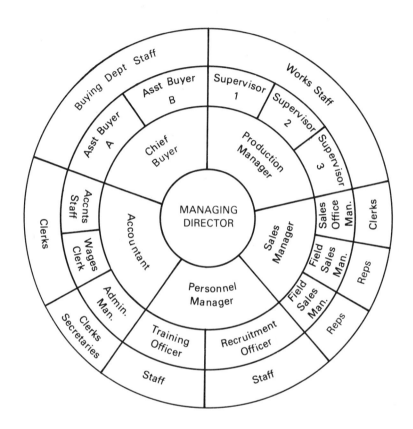

Figure 2.7 *Circular or concentric organisation chart.*

The spatial implication here is the nearer the centre you are, the greater your position, power and authority; conversely, those at the outside of the circle have lower status and position (see Figure 2.10).

This brief survey does not cover all the possibilities. You can use any device you like to 'picture' or model the organisation, always provided the chosen method is:

(a) appropriate;
(b) accurate (about the aspects to be shown);
(c) easily understood.

However, as long as we realise that charts should *describe*, not *prescribe*, and that there are inherent shortcomings in every model, we can make much fruitful use of organisation charts.

Essential features of organisation charts

Charts are used to show:

(a)   the whole business;
(b)   the individual constituent companies or divisions of the whole;
(c)   the departments or sections in a company;
(d)   the details of one department or section only.

Compared with a map, the first could be a map of the world, the second the British Isles, the third counties, and finally a street plan of a town.

At present there are no international or BSI standards covering the symbols used, but certain conventions are normally followed, as is shown in Figure 2.8.

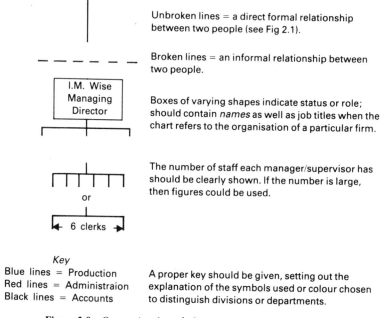

Figure 2.8   *Conventional symbols used for organisation charts.*

We have already noted that models often highlight only a few aspects of the thing they model. So it should be with organisation charts: too much detail or too many symbols, lines or colours could confuse rather than aid understanding.

2.3 Types of organisational structure

Now we have seen how organisation charts can be used to model organisational structures, we must next consider what kinds of structures the charts attempt to model. As with much in management, it is dangerous to set everything under neat headings, and although we shall review some basic structures, any given organisation may exhibit any or even all of the structures at the same time. A further difficulty we have to overcome is that not everyone is agreed on the definitions used for the basic structures.

Line organisation

Joan Woodward[2] carried out a study of a number of firms in Essex in the early 1960s. She came to the conclusion that each firm had two kinds of function: *task* and *element*.

1. Task functions. These, she maintained, were those functions vital to the achievement of the organisation's *primary* objectives. Most firms would have four such functions: production, sales, accounts/finance, and research and development. (There could be differences in firms like transport contractors, and in those where there is no production, for example in a wholesale warehouse.)
2. Element functions. Functions of lesser importance such as quality control or personnel are not in existence to meet the primary objectives, but rather to *help* by acting as 'back-ups' to task functions. By taking, for example, inspection problems away from direct production, quality control offers a service; the services the personnel department offers are too numerous to mention here.

'Line organisation' is that part of the organisation which relates to task functions. 'Line managers' are the managers of task functions: works managers, chief accountants, managing directors and sales managers would all, under this definition, be line managers. A simple form of line organisation is shown in Figure 2.9.

Line and staff organisation

The first problem with 'line and staff' is the use of the word 'staff'. Sometimes it means the whole labour force of a firm, but more often it means that part of the labour force which has better terms of employment, is paid monthly rather than weekly, and has a pension partly provided by the firm. 'Being on the staff' is an expression of status, if not of extra income.

   'Staff' in 'line and staff' does not mean *either* of these things. Staff personnel are, in fact, people employed in the 'element' functions, such as personnel or quality control officers, or as special helpers to managers or supervisors. Figure 2.10 illustrates this definition.

   Another explanation of 'line' and 'staff', differing from Woodward's analysis of task and element functions, can be expressed in terms of the *authority* vested in the

---

[2] Woodward, J. (1965) *Industrial Organization: Theory and Practice.* Oxford: Oxford University Press.

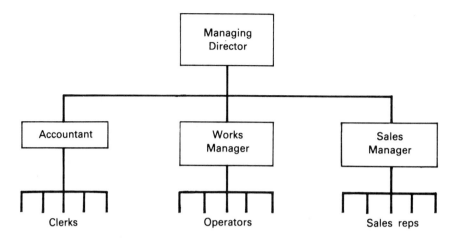

Figure 2.9 *Line organisation.*

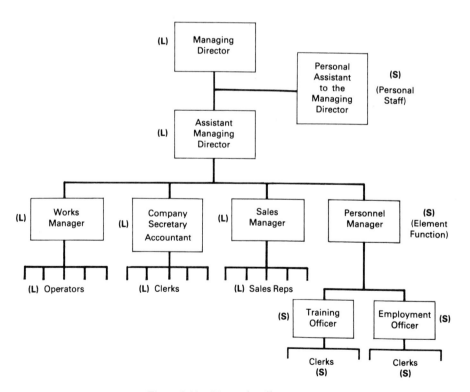

Figure 2.10 *Line and staff organisation.*

manager of a department.[3] Consider the authority of the works manager and the personnel manager shown in Figure 2.10.

(Note that in Figures 2.14, 2.16 and 2.17, 'staff' is used to indicate the work-force employed in particularly departments — yet another common use of the word 'staff'.)

While, of course, personnel managers are in charge of their own departments, their authority is limited to carrying out policy laid down by the board and/or the managing director; works managers, on the other hand, may have wide executive powers and may make their own decisions on a variety of matters without necessarily referring such decisions to the managing director.

Functional authority

The matter is, however, complicated by the fact that certain managers (usually 'staff' managers) actually have and exercise authority *outside* their own departments. While such authority is limited and refers to specific areas, it does affect the line manager. A clear-cut example would be the firm's safety officer, who might walk through a workshop and find an operator using a machine which was, in the safety officer's opinion, in a dangerous condition. The safety officer, without reference to a supervisor, could order the worker to stop work and switch off the offending machine. But there the authority would end. The safety officer could not instruct the worker to start another job or another machine. Similarly, the personnel department may have authority to discipline workers when certain grades of punishment — dismissal, suspension, etc. — are involved. Such authority, once the prerogative of the manager, is now transferred to the specialist. Perhaps we should call 'functional authority' 'specialist authority'.

Line and staff problems

Managers and supervisors quite rightly feel that the employment of such specialist staff and departments does take away authority, the more so when certain 'staff' personnel are introduced into their departments (from quality control, for example). The fact that personnel and other specialists have invented their own jargon does not help.

Some managers are eccentric, wilful or just non-conformist, and, while being excellent servants to the organisation and 'good' managers, they may bend a few rules or fail to fill in the right forms, achieving the right ends by totally unorthodox means. The specialist who works 'to the book' or likes to see everything run exactly may object to the irregular behaviour of such managers, and even report them to top management.

Another cause of friction is that, rightly or wrongly, line managers often consider themselves (and their departments) as being 'more important' than the 'staff'

[3] Bullock, Lord and Stallybrass, O. (1977) *Fontana Dictionary of Modern Thought*. London: Fontana. A useful book for all interested in modern science and technology which defines 'line positions' as those in the chain of command for decision and action. A line manager is part of the direct line from managing director to shop floor.

managers, who cause overheads, because the line staff are engaged in accomplishing the organisation's primary objectives. Conversely, the specialist (functional) staff are becoming ever more qualified and may be culturally distinct from the line managers, particularly if the latter have been promoted from the shop floor.

Delegation

Delegation is an important concept, and very much related to the organisation structure. If we look at a typical organisation chart, we see the seemingly all-powerful managing director at the top, but we must quickly realise that he or she cannot take all the decisions and do all the work: that is what the managers are for. However, subordinates cannot do what is required of them without the necessary authority and power to act.

Delegation, then, is where one person, A, give someone else, B, the power and authority to perform work or to give orders to others on behalf of A. B accepts the power and authority, but in return also accepts the need to justify his or her stewardship, to 'be accountable' to A in due course. Delegation is usually *downwards*, although in a trade union it could be argued that the power of the branch (and other) officers is delegated *upwards* by the members.

In Figure 2.11 one can see the chain of delegation, starting with the shareholders, who are the owners of the business, but who in many companies are too numerous,

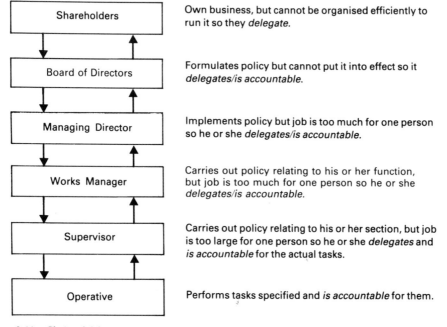

Figure 2.11 *Chain of delegation. Adapted from Evans, D. (1981)* Supervisory Management. *Eastbourne: Holt, Rinehart and Winston. Note.* Downward arrows = delegation; upward arrows = accountability.

too widely dispersed to take decisions about the day-to-day running of the firm. The shareholders *delegate* the running of the business, both policy-making and the implementation of policies, to a committee, called the board of directors (all, of course, shareholders), but require the board to be *accountable* at the company annual general meeting held once a year.

The board decide on policy, but *delegate* the carrying out of the policy to the managing director, who, besides being a shareholder and director, is usually a full-time employee of the company. However, even in a relatively small firm, the task of supervising every job, and making decisions in sales, purchasing and production, is too much for one person to do effectively. So the managing director *delegates* the running of the separate functions of the company to senior managers (only the works manager is shown here in Figure 2.11) who take upon themselves the job of carrying out company policy in their function (usually called a department). The senior managers, however must *account* to the managing director for all the decisions they take.

In the same way the works manager is unable to oversee every job done in the factory, and will need to *delegate* to junior managers (supervisors), who supervise, say, 25 operatives, the task of running a particular section, for example a press shop. The supervisor is, in turn, *accountable* to the works manager (see the next section).

At the end of the chain are the operatives. The supervisor *delegates* to them the actual performance of various tasks in the shop. In turn, the operatives are *accountable* to the supervisor for the work they turn out.

Delegation is practised much less than it should be; some managers are insecure, and feel that others may do jobs better than they can, if given the chance; others perhaps genuinely believe their subordinates are incapable of doing certain jobs, and only the 'big white chief' can cope. Inevitable consequences flow from a serious failure to delegate: at best, an enormous workload leading to inefficiency on a large scale; at worst, a nervous breakdown or an ulcer; and a demoralised, untrained workforce.

Accountability

Authority and accountability must go hand in hand (see Figure 2.11). A fair system demands that every manager or supervisor should be answerable for his or her actions. People given authority without accountability can become either ruthless dictators, acting on unchallenged whims, or lazy and uncaring in their work. Conversely, people given responsibility without authority either do nothing, or assume authority they do not have. Both situations are obviously unsatisfactory.

Just because a manager delegates a job to someone else, it does not mean the manager ceases to be accountable for the carrying out of the job. For example, imagine a supervisor who is responsible, in addition to organising production, for the security of his department. As the supervisor knows a meeting he is to attend is likely to last until late, he deputises Tom Smith, a charge hand, to close the windows, lock the filing cabinets, and see the workshop door is shut at the finish of work. Late that night, an intruder gains entry, and makes off with important documents as well as loose tools.

Tom Smith has failed in his job, and is accountable for this failure. However, the supervisor is still accountable in turn to his boss, and cannot evade the issue by saying 'It's Tom's fault!'.

Spans of control

By 'span of control' we mean the number of people reporting *directly* to one superior. This number can vary enormously from one department to another, from firm to firm and from industry to industry (Figure 2.12).

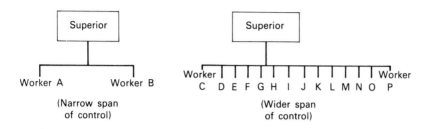

Figure 2.12 *Narrow and wider spans of control.*

How many people can a manager or supervisor control? Unfortunately, the answer is not simple. The limits are set by a number of different factors, all of which are important.

The nature of the job.   This is a significant factor. If the job is relatively simple, and most employees in the department are doing the *same* job, then larger numbers can be handled easily. On the other hand, if the jobs are complex, fewer people can be supervised effectively.

Imagine a managing director with 25 senior managers reporting directly to him or her, all with vastly different areas of work and with vastly different problems! In contrast, think of a manufacturing department where all the employees have been with the company a long time and know the job and the machines; in this situation a supervisor could comfortable cope with such a number.

The time available.   The less time managers actually have in which to manage, the fewer people they can control effectively. This applies where managers have special duties which frequently take them away from their nominal job, or when they run more than one department.

The nature of the employees.   The amount of experience, training and expertise possessed by the workforce is crucial. New entrants, untrained personnel and inexperienced workers all need extra care and attention. Effective control depends to a great extent on the nature of the employees.

How many employees?   Many writers on management have expressed opinions on the correct number of subordinates a manager should have. In 1937 V. Graicunas suggested that six direct subordinates could be effectively supervised; in 1938 L. Urwick was more cautious, with five or six at the most. A famous general, Sir Ian Hamilton, maintained that four was the ideal figure. From what we have already considered, such statements are questionable, to say the least. The total situation dictates the span of control. Joan Woodward found South Essex firms in the mid-1950s with spans of control for the first-line supervisors which varied from seven to ninety.

Assuming, however, that the ideal number could be determined, a manager could be faced with more subordinates than the ideal (too wide a span), or alternatively, fewer subordinates than the ideal (too narrow a span). Too wide a span entails lack of control. Too narrow a span can lead to a waste of personnel, too many grades of staff and more levels of communication. Both situations lead to increased costs.

2.4 The organisation of a typical firm

Talking about a 'typical' firm is rather like talking about the 'average' person; we are dealing with something which does not exist, but, for our purposes, we will designate a medium-sized engineering firm, with a factory and offices on one site, as typical. Even so straightforward a choice could lead to a confusing chart, so for the sake of clarity we will first look at an overall view of the divisions or departments, and then consider each department separately (see Figure 2.13).

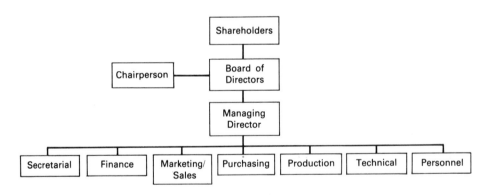

Figure 2.13 *Basic organisation chart: medium-sized manufacturing company.*

The *shareholders* acquire their interest in the company either by buying shares when the company is launched, or by purchasing (or being given) shares at a later stage — via the Stock Exchange in the case of public companies. They exercise their right of control by voting at annual general meetings or special general meetings of the company. They elect some of their number as *directors*.

The *directors* together constitute the *board of directors*. They elect a chairperson, who may be a retired senior employee (an ex-managing director), a member of the controlling family (if the original family still retains a large shareholding), or someone with considerable standing in business. The power of the *chairperson* is often difficult to determine or define, but in some companies it includes the power to dismiss the managing director.

The board delegates the day-to-day running of affairs and the carrying out of policy to the *managing director*, the chief executive of the organisation. He or she has great authority and influence in the firm, appointing all senior staff and making or shaping all major decisions.

The departments shown reporting to the managing director in Figure 2.13 are those found in our typical, medium-sized firm. Students may find other organisations are different, having a separate organisation and methods/work study section, or a business data processing (or electronic data processing) department; or there may even be a research and development department distinct from the technical side. The permutations are endless.

Some departmental functions

The *secretarial* function is headed by the *company secretary* (often professionally qualified). By law, each limited company must have a secretary, who has specific legal functions and who will frequently deal with all matters relating to shareholders, general administration, policy statements, and directors' meetings.

The *financial/accounting* function is headed by the *accountant* (normally qualified) and covers: the keeping of records, including account books; cost accounting (see Chapter 13); general financial management, including advice to the board; wages and electronic data processing. In smaller firms, the accountant may also be the company secretary.

The *marketing manager* (increasingly a person professionally qualified) runs the marketing/sales function. Precise duties vary from one organisation to another, but basically the function is concerned with bargaining and selling, contracting and supplying, and generally doing everything to generate, stimulate or facilitate sales. Responsibilities include market research, advertising and sales promotion, and managing the outside sales representatives and the internal sales office. Production staff may also find the marketing manager has a considerable say in the development of new products.

The purchasing function

The purchasing (or buying) function (see Figure 2.14) is headed by the *chief buyer*, sometimes called the 'head buyer', the 'purchasing manager' or even the 'chief purchasing officer'.

In Figure 2.14 the purchasing function is shown as independent, buying materials and equipment for *all* aspects of the business. Some firms prefer to place purchasing under the control of production, presumably based on the argument that purchasing's main purpose is to *serve* production.

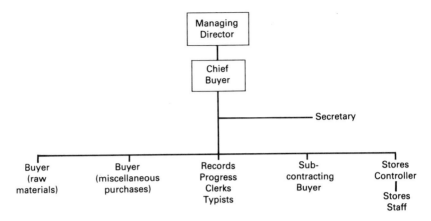

Figure 2.14 *Purchasing function.*

Buying raw materials usually calls for a great deal of skill and knowledge, not only in selecting the products themselves, but in estimating price trends. Buying metals, for example, can be a tricky business in a fluctuating market. In addition, *consumable items* — that is items used up during production, such as oils, rags, and drill bits — will be needed as well as office equipment and stationery. Where the firm cannot undertake all the work for which it has orders, purchasing is required to pass out the work (subcontract) to other firms to complete.

Stores, shown in Figure 2.14 as part of the purchasing function, can be considered a logical extension of buying — a store-place for products or materials purchased in advance. Some organisations, however, prefer to place the stores under the control of production, on the grounds that the primary task of stores is to provide every kind of material for production. There are also some firms which leave the stores relatively independent from either production or purchasing.

The details of material and stock control are dealt with in Chapter 15.

The personnel function

Although a vital function, particularly to production, it is not appropriate here[4] to consider it in detail (see Figure 2.15). *Personnel planning* is concerned with predicting the future make-up of the workforce in terms of numbers required and the skills needed, and controlling the use of presently available resources. *Recruitment* involves clarifying the exact nature of a job to be filled, drawing up a profile of the ideal job holder, and attracting a field of suitable candidates. *Selection* involves choosing the most suitable candidate for the job.

---

[4] Students who would like to learn more about the personnel function are recommended to read Unit III of Evans, D. (1981) *Supervisory Management.* Eastbourne: Holt, Rinehart and Winston, particularly Chapters 9 and 19.

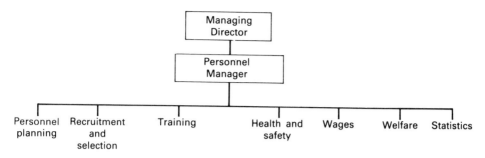

Figure 2.15 *Personnel department.*

Training has a wide field to cover, from imparting the minimum knowledge and skill needed to do a job, to developing people's full potential and capabilities; it also includes mandatory training in health and safety. Besides the administration of the wages structure, a wide range of welfare services (including medicinal, first aid, etc.) and a range of records and statistics on the workforce are maintained.

In some firms, the responsibility for industrial relations is placed on the personnel department, but, in most, such bargaining is carried out by senior management.

2.5 The organisation of production

The production (or manufacturing) function is headed by an executive who could be variously titled *production director, production manager, works director* or *works manager*, depending upon the size of the company. Where there is a production director or manager, his or her deputy could be called works manager.

The organisation of production is so varied from firm to firm, or industry to industry, that it is impossible to describe a 'standard' organisation layout. To give some idea of the possibilities, the following three examples cover a medium-sized engineering firm, a 'process' manufacturing company and a small, specialist set-up. (It must never be forgotten that the majority of manufacturing organisations employ fewer than 50 people.)

Medium-sized firm

The production function illustrated in Figure 2.16 is split into two. The works branch, headed by the works director, is responsible for:

(a) production planning;
(b) production control (including staff who investigate the progress of various orders — 'progress chasers');

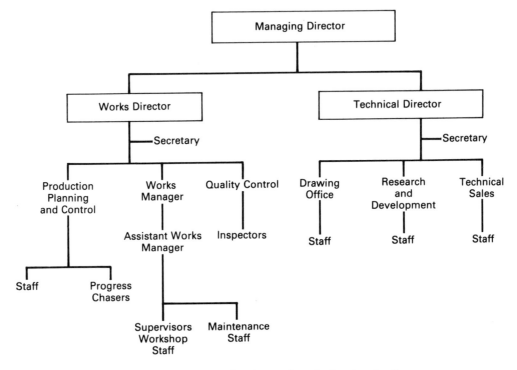

Figure 2.16 *Production function: medium-sized engineering firm.*

(c)   production departments (machine shops, assembly departments, foundries, heat treatment rooms, etc);

(d)   maintenance (of buildings, plant and machinery, fixtures and fittings);

(e)   quality control (usually *not* under the direct supervision of the works manager).

The technical director heads those departments which give a *technical service* to production.

Process manufacturing company

The production function illustrated in Figure 2.17 is allied to design, maintenance, quality control and stores. The production manager in this case is restricted to the three major production processes: cutting, sewing and finishing.

Small firm (special orders, small runs)

The small firm illustrated in Figure 2.18 is typical of a great many in the UK, particularly in areas such as the South East of England and the West Midlands. The

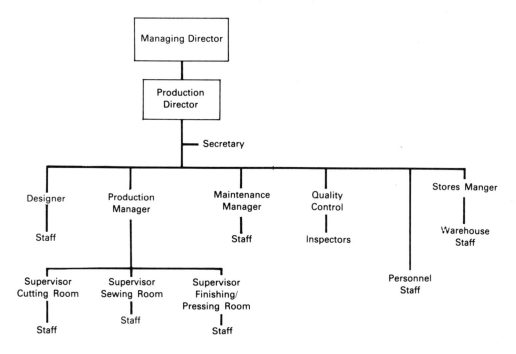

Figure 2.17 *Production function: process manufacturing (textile industry).*

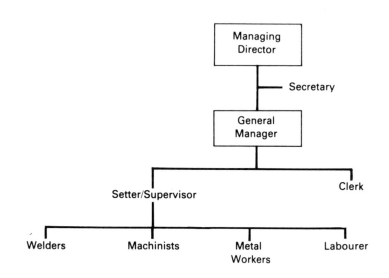

Figure 2.18 *Production function: small specialist firm.*

general manager does not only oversee the workshop but often acts as a sales manager as well.

The workforce of 10–15 employees includes supervisor/setter who keeps control of the shop floor. There are welders, sheet metal workers and machinists, though it would be expected that all would be able to tackle the others' jobs, as the situation demanded. One general labourer would be needed for cleaning, carrying, etc. The whole emphasis is on flexibility.

2.6 Job descriptions

In earlier, post-1945 times, when demand was high, efficiency was of lesser importance than production. Many firms relied upon a generalised knowledge of jobs for recruitment purposes, and did little training or work in such fields as job evaluation. Because of economic necessity, firms are increasingly now looking at labour carefully, as it is a costly resource: it is difficult to know whether staff are being used in the best possible way unless *what* they are doing is known to a high degree of accuracy.

The organisation chart (which is usually more informative about managerial and administrative jobs than manual ones) does, as mentioned earlier, identify the titles of jobs and the job holders, that is, people are described in *occupational* terms. In fact a full catalogue of a job's tasks would be inappropriate to such a chart. However, when we come to look at questions raised by studying organisation charts — whether existing jobs should re-allocated, divided or combined, or whether people working for the firm are reaching desired standards of output, or doing their jobs in the most efficient manner possible — much more information is needed. This is obtained through job analysis.

Job analysis

Any job can be seen as a series of tasks; some may be important, such as deciding how to spend thousands of pounds, and others less so, such as stapling two sheets of paper together, but all are part of the total job. Very few jobs have just one single task: such jobs would be highly repetitive and probably very boring. Job analysis is the total process of investigating and evaluating jobs, during which the facts concerning each job are systematically recorded, including:

(a) tasks (individual work activities);
(b) procedures;
(c) responsibilities (of the job holder);
(d) personal attributes, qualities and qualifications required of the job holder.

From such information we can see how jobs may resemble or differ from each other, and get some indication of the status and rewards of the job as well as its content. (As we can see from Figure 2.19, job analysis has other uses apart from recruitment and selection, e.g. training.)

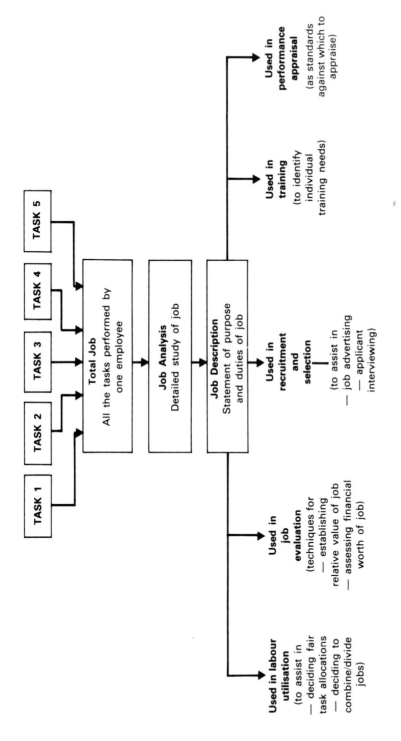

Figure 2.19 *The nature and purpose of job analysis and job descriptions.*

Collecting the information. Collecting information about jobs is difficult, complicated and time consuming. Try to write down on two sheets of paper *exactly* what your own job is! Even if you could do this reasonably quickly, and to your satisfaction, do you feel your boss (if given the task to write what he or she sees your job to be) would come up with a list of tasks similar to your list?

Probably the best method is to have an independent fact-collector to question both the present job holder and his or her manager, and perhaps others with whom the job holder comes into contact. Ideally, the information should be collected and available before a vacancy arises, and fairly regular revisions of information are required, as jobs change over a period of time. Information about the job may be held by other specialist departments, such as training or work study departments.

The nature of a job description

This is a formal document, based on the information obtained during the job analysis, and defines the job that needs to be filled. Usually the job description states the purpose, duties and relationships of the job and lists the physical, social and economic factors that affect it. The information given in a job description is often given under a series of headings.

Identification of job. This includes current job title, the department concerned and the number of people doing the job.

Purpose of job. This is a brief, general statement of the major objectives of the job. (For example, the purpose of a works manager could be: 'To manage the manufacturing unit of the company making valves and pistons'.)

Duties. There should be a list of all the tasks and duties involved in the job. Ideally one of two methods is used:

(a) where each duty is preceded by an *active* verb (for example 'Lists totals of debtors', 'Types letters to customers')
(b) where each duty is preceded by an *infinitive* (for example 'To prepare budgets for expenditure on loose tools', 'To suggest improvements in security').

It is important that *one* method is used throughout.

Responsibilities. A statement of responsibilities for resources — labour, money, machines — is set out. This is important for managerial staff, but it could also apply to operator-level staff.

Relationships. There is a statement of (human) relationships involved in the job, with other people inside and outside the firm. This should include the job title of the person to whom the employee is accountable.

Physical conditions. Details are given of noisy, dirty or dangerous conditions, or the reverse if pleasant conditions apply. Hours of work, overtime possibilities, unsocial hours, etc. should also be mentioned.

Social conditions. There should be an indication of the work group or groups with which the employee will be concerned.

Salary/wages/other benefits. There should be a statement of salary/wage rates, bonuses, increments, piece work, commissions and any 'extras' or 'fringe benefits' such as pension arrangements, holidays, car allowances, etc.

Promotion prospects. A statement of the prospects of promotion, transfer to other departments, etc. is included if appropriate.

The uses of job descriptions

There are a variety of uses for job descriptions, but the five main uses are shown in Figure 2.19.

Labour utilisation. Labour utilisation is the activity of ensuring the existing labour force is used to the best effect. A review of the work done and the tasks to be performed could result in a re-allocation of the tasks among the workforce. Such a re-allocation is made all the easier if the *present* jobs (and tasks) of the workforce are known in detail. From the data provided from job descriptions, jobs can be re-allocated among personnel in a department or individual jobs can be redefined, divided or combined as necessary.

Job evaluation. Job evaluation is a collection of techniques of differing method and approach. However, all have the same end in view; they attempt to find the 'money's worth' of jobs.
   It is possible to do this for a firm or organisation where:

(a)   the jobs can be easily identified;
(b)   there are sufficient differences between jobs;
(c)   agreements on the relative importance of various jobs can be made between workers (unions) and management.

An essential part of job evaluation is job analysis, though different systems require different levels of sophistication in analysis. Unless the relevant facts about a job have been revealed, and the similarities to and differences from other jobs investigated, we cannot compare one job with another. Job evaluation essentially implies comparing jobs to determine differentials and relativities. Job evaluation is a set of methods designed to help produce a structure of wages and salaries in an organisation.

The first and most important point to grasp in understanding job evaluation is that we are not concerned with the individual worker doing the job; this is a matter for assessment and appraisal by the supervisor or manager. If any rewards are to be made for merit, such rewards would be superimposed on job evaluation gradings. So job evaluation is concerned *only* with the qualifications, training, experience, expertise, strength and intellectual abilities required for the demands of a job.

The four commonest methods are:

1. Job ranking. This treats each job as a whole, and ranks the whole in relation to other jobs in the organisation. There is not much emphasis on detailed job analysis.

2. Job classification. This method is to select a number of grades into which jobs can be grouped, and to select one key or 'bench-mark' job as typical of that grade. The job description of each job in the organisation is then examined and compared with the bench-mark jobs, and from that examination it is allocated to the same grade as the bench-mark to which it relates most closely. Job descriptions are essential to this method.

3. Points evaluation. An American inspired system, points evaluation relies upon the identification of *parts*, *elements* or *factors* of a job, rather than the whole job. Jobs are evaluated under categories of factors varying from three to eleven or more and the initial job description assists in the selection.

4. Factor comparison. The fourth method both ranks jobs and calculates appropriate money values. Key jobs are selected as bench-marks and then analysed under factors such as mental effort, skill required, physical effort, job responsibilities and working conditions. By analysing other jobs in the organisation, and comparing them factor by factor with bench-mark jobs, assessments can be made of money values to be attached to the end factor. Again this analysis is considerably assisted by the use of job descriptions.

Recruitment and selection. Job descriptions are used in recruitment (assembling sufficient candidates for interview) and selection (the choosing of the strongest candidate).

At the recruitment stage the job description is used to create an *employee specification*, and is a profile or 'pen portrait' of the kind of person who would be suitable for the job vacancy. In the specification would be listed the personal characteristics and qualities looked for in job applicants. The nature of the job might enforce physical limits (height/weight/age), or stress the need for such skills as planning, organising, negotiating or selling. The employee specification is directly derived from the job description.

The employee specification leads straight on to the *advertisment* in a suitable medium, such as a newspaper or technical journal. The advertisement is derived directly from the employee specification.

Finally, when completed job application forms are received in response to advertisements, they can be checked against or compared with both the employee specification and the job description. Promising candidates are those whose experience, skills and qualifications most closely match the standards set by the job description. At the interview stage, candidates will have had a copy of the job description to assist them in appreciating the type of job on offer, and interviewers can use the same document to help them to frame suitable questions to ask the candidates.

Training. Any attempt to carry out purposeful and systematic training in an organisation needs to begin by identifying the skills and knowledge required in each job. This information is derived from the job description, and then compared with the skills and knowledge possessed by individual job holders.

For each individual we shall obtain from this comparison a deficiency list — his or her training needs. The total of all deficiency lists forms the basis of the firm's total training plan.

Performance appraisal. Appraisal (often called 'performance appraisal') is that process during which the progress, performance, results and sometimes personality of an employee are reviewed and assessed and the employee is interviewed by his or her immediate superior, and often by other, more senior managers. Appraisal is part of the 'control' system, this time the control of the staff or employees.

In appraisal the aim is to review and change, to inform and monitor, to examine and evaluate employees, with a view to spotting 'variances' from expected standards — good or bad — and taking appropriate action as required to correct inadequate performance.

An appraiser will need a copy of the employee's job description against which to evaluate his or her performance, as well as some statement of the employee's performance over a given period. The job description can indeed be the central document around which the appraiser conducts the appraisal interview.

Summary

1. Models aid understanding. Diagrams and maps are models. Organistion charts are structure maps of organisations (firms).
2. Spatial relationships are used as analogues of power and authority relationships in the organisation.
3. The *scalar chain* (Henri Fayol) is a type of organisation chart highlighting the chain of command and communication.
4. The *'T' chart* is the most popular chart in use: others are wheel, concentric and circular.
5. Joan Woodward divides the organisation into *task* functions and *element* functions. The former are those functions (production, sales, accounts/finance, research and development) which are vital to the achievement of the firm's

objectives. The element functions, of lesser importance, help out as 'back-ups' to task functions.

6. 'Line' personnel are those people employed in task function departments. 'Staff' personnel are those employed in element functions.

7. 'Line' managers have authority within their departments, or areas of responsibility. However, some specialist 'staff' managers have authority outside their departments, in fact factory-wide (e.g. the safety officer). A staff person exercising this type of authority is said to exercise *functional* authority, i.e. authority derived from carrying out a particular function.

8. *Delegation* relates to how far down the chain of command a decision is made. It is where one person, A, gives another, B, the power and authority to take decisions. B, having been delegated powers, will now become *accountable* for his or her decisions to A.

9. *Span of control* is the term used to describe the number of people directly supervised by one person.

10. A 'typical' firm will have a structure of shareholders, board of directors, a managing director, and a series of departments under him or her. These departments are frequently secretarial, finance, marketing/sales, purchasing, production, technical and personnel.

    The secretarial department deals with shareholders and board matters; accounts, wages, etc. are handled by the finance department. Marketing covers all kinds of sales promotion as well as selling. Purchasing is responsible for buying new materials and consumable items. Personnel has a wide-ranging set of duties including labour planning, recruitment and selection, training and sometimes industrial relations.

11. The organisation of production is so varied that it is impossible to describe a 'standard' layout. Figures 2.16, 2.17 and 2.18 show three contrasting organisation structures.

12. Job analysis is the detailed study of jobs, during which the facts concerning each job are systematically recorded.

13. A job description is a formal document based on the information obtained during job analysis. It covers:
    (a) the identification of the job (title, etc.);
    (b) the purpose of the job (major objectives);
    (c) the duties of the job (all carefully listed);
    (d) responsibilities (for resources and labour);
    (e) physical conditions (especially any which are dirty or dangerous);
    (f) social conditions (work groups encountered);
    (g) salary/wages/other benefits;
    (h) promotion prospects.

14. Job descriptions are used in:
    (a) labour utilisation (the more efficient use of labour);
    (b) job evaluation (attempts to calculate the 'money's worth' of jobs);
    (c) recruitment and selection (ensuring the best candidates for jobs are selected);
    (d) training (identification of training needs);
    (e) performance appraisal (assisting in provision of standards against which employees' performance can be judged).

Questions

Review questions

2.1 What is meant by a 'model'? Why do we use models when they are not *exact* copies of the original?

2.2 What are 'organisation charts'? What do they show? Give examples of *two* types of chart.

2.3 Distinguish between 'line' and 'staff' personnel. What is 'functional' authority?

2.4 Explain the meaning of the following terms:
(a) delegation;
(b) span of control;
(c) accountability.

2.5 What departments (or functions) other than production are commonly to be found in most medium-sized or large manufacturing organisations?

2.6 Describe the responsibilities of the following functions:
(a) accounts/finance;
(b) production;
(c) personnel.

2.7 Why is it necessary to prepare a job description before:
(a) writing a job advertisement;
(b) carrying out a job evaluation?

2.8 What kinds of information about a job would be included in a job description, and to what uses can a job description be put?

Discussion topics

2.9 Discuss the value and use of the following models:
(a) an architect's model of a new purchasing department office block;
(b) a plan of the office block's ground floor;
(c) the purchasing function's organisation chart.
Does each explain the total situation? Do you agree that taken together they explain more than each does individually?

2.10 Is there any justification for distinguishing between 'task' departments and 'element' departments?

2.11 Discuss the view that delegation is not necessary, and all decisions could be taken by one person. Such a situation would surely be simpler and cheaper to run?

Assignments

2.12 Prepare an organisation chart for the organisation to which you are attached, paying particular attention to the way the production function is organised. (Students not yet apprenticed could use their college for this assignment. For 'production' substitute 'engineering department.)

2.13 Visit by arrangement any organisation to which you are not attached. Try to prepare an organisation chart of its various departments. Compare the results with what you know about your organisation.

2.14 If you are in employment, write your own job description. If still at college, write the job description of a friend, relative or college official such as head porter/caretaker or librarian.

Case study

2.15   Things were certainly going wrong at Greyhound Electrics. There had been a thunder-
storm and water had leaked through the roof. It was dripping slowly but steadily on a
junction box. Terry Sparkes was replacing a fuse in the box (there had been a surge of
power during the storm, the fuse had blown and work had stopped in the workshop) with
a great deal of haste, as production needed to restart quickly.

   Paula Pry, the safety officer, entered the shop just as Terry pulled the lever over to
'on', and the machines started. 'Just a minute,' she shouted. 'Switch that thing off again
at once!' Terry obliged. 'Now,' continued Pry, 'leave your machines, and organise
someone to get into the roof to plug the leak. Come on, you're wasting time.'

   At that moment, Tom Shepherd, the supervisor entered the shop. 'What are you
playing at, Pry?' he shouted. 'These are my staff, not yours!'

   'They're on safety work now, and that is my responsibility,' Pry replied.

   (a)   Was Pry right to intervene when she did? What kind of authority was she
         exercising?
   (b)   Did Tom Shepherd have a right to argue with Paula Pry about the safety job she
         had set the workforce?

3
The Firm as a System

In this chapter, the basic ideas of systems theory are introduced and the inputs and outputs of a manufacturing system are identified. Human organisations are goal-seeking, and the particular goals of a manufacturing system are analysed.

3.1 Introduction to systems theory

If someone asks the question 'Where does a physical object end?', the answer seems simple: the outside. But when we look more closely at an object like, for example, the sun, we find it has no finite boundary, but just becomes dimmer as we move further into space. Consideration of a more mundane example, the motor-car, brings out a further point: we cannot really consider the role and function of the car — to transport people and goods from point to point — without considering its *environment*. We cannot isolate the car from its surroundings: if we describe it in motion we can talk about its suspension, its road-holding abilities and its speed — all of which will be related to and affected by such characteristics of its environment as road surfaces, weather conditions, the amount of traffic on the road and the time of day.

So it is with all organisations, including manufacturing ones. To talk about a firm without considering its location, its customers, its suppliers and a great deal more is only to tell part of the story. It is how a firm or organisation *copes* with its environment — importing inputs from outside, working on them, and re-exporting them — which is of significance, just as the petrol/mileage ratio or road-holding performance of a new car is of significance to its purchaser.

Systems theory was born out of the Second World War. A team of scientists assembled at the Massachusetts Institute of Technology — a 'think-tank' of mathematicians, engineers, biologists and others — worked to improve the functioning of anti-aircraft guns and similar weapons. Soon the team realised they were all working to the same end: a theory of *control*. From this research the science of control, *cybernetics*, was developed in 1947, and in 1950 came general systems theory (GST), based on the notion that there were basic similarities in the ways that *all* systems function, and that a system is a related group of elements organised for a purpose.

It is clear that the definitions of a system as used in GST include all human and social systems, including manufacturing ones. Thus what can be said of systems can be applied to organisations.

3.2 Classification of systems

Systems can be classified under various headings, but the most important for our purpose is the major division into closed and open systems, and the relations of these two kinds of systems with their environment.

Closed systems

A completely closed system is one with sealed boundaries against any influence from or interaction with the outside environment. Nothing enters or leaves a closed system. A characteristic of such systems is an inherent tendency to move towards a static equilibrium and random state in which there is no potential for work (entropy). A closed system will tend to increase in entropy over time. Possibly the only *totally* closed system is the whole universe.

Open systems

An open system, on the other hand, while it can have or be given boundaries, does have relationships with its environment (other systems). When an open system *is acted upon* by other systems it is said to go through an *import process* or, to use a term from computer language, it receives *inputs*. When it *acts upon* the inputs, the open system is said to carry out a *conversion* or *transformation* process, and when it *reacts outwards* to the environment (other systems), this is called the *export process*, or *outputs*.

The organisation or firm can be considered in terms of a general open-system model as illustrated in Figure 3.1.

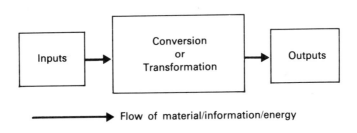

Figure 3.1 *An open system.*

Such a system is in constant interaction with its environment, and at the same time strives to achieve a *dynamic* equilibrium: the biochemistry of the human body tries to maintain an equilibrium between its inputs (food, water, information, etc.) and energy expended/work done and waste products. The survival of an open system ultimately depends upon a continuous inflow, transformation and outflow process. It goes without saying that the system must receive sufficient inputs at a suitable rate of entry to maintain the rest of the cycle.

Adaptive systems

Adaptive or *self-adjusting* systems adapt themselves to changes in the environment, that is, they contain some mechanism which enables them to respond to increased or decreased inputs, or the demands for increased or decreased outputs. Human beings are able to adapt in this way, for example in dealing with temperature changes by putting on or taking off clothes, perspiring and shivering. It is not surprising that organisations — groups of people — share this adaptive ability.

Probabilistic systems

These are systems in which certain events can be predicted but not others, even given large amounts of information about them. With a roulette wheel in motion, for example, you can predict that *some* number will come up, but not which one.

Contrived systems

Contrived systems are not naturally occurring ones like biological systems, but are deliberate, artificial creations.

Industrial firms

We can now see that firms and business organisations are examples of open, adaptive, probabilistic and contrived systems.

3.3 The manufacturing system

It is clear that manufacturing systems are many and varied and it is therefore difficult, except at a very general level, to establish what the inputs and outputs of manufacturing systems are.[1] However, it can be said that all manufacturing systems interact

[1] See Parnaby, J. (1981) Concept of a manufacturing system, in Open Systems Group (ed.) *Systems Behaviour*. London: Harper & Row and Open University.

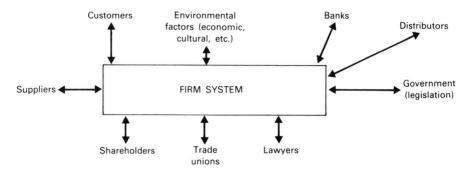

Figure 3.2 *Factors operating on the firm/system.*

considerably with their environment (other systems). Some of the factors operating on them are shown in Figure 3.2.

Inputs to the system

The major inputs can be classified as follows.

Information. No open system can continue to function without information from its environment. In the case of the manufacturing system, inquiries, opinions and orders from customers (particularly the latter) are of extreme importance. Data and standards accepted throughout the industry (e.g. British Standards), legal requirements (health and safety legislation), known fashion trends, market research information, information on competitors and the like must also be treated as essential inputs. Raw material availability and cost must also be known.

Money (capital). Contrived systems need an initial impetus to start them off, equip the conversion processors with adequate technology and provide other necessary inputs. The almost universal way of doing this for manufacturing systems is to borrow money from shareholders or banks.

Cash inputs will be required constantly once the system is functioning. Much of the necessary finance will come from the sale of the outputs, though further loans may be necessary to expand the business, and to be used for the purchase of raw materials, labour, etc.

Raw materials. This term covers not only the basic products used in the manufacturing process but also bought-in components, sub-assemblies and finished items (i.e. outputs of other firms).

Consumable items. These are items which are used up or 'consumed' during the manufacturing process — lubricating oils, rags, etc.

Labour. Staff, both manual and non-manual (i.e. technical, administrative and managerial), are needed to operate and manage the conversion processes within the system.

Assets (plant and equipment). 'Assets' covers a wide range of items including the premises in which the processes are housed, computers, machinery (large and small), spares, tools and transport vehicles. These assets are purchased from capital.

Services. A constant supply of energy in the form of gas, electricity, oil, etc. will be needed. Other services, such as water, sewerage and drainage, specialist maintenance by outside contractors, telephones, and mail collection and delivery, are also examples of essential inputs.

Business environment. The general climate of business opinion (for example about the current economic situation) and the values, norms and ideals of other firms will affect to a greater or lesser extent the way the manufacturing system behaves.

Social pressures. Firms are usually keen to create a 'good image' of themselves. Criticisms in respect of dangerous practices, unsightly buildings or nasty smells can affect the technology and conversion processes operated.

Trade union pressures. The attitudes, aspirations and policies of trade unions and their members can produce sudden and traumatic inputs to a manufacturing system.

General economic/political environment. The current state of the economy, interest rates, political stability, etc. can affect *all* business systems.

Outputs from the system

The major outputs can be classified as follows.

Finished products. These are the result of the conversion process being applied to the raw materials, and undoubtedly are the most important tangible output from the system. They can be measured in terms of *quantity*, *quality* and *sales value*.

Profit (or loss). This is the amount of money left over after all the expenses incurred in paying for inputs, the conversion process and facilitating outputs have been paid out of sales revenue. A loss is a 'minus profit'.

Information. Contrived open systems generate considerable amounts of information (usually by design). Provided available data are captured and ordered into significant information, much can be learned about the nature of the outputs, for example whether they have met the targets set. Provided this information is fed to a control process in the system, it can be used to help improve the control and general running of the system.

Reputation. Every manufacturing organisation will strive to establish and maintain a good reputation. Such a reputation will be one of the outputs, provided the firm fulfils orders promptly, to specification, in the right quantity at the right price. However, if the firm supplies poor-quality goods at uncompetitive prices, with delays in delivery, a less acceptable output — a bad reputation — will result. A good reputation (hard earned and easily lost) is a key factor in obtaining both new and repeat business.

Inputs and outputs: an overall view

The manufacturing system can now be represented diagrammatically as in Figure 3.3.

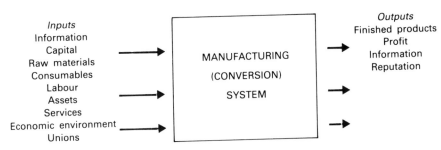

Figure 3.3 *An overall view of inputs and outputs: manufacturing system.*

Controlling the system

As mentioned already, a significant output is information. Some of this information will in fact be taken back into the system for control purposes. In Chapter 1 it was noted that 'controlling' involves the setting or establishment of standards of performance, devising and using methods of measuring and monitoring performance, comparing the standards set with actual performance, and (where necessary) making appropriate adjustments to the system to correct significant deviations from the standards set.

In systems language this is described as measuring the *outputs* of the system against some predetermined standard and *feeding back* the results of this measurement process to a monitor/controller (i.e. some person or piece of equipment capable of noting and dealing with the information appropriately). If deviations or variances from the desired outputs are noted, the controller can make necessary adjustments to the *inputs*. For example, the quality control department could be regarded as the 'monitoring' process. If the chemical analysis of a product reveals the product is not up to standard, then changes to inputs can be made, for example new manufacturing instructions (information), the use of better-quality raw materials, or more highly trained labour.

In this way there is a loop in the system known as a *feedback loop*. The process is illustrated in Figure 3.4.

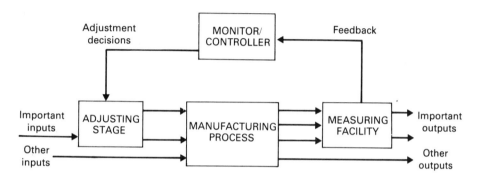

Figure 3.4 *A system with a feedback loop (for control).*

3.4 Objectives of the manufacturing system

In Chapter 1 organisations were defined as groups of people working towards a common objective or set of objectives. As manufacturing systems are examples of organisations (accepting they have physical as well as human resources), it makes sense to ask what the major objectives of a typical manufacturing company are.

A possible way of doing this is to draw up a series of headings round which to frame objectives — market share, new product policies, financial resource needs, labour relations, productivity and so on. An analysis of such a list reveals that we can relate most of the resulting objectives to one which is more fundamental: profitability. Thus many objectives, for example 'to bring out a new product', 'to try a new market' or 'to increase the amount of capital available', can be linked with the major goal of increasing profitability.

Profitability

Profits are desirable, even essential, to any manufacturing company. Such organisations need a continuous stream of financial inputs to buy materials, pay wages and cover other expenses. Where such financial inputs are exceeded by financial outputs, there is a net loss of financial resources in the system. Should such a loss continue over a period, then decline, decay or destruction of the system is inevitable. But even increasing profit (which means a firm can grow and expand) is basically a means of ensuring the survival of the organisation.

Survival

The minimum acceptable objective is the continuing survival of the organisation. Indeed small manufacturing organisations may not wish to grow and expand but just to generate enough profit for survival. (It is even possible in the shorter term that a break-even result (a zero profit) could still ensure survival.)

This means that objectives directly associated with profitability and increased profit will have to be suitably modified (for example 'to maximise increased profits consistent with survival') to include this essential survival objective. Indeed the pursuit of profits, or increased profits, should be regarded as a *long-term* objective. It may be necessary to forgo increased profits (or even any profits at all) in years when the company is being re-organised or re-equipped to meet a new challenge in the environment.

Increased market share

This is another objective which has a 'survival' element in it. Indeed when the total market for a manufactured product is declining, to obtain an increasing share of that market (i.e. take work from competitors) may not result in more sales, but at least ensures survival. When the market is static or expanding, naturally increased sales (and revenue) will result from a successful attempt to increase market share.

Social acceptability

The three objectives mentioned above are *economic* objectives, and until recent times all organisational goals (particularly for firms in the private sector) were stated in economic terms. However, in the last 25 years a feeling has arisen in the Western world that customer service and profit making are *not* the only possible goals. Groups outside firms claim they should have a say in business activities and are able, by forming pressure groups, to attract considerable publicity and influence public opinion.

Firms in today's more open climate of discussion and debate want to be well thought of by society, that is, the general public. However, there are specific sectors they may wish to appeal to, for example customers and suppliers, employees, local communities and pressure groups.

Customers and suppliers. The need for a good reputation among customers and suppliers has already been mentioned. Fair trading practices, honest dealing, truthful advertising and strict observance of the law will assist in the creation of a 'good image'.

Employees. The Government, through industrial legislation (especially health and safety laws), has helped business define what socially acceptable behaviour is. The Sex Discrimination Act and the Race Relations Act have affected employment policies, and tend to cause managements to act in ways that society thinks they should. Firms always like to think they are 'good employers'.

Local communities. A firm cannot pretend to be an island shut off from its local environment. Bad smells, smoke, noise and litter all attract public criticism and perhaps legal consequences. On the positive side, many firms take an active part in local affairs, promoting local charities, providing use of sports facilities or assisting educational establishments in the training of students.

Pressure groups. Particular groups may plead for the retention of old buildings, the preservation of special areas of interest, or the use of particular materials in building. Many firms feel that their social acceptability is enhanced if they can make such concessions.

3.5 Productivity

The term 'productivity' is one which is often misused and misunderstood. It is frequently confused with the similar-looking term 'production'. *Production* is simply another term for output, whilst *productivity* is a measure of *how well* a manufacturing system performs. The concepts of systems theory already discussed in this chapter are helpful in understanding productivity.

Assume a chemical process X has an input of 100 tonnes of raw material and an output of 96 tonnes of saleable product, as shown in Figure 3.5. The relationship or ratio between the output (96 tonnes) and the resources used (the input of 100 tonnes) is the productivity of the process. This ratio is normally expressed by the formula $^o/_t$,

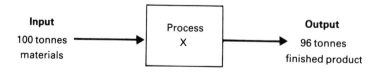

Figure 3.5 *Inputs and outputs compared.*

in this case $^{96}/_{100}$. Now if alterations can be made to process X so that 97 tonnes is produced, the ratio becomes $^{97}/_{100}$ and productivity is said to have *increased*. (It will also be noted that increased productivity can result if the same output as before (96 tonnes) could be achieved with a smaller input of raw material, say 99 tonnes.)

Conversely, productivity of process X would decrease if output were to fall to 95 tonnes with an input of 100 tonnes, or if more inputs (say 101 tonnes) were required to maintain the 96-tonne output.

Productivity and production equipment

It is now clear how production equipment (part of a firm's capital assets) can be used to contribute towards increased productivity. By using specialised, dedicated machinery not only can costs be reduced, but more output can be achieved within a given time than that attainable by less specialised, more labour-intensive machinery. It is hard to conceive how productivity in the oil refinery and processing industries could be as high as it is at present if the equipment used was not capable of high-volume, large-scale production.

Capital assets can be more efficiently used by shift working, for example.

Productivity and product design

Various aspects of product design, through particular attention to the concepts of value analysis and value engineering, are discussed in Chapter 5.

At this stage it is sufficient to note that the aim of a designer or design engineer when developing a product will be to minimise inputs — in fact all the costs of production — without affecting the product's ability to perform the functions required of it or its acceptability to customers. This implies that a designer recognises that:

(a)   some materials are more costly than others for the same use demanded;
(b)   specifying very close tolerances on components will increase costs of production, increase the possibility of scrap/reworking, and increase the cost of quality control;
(c)   special 'finishes' to products will add to production costs;
(d)   the simpler the manufacturing processes used, the less energy is likely to be consumed;
(e)   the use of standard components reduces overall cost.

In these, and many similar ways, the careful design (or redesign) of a product can help to reduce total input costs of production, and thus increase productivity.

Productivity and work methods

Management is constantly encouraging the production function to produce more from the same resources. While Chapter 12 deals with the whole field of work study, here it can be said that *method study* is an activity wholly aimed (by internal examination of the *way* in which a product is made) at making production methods more effective. Typical examples would be: the elimination or combination of processes; the mechanisation or automation of particular jobs, such as handling large quantities of materials or machining large numbers of similar components; or better training of workers so that they produce more efficiently.

The net result of investigations into methods and subsequent changes is to increase productivity by the better use of resources.

Productivity and motivation

Some of the problems of motivation were discussed in Chapter 1. Financial motivation (incentives) are dealt with in Chapter 12, as such incentives are normally based on a work-study investigation of some kind. The basic assumption here is that individuals will work harder (and more efficiently) if there are sufficient rewards for efficient working or good performance.

Financial incentives can work, provided individual workers see the extra reward to be worth the extra effort, that they want (or need) the extra reward, and that they are satisfied that their performance can be measured and attributed to them fairly. From the firm's viewpoint financial incentives are less costly and much simpler to implement than schemes for job enrichment, worker participation, etc.

Another approach is to make sure all workers in a company are *satisfied* workers, the assumption being that contented workers will work hard. (Research tends not to confirm this assumption, though there is likely to be less sickness and absenteeism in firms which attempt to be 'satisfying' organisations.)

A further approach is to assume that workers, like all human beings, have various sets of *needs* (such as money, security, meeting other people, recognition, and some degree of freedom in determining what their jobs will be and how they will do such jobs). Firms which provide work that can offer workers opportunities to satisfy these needs will create conditions in which workers will (it is hoped) work willingly *and* effectively.

Research into such assumptions tends to demonstrate that the 'needs-satisfying' schemes work better for some groups of employees, or individuals, than for others: for the intelligent, highly skilled and independent employees rather than those working in jobs in, say, process, mass, or large-batch production, who necessarily have few opportunities for control over the work.

Finally, there is the notion that motivators are very large in number, and each worker has his or her own individual set of needs/motivators which can change over time, plus other factors like life-experiences, education, fear, need for power or achievement, etc. The aim here is to discover what needs motivate worker *A* today, and provide him or her with suitable opportunities to satisfy them.

What is not in dispute is if the right 'mix' of motivators can be found for groups of workers or individuals, they will work harder, become more efficient, and thus increase their productivity.

Summary

1. A *system* is a related group of elements organised for a purpose.
2. Systems cannot fruitfully be considered in isolation from their environment, as virtually all systems are 'open systems', that is, interacting with the environment.
3. Systems can be classified as:
    (a) closed systems — those with no interaction with their environment;
    (b) open systems — those which interact with their environment, by receiving *inputs*, acting upon the inputs (*conversion process*), and exporting the converted (or transformed) inputs to the environment as *outputs*; the survival of a system depends on receipt of sufficient imputs;
    (c) adaptive systems — those which possess a self-adjusting mechanism which enables variances in input to be coped with;
    (d) probabilistic systems — those about which only general predictions can be made, and with degrees of uncertainty about both inputs and outputs;
    (e) contrived systems — those constructed by people; industrial firms are open, adaptive, probabilistic, and contrived systems.
4. The major inputs to manufacturing systems are:
    (a) information, including orders and information about the economic, cultural and legal environments;
    (b) money with which to start and maintain the business;
    (c) raw materials, the basic products and components used in the manufacturing (conversion) process;
    (d) consumable items, used up in manufacture;
    (e) labour, involved in the conversion processes in the firm;
    (f) assets — the plant and equipment;
    (g) services — energy and outside services supplied;
    (h) business environment — general climate of business opinion;
    (i) social pressures — public views about what is acceptable for manufacturing enterprises to do and what is not;
    (j) trade unions;
    (k) general economic environment of the nation.
5. The major outputs from manufacturing systems are:
    (a) finished products;
    (b) profit (or loss);
    (c) information — data about the outputs; such data, if fed back into the system, can be used to assist in the control and general running of the system;
    (d) reputation — basically a combination of outputs and information about them; acceptable outputs tend to establish a good reputation, while outputs less acceptable to the business environment will help form a bad reputation for the firm.
6. Control of a system involves measuring its outputs against predetermined standards and comparing the two. Variations or differences between the two are noted, and if significant the necessary adjustments are made by the control element. The process is known as a feedback loop.

7. The major objectives of a manufacturing system are:
   (a) profitability;
   (b) survival;
   (c) increased market share;
   (d) social acceptability among customers and suppliers, employees, local communities and pressure groups.

8. 'Productivity' is how well a system performs, and is the relationship between the outputs and the inputs (resources used) of the system, usually expressed by the formula O/I, where O = the production outputs and I the material inputs.

9. 'Production', on the other hand, is the amount of physical output produced by the firm, and is expressed in some quantifiable form — volume, weight, money value, etc.

10. The level of productivity depends a variety of factors, but particularly is affected by:
    (a) production equipment — the use of specialised, dedicated machinery can enhance productivity;
    (b) product design — by building into the design specifications minimum tolerances necessary, using the cheapest material available consistent with safety, function, customer acceptability, etc., productivity is increased through lower manufacturing costs;
    (c) work methods — by selecting the quickest/most efficient ways of manufacturing products, productivity is increased;
    (d) motivation — getting people to work willingly, consistently and efficiently helps to keep costs down and reduce manufacturing times, both of which increase productivity.

Questions

Review questions

3.1 Why cannot we isolate an object, person or manufacturing system from its surroundings?

3.2 What is the definition of a system?

3.3 Compare and contrast open and closed systems. Is a prison a closed system? If so, why?

3.4 Describe, with appropriate diagrams, the flow of information and materials through a manufacturing system.

3.5 In what ways can a manufacturing system be 'adaptive'?

3.6 List and discuss:
   (a) the inputs;
   (b) the outputs;
   of a manufacturing system.

3.7 Show how two of the major objectives of a firm — profitability and survival — are related.

3.8 Why is social acceptability now such an important objective for firms? What are the consequences of performing unacceptable acts (e.g. polluting local rivers or streams, or allowing the escape of dangerous chemicals in the atmosphere)?

3.9   Distinguish between production and productivity.
3.10   Explain how production equipment, product design, work methods and motivation can enhance productivity.

Discussion topics
_____

3.11   In what ways are a college, a canned baked-bean factory and brewery similar as systems (i.e. in terms of the flow of information and materials through the systems)? Discuss how the inputs, conversion processes and outputs differ.
3.12   What would happen if a business organisation stopped receiving most of its inputs (for example if there were a postal/telegraphic/road delivery strike)? What would happen to the equilibrium of the organisation? Could it be restored?
3.13   Discuss the view that the major objective of a manufacturing company should be to increase production.
3.14   Consider what people want from work. Discuss in groups *five* possibilities other than money and compare the results.

Assignments
_____

3.15   Take any local manufacturing organisation and draw a systems diagram listing as many inputs as possible (specifying by name individual material inputs, for example), explaining the conversion processes in the system, and finally listing the outputs.
3.16   Taking the same or any other manufacturing organisation, explain in what ways the firm attempts to achieve the major objectives discussed in this chapter.
3.17   Visit, by arrangement, a local manufacturing firm. Examine the production machinery and write a short report on how it contributes to productivity. Suggest what changes are necessary so that productivity can be further improved.

Case study
_____

3.18   John Standfast, General Manager of Volatile Chemicals' Northville Plant, had a meeting last week with the Northville Ecology Group and some local councillors. They pointed out there had been numerous press stories, as well as individual letters of complaint, about the noisy operations of the plant, the frequency of very nasty smells in nearby residential areas, and the occasional leakage of liquid chemicals from an outside holding compound into local streams.

John had explained the company's policy of gradually reducing atmospheric pollution by installing the latest plant as the old became obsolete, and the difficulties they had in storing chemicals before delivery. The noise resulted from urgent maintenance work carried out at night and on Sundays, when the plant was closed. However, John had promised to look into the matters raised again.

Shortly after the delegation had gone, John spoke about their complaints to Charlotte Bunsen, the chief chemist. 'We must do something soon,' he said, 'These people are well known, and before long we'll have enforcement orders and health and safety inspectors on the doorstep.'

'We're doing all we can,' replied Bunsen, 'but the major problem is that of cost. Things are not easy now, especially as large shareholders are pressing us to increase our market share and keep profits up.

'To re-equip the whole plant would cost three years' profits now: we just haven't the money available. Worse, we'd be scrapping plant with years of useful life in it, and we'd be losing lots of production capacity while the changeover took place. Productivity as well as production would be low and our very survival as a plant would be threatened.

'The last straw would be if the council issued enforcement notices or prosecuted us: we'd have to close down. After all, we do employ 40 per cent of Northville's working population. Tell that to your visitors!'

(a) Do you agree with Bunsen that profits now should be the company's primary objective?

(b) Can the company in fact survive without some changes?

(c) What do you feel John Standfast should decide, and what should he tell his visitors when they follow up their visit next month?

4

Product Performance and Production Methods

The first part of this chapter consists of an introduction to *costing* (considered in more detail in Chapter 13) and in particular deals with the contribution made by an individual product to a firm's overall (i.e. financial) performance.

The second part considers different types of production, and the factors which constitute them.

4.1 Product performance

The primary objective of a firm should be to make a profit.[1] Indeed, when we are called upon to measure the performance of a company, we would normally concentrate on the amount of profit (or loss) it has made. The quality of its products, the calibre of its staff and the excellence of its technology would all be important, but the most significant yardstick is profit.

What exactly is meant by 'profit' (sometimes called 'a profit', or simply 'profits')? A profit is that sum of money left over (the balance) from all the money taken in sales (the sales revenue), after all the bills have been paid. More simply, for the operations of a firm, this situation can be expressed as:

Profit = Sales revenue − Total costs

Figure 4.1 shows the relationships between sales, costs and profit diagrammatically. Sales revenue is £25 000 and the total costs are £15 000. The remainder, the balance of £10 000, is profit. This example deals with the operations of a firm, XYZ Ltd, making one product over a period, but the same idea would hold good for other individual products, and similar diagrams could be constructed.

---

[1] Some organisations, particularly state-owned ones, may be run at a loss knowingly, but, even here, the aim is to keep that loss as small as possible.

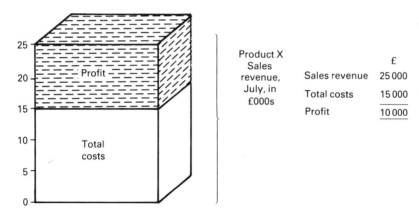

Figure 4.1   *Relationships between sales, costs and profits, XYZ Ltd.*

In the real world, however, selling prices (and thus sales revenue) are influenced by the competition of rival manufacturers, and there is often a 'maximum desirable' selling price. To increase the selling price of a product beyond this level could lead to a considerable, if not total, loss of business.

If costs are not known they cannot be controlled; if they cannot be controlled they could exceed the selling prices imposed by competition. It is vital therefore for any firm to know what the total costs of a business are at any given time, and indeed forecast what they might be in the future to a fair degree of accuracy.

If the firm concerned is a small one, and only one product is made and sold, Figure 4.1 explains the whole story simply and clearly. The money from sales comes from the sales of one product alone. The total expenses of the business — down to the last nut and bolt, even the last paper clip — can be set against the production of the one product. What is left is the profit from the manufacture and sale of one product.

However, most manufacturing businesses do not depend upon one product alone: even where one kind of product is made — fork-lift trucks, for example — there can be a wide range of models, with different features and optional extras. The difficulty now arises in identifying the performance of each different product or model, or deciding which is worth while continuing to make, and which is not.

To appreciate why this difficulty is an important and a real one, it will be necessary to look at the process of 'costing' in more detail.

4.2 Costing

The process of 'costing' involves identifying, classifying and recording money paid out arising from the manufacture of goods (or provision of a service), so that the total costs of products or services can be ascertained.

Classifying costs

Costs can be 'classified' or grouped together in different ways. It will be useful at this stage to consider a detailed example.

Example. Bill Makegood, a leading fitter with a bicycle manufacturer, lost his job last year. With his redundancy money, plus a bank loan, he set up Makegood Ltd to manufacture handmade racing bicycles to order. The new firm was sited on a council trading estate to take advantage of two years' subsidised rent and rates, and a lease/hire scheme for expensive equipment.

Quite quickly Bill found a market. He also discovered the need for a telephone, electric power, and a postal franking machine to deal with overseas inquiries. He took on two fitter/mechanics. He also purchased outright a whole series of small tools, oils and miscellaneous equipment, and steel tubing for frame making, as well as metal for other parts. The part-time typist he engaged suggested appropriate stationery, and helped organise a storeroom for the spokes, saddles, tyres and other spares that Makegood Ltd would make themselves. A local carrier was employed to deliver bicycles to customers.

To begin with, Bill made only one model, the 'Speedmaster', but when Tom Figgures (the accountant Bill hired to check the books) drew up a balance sheet after six months, it was clear that Bill had a profitable business. Last week, however, Bill told Tom he intended to launch two new models — the 'Velocity' and the 'Swift'. 'I shall need,' he said, 'to know how each model contributes to the success of Makegood.'

A standard primary method of classifying costs is under *three* headings:

1. Materials costs: the costs of raw materials, components or finished goods supplied to a firm.
2. Labour (wages) costs: the costs of wages, salaries, bonuses, commissions, etc. paid to the employees of the company.
3. Expense costs: the costs of the various services rendered to the firm by outside agencies. (It is also usual to include under this heading amounts to cover the wear and tear ('depreciation') of assets owned by the company, such as plant and equipment used in manufacture.)

Using this classification in the case of Makegood Ltd, we can obtain the split of costs shown in Table 4.1.

These costs can also be represented diagrammatically as in Figure 4.2. (To arrive at the total figures shown, it would have been necessary to work out each individual cost, and add together all those within the same classification.)

The direct/indirect classification

A second method of classifying costs is into direct and indirect costs.

Table 4.1 *Breakdown of costs: Makegood Ltd.*

Materials	Labour	Expenses
Oils	Two mechanics'	Bank loan interest
Small tools	wages	Rent (part)
Steel tubing	Part-time	Rates (part)
Spokes	typist's wages	Equipment lease/hire
Tyres, saddles, etc.		Telephone
		Power (heat, light, etc.)
		Postal charges
		Carrier's fees
		Accountant's fees
		Insurances

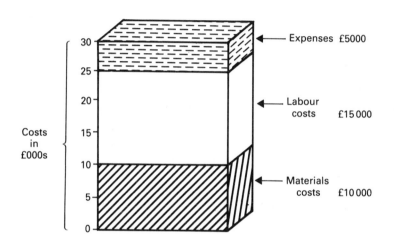

Figure 4.2 *Makegood Ltd: cost breakdown.*

Direct (production) costs. These are costs which can be clearly identified as relating to the actual production of one of a firm's products. Such costs can be further split into:

1. Direct material costs: costs of new materials, or components (even other firms' finished products) incorporated in the final product.
2. Direct labour (wages) costs: costs of wages which arise from work carried out during the manufacture of the final product, and which can be clearly identified as belonging to that product. Basically such personnel as machine operators, bench hands or assembly-line workers come under this heading.
3. Direct expenses: costs other than material or labour costs which can be identified as relating to the manufacture of a specific final product. Working drawings, special tools and even travelling expenses involved in the design stage would be included, provided the whole charge is related to the one specific final product.

The combined total of the three direct (production) costs (material, labour and expenses) is called the *prime cost*.

Indirect (production) costs.   These are costs which cannot be clearly identified as relating to the actual production of one of a firm's products. Such costs can be further split into:

1. Indirect material costs: costs of materials which are used in production, but which cannot be easily or clearly traced back directly to a specific product, for example, oils, cotton waste, nuts, bolts, screws or nails. (Most of such items are used up in production and are generally termed 'consumables'.)
2. Indirect labour (wages) costs: costs of wages paid to personnel who, although not engaged in the actual production of specific products, are indirectly connected with production. Such personnel would include employees working in staff departments — maintenance, quality control or welfare, for example — as well as labourers, utility workers, and even supervisors in production departments.
3. Indirect expenses: costs other than indirect material or wages costs which relate to production, but which cannot be allocated easily to any specific product. For example, splitting up the total heating charge that Bill Makegood has to meet between his three models — Speedmaster, Velocity and Swift — could be a difficult undertaking. Power generally, and such items as rents, rates and insurance of factory premises, are indirect expenses.

The combined total of these indirect production costs — material, labour and expenses — is called the *factory overheads*. These overheads are sometimes called 'on cost'.

Other overheads (non-manufacturing overheads)

The remaining costs incurred by an organisation are neither directly nor indirectly related to the production function. Such costs include:

(a)   wages paid to office staff, executives and directors;
(b)   research and development;
(c)   selling expenses;
(d)   transport.

These 'other overheads' can conveniently be split into:

1. Administration. This will include costs incurred by all departments *not* concerned with production, selling/distribution, or research and development. Examples of such costs are those incurred in running departments like personnel, accounts and secretarial, and reception, telephones, lifts, etc. — in fact all typical office-block costs.
2. Selling/distribution. This will include the costs of all marketing, selling and distribution activities. Examples of such costs are sales manager's salary, sales representatives' commission, running and maintenance costs of delivery vehicles, drivers' wages, and advertising and other sales promotions.

3.   Research and development. This will include costs incurred in researching into, or developing, new products, or in seeking to improve existing ones. As research and development staff are usually engaged simultaneously on several projects — and many projects indeed fail before completion — it is difficult to relate the costs incurred either to individual products or indeed to production at all.

The combined total of these three other overheads — administration, selling/distribution and research and development — is called the *non-manufacturing overheads*.

Elements of cost

It will be seen from the above direct/indirect classification that the total costs of a factory's operation can be divided into a number of elements, which can be grouped together in various combinations. Each element is given a particular name.

Element 1: the prime costs.   The prime costs comprise the labour and materials used in production, plus any expenses clearly identified as being manufacturing ones, as shown in Figure 4.3.

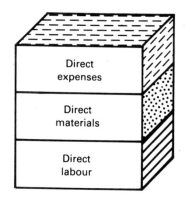

Figure 4.3   *Prime costs.*

Element 2: the factory overheads.   Factory overheads comprise the labour and materials used indirectly in association with production, plus any running expenses which cannot be clearly allocated to particular products, as shown in Figure 4.4.

Element 3: the non-manufacturing overheads.   The non-manufacturing overheads comprise the administration, selling and distribution expenses, and the costs of research and development in the organisation, as shown in Figure 4.5.

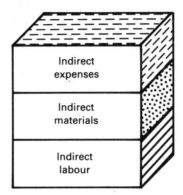

Figure 4.4   *Factory overheads.*

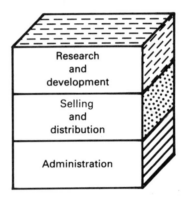

Figure 4.5   *Non-manufacturing overheads.*

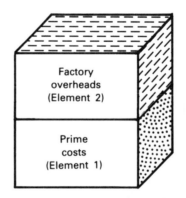

Figure 4.6   *Factory costs.*

Element 4: factory costs. 'Factory costs' is a term given to the combined totals of Elements 1 and 2, i.e. prime costs and factory overheads, as shown in Figure 4.6.

Element 5: total costs. 'Total costs' is a term given to the combined totals of Elements 1, 2 and 3, i.e. prime costs, factory overheads and non-manufacturing overheads, as shown in Figure 4.7.

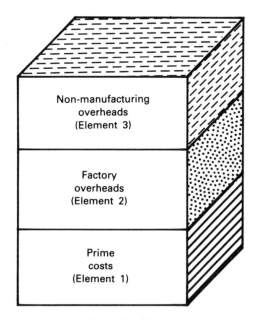

Figure 4.7 *Total costs.*

4.3 Sales revenue, costs and profits

We can now return to Figure 4.1 (at the beginning of this chapter). The example of XYZ Ltd can now be seen to be incomplete: the total costs have not been broken down into Elements 1, 2 and 3. Figure 4.8 now shows this breakdown, assuming each element of cost totals £5000.

4.4 Individual product costs

So far we have concentrated on breaking down a firm's total costs, that is, the combined total of all the costs of all the products it makes. The next step will be to apply this analysis to individual products.

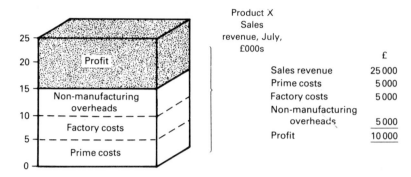

Figure 4.8 *Relationships between sales, the various costs and profit, XYZ Ltd.*

Material costs

These will be the direct material costs applicable to the individual product. Thus, in the case of Bill Makegood's Speedmaster model, the costs of everything bought (such as tubing, tyres, spokes, etc.) for the manufacture of that model can be recorded and totalled. The final figure is normally easily calculable.

Labour costs

These will be the direct labour costs applicable to the individual product, for example the time spent in bending, shaping, braizing, filing, drilling, polishing and assembling Speedmaster bicycles. Such time can be recorded and converted into the wages paid for each task. Again the final figure for labour costs is normally easily calculable.

Expenses

These will be the direct labour costs applicable to the individual product.

Other costs

As we have seen, the direct costs for each product can quite easily be recorded and calculated. Even where sub-assemblies (such as wheels) are used on more than one model, a check on production records will quickly reveal how many wheels were allocated to each model. Labour and expenses are also relatively easy to allocate correctly.

Problems arise when we start to ask what proportion of indirect costs should be allocated to a particular product. Which model — Swift, Velocity or Speedmaster — should bear the cost of the rent, rates or wages of the part-time typist? How should the carrier bills be split when a load of all three models is delivered to a retail outlet? How can Bill Makegood work out the profitability of each model when some costs are virtually unidentifiable with any one of them (the telephone bill, for example). Answers to some of these questions are discussed in Chapter 13, but it must be stressed at this stage that *any* method used to allocate 'other costs' is bound to be arbitrary. Bill can, however, use another yardstick to compare his models: he can work out the *contribution* of each.

4.5 Product contribution

Working out a product's contribution is called 'contribution costing' (sometimes 'marginal costing'). Contribution costing is based on a third classification of costs: between 'variable' and 'fixed' costs.

Variable costs are those costs which vary virtually in step with output.[2] It will quickly be seen that all prime costs are variable ones: every batch of bicycles Bill makes will need more material and more labour. Some factory overheads will also vary with output.

Fixed costs, on the other hand, are those costs which tend to remain unchanged even if output fluctuates: typical fixed costs are rates, rent, building maintenance and management salaries. All non-manufacturing overheads and some factory overheads are fixed costs.[3]

The term 'contribution costing' is used because in this method of looking at costs, it is the *contribution* the product makes (or fails to make) to:

(a) paying off the firm's fixed costs;
(b) profits

which is being measured. The formula, then, for any given period of time, is:

Contribution = Sales revenue − Variable costs

Example. Product X has a sales revenue in July of £25 000. Labour and material costs total £10 000, and variable costs are £5000. Fixed costs are £8000. Calculate the contribution and profits. The answer is shown diagrammatically in Figure 4.9.

Calculating a product's contribution

The steps for calculating a product's contribution are:

1. Work out the prime costs incurred in a given period.
2. Work out the variable overheads applicable to the product in the period.

---

[2] The amount of scrap must affect this proportion slightly.
[3] Some of the latter are also 'semi-variable', i.e. partly fixed, partly variable. Consideration of this group is not included here in the interests of simplicity.

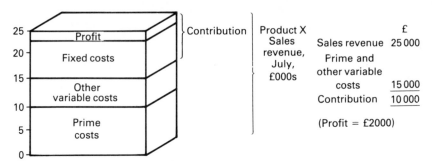

Figure 4.9   *A product's contribution.* (Note: *Contribution is* not *the same as profit, though it can include* some *profit.*)

3.   Add the totals of steps 1 and 2.
4.   Work out the sales revenue obtained in the period.
5.   Subtract the total of step 3 from the total of step 4.

Total company contribution (contribution addition)

By adding together the contributions from each product in the company's range a total company contribution (TCC) can be calculated. By subtracting from the TCC the sum total of all the fixed costs, a profit figure can be obtained for the firm as a whole.

4.6 Comparing product contributions

The following example shows, by concentrating on a product's contribution, that comparisons can be made with other products.

Example.   Makegood Ltd manufacture four models of bicycle: Pegasus, Speedmaster, Swift and Velocity. The accountant produces a set of figures detailing sales, costs and profits. (The total of £51 500 of fixed overheads is allocated arbitrarily by Tom Figgures among the products.)

Model	Pegasus	Speedmaster	Swift	Velocity	Totals
	£	£	£	£	£
Sales revenue	20 000	60 000	50 000	30 000	160 000
Prime costs	10 000	17 500	22 500	10 000	60 000
Variable overheads	4 000	10 000	10 000	5 000	29 000
Fixed costs	4 000	20 000	22 500	5 000	51 500
Profit	2 000	12 500	—	10 000	19 500
Loss	—	—	5 000	—	—

Bill Makegood sees the figures and concludes that the Swift was a loss-maker and should be discontinued. However, when he calculates the effect of dropping the Swift — assuming the sales of the other models remain constant — he finds the following result (remembering that the £51 500 of fixed overheads will remain, and will not be reduced by £22 500 if the Swift is discontinued, the accountant redistributing the £51 500 among the remaining products):

	Present totals	–	*Swift*	=	*Revised totals*
	£		£		£
Sales revenue	160 000		50 000		110 000
Prime costs	60 000		22 500		37 500
Variable overheads	29 000		10 000		19 000
Fixed costs	51 500		—		51 500
Profit	19 500				2 000

Bill then discovers that the drop in profit, £17 500 is exactly equal to the *contribution* of the Swift (i.e. SR £50 000 – PC and VO £32 500). It would be disastrous to drop the Swift. He also discovers the contributions of the four models to be: Pegasus, £6000; Speedmaster, £32 500; Swift, £17 500; and Velocity, £15 000.

It will be seen from this example that in planning for maximum profit, emphasis should be given to each product's contribution.

4.7 Types of production (production systems)

Following the scheme adopted by Joan Woodward,[4] based on research carried out between 1953 and 1957 in South Essex, within 203 manufacturing firms, production systems can broadly be divided into three major categories. Little dispute exists about the categories themselves, although there is some difference of opinion about the names given to them. Typically the three categories are called job/small batch, large batch and mass production, and process production. The divisions between each are not sharp, and there is a degree of overlap between them.

Job/small batch production

This category includes 'one-offs', special orders, fabrication of equipment in stages, technically complex units, prototype equipment and research (i.e. purpose-built) machinery. Also under this heading come repairs, special modifications, runs of two

---

[4] Woodward, J. (1958) *Management and Technology*. London: HMSO.

or three only, and sufficiently small batches for a large proportion of 'hand-made' work, or unusual methods of production.

Job/small batch production could entail either the bringing of raw materials, components and sub-assemblies to one place for building up a finished product, or the passing through of an item from department to department in a firm, with a new, non-routine operation being performed upon it at each stage.

A wide variety of enterprises (usually small but not necessarily so) use this production system: bespoke tailors, ship- or bridge-builders, garage repair workshops, specialised prototype manufacturers or makers of specialised machinery, racing car manufacturers, coach builders, welders — even monumental masons.

Implications for management

1. This 'one-off' type of production (whether building a factory or supplying purpose-built equipment) is usually made to order, and rarely for stock. No current orders = no current work.
2. Plant, machinery and tools used will need to be wide-ranging and versatile, with the same equipment being used on different jobs.
3. The workforce will also need to be versatile and flexible, possessing various skills and being able to think of ways round problems.
4. Time spent in planning each job, setting up tools and equipment, checking fits, etc. will be relatively high.
5. Management/supervision will need to be technically qualified, imaginative and good at problem solving; they will act as advisers to their trained workforce.
6. The cost of manufacture/individual repair will be high, direct labour being the largest single element of cost except possibly where very expensive materials (e.g. gold) are used.

Machinery layout.   There will be no 'standard' form of layout: often the siting of materials and equipment will be dictated by the premises used and the most suitable place for assembly to take place.

Large batch/mass production

This is a fairly wide category: at one end of its spectrum we find production of components in medium or large batches, subsequently assembled in diverse ways (almost overlapping with the first category), and at the opposite end, a mixture of batch and 'flow' production (discussed in the next section).

Large batch/mass production systems have in common one special characteristic: *all* the items or components in a particular batch are put through a specific operation before *all* are moved on to the next operation. Each batch thus assumes a separate identity, and is often individually labelled or ticketed.

This production system is commonly found where quantities of identical items are required (varying from a few dozen to several thousands). Examples of products made in this way include 'off the peg' suits or military uniforms, books, a large range of motor-vehicle parts from engines to electric motors for car heaters, standard ranges of furniture and tape cassettes — in fact a myriad of everyday items.

Implications for management

1. While production will endeavour to match sales, production can proceed (for a time at least) without current orders for specific lines. Storage space for components, and adequate capital (money) to finance such stocks, will be required.
2. A wide range of different tasks and jobs are carried out, so machinery used is (as for job/small batch) general- and multi-purpose, but the machines themselves will be 'grouped to function', that is, particular types of machines will be concentrated together.
3. This grouping to function entails specialist supervision, tool-setting, and final inspection procedures.
4. Production is either to fulfil customers' orders or to build up stocks in anticipation of sales. In either case there is a need to control stocks and to schedule orders correctly to ensure the most profitable and convenient quantities are produced. Stopping lines to change over to other products halfway through a run is very expensive: machine loading planning is also crucial. Order progress needs careful monitoring.
5. Production control is even more necessary if there is a basic product sold with small differences or optional extras — varying thread sizes, different colours or finishes, for example.
6. The degree of skill of the labour force will vary with the degree of automation: high with the smaller batches, and semi-skilled or even unskilled labour in assembly departments. Such labour must be versatile, however, to cope with a wide range of different products.
7. Both a product design/drawing office function and a sound purchasing back-up are essential.
8. Whilst management/supervision need not know every detail of every job, or be experts in all the machinery used, they must be able to spot trouble and seek appropriate assistance.
9. A well-developed costing system to monitor all cost elements is called for, as material as well as labour costs are significant.

Machinery layout. This category (i.e. large batch/mass production) is a wide one. The process or 'functional' (i.e. grouped to function) layout of machinery predominates in firms producing batches of a wide range of different products. On the other hand, in mass production, where very large quantities of a few products are made, then a layout by product, or 'line layout' as it is sometimes called, is more appropriate.

Hybrid arrangements — a combination of the two processes (group technology) or process and product existing side by side in the same factory — are a third variation.

A fuller description of these layouts is given in Chapter 9, 'Facilities Layouts'.

Flow/process production

A major characteristic of this production system is the ordering of all the various operations in a fixed, predetermined sequence. Products pass from one operation to the next, often without any delay (as opposed to the waiting/queuing which could occur between operations in the large batch type of production). Examples of goods made by this method include motor vehicles (i.e. the assembly of the components) and a wide range of household articles such as washing machines and dishwashers; a completely different group includes various food products — sweet bars, chocolates, etc. — and beverages such as milk and beer. In its purest form, flow production is used for the manufacture of industrial gases and other chemicals, and the refining of petrol.

Thus a wide variety of firms, some very large, use flow production: engineering could be represented by British Leyland, chemicals by ICI, glassware by Pilkington, milk pasteurisation and bottling by Unigate, paper-making by Bowaters.

Implications for management

1. Large capital (money) investments in plant (often specialist) are required: to be assured of a profitable business, a secure, known market must exist, with a steady demand for the product(s).
2. The sequence of operations needs the most careful planning: there can be no 'rescheduling' once a job has started — particularly where food and drink are involved.
3. Particularly with engineering/manufacture, all components and sub-assemblies must arrive where they are expected on time. (Work in progress needs constant monitoring.)
4. The flow must be kept going: management are vulnerable to union pressure or threats, as heavy losses can be incurred by a shutdown.
5. Similarly, breakdowns are a threat: procedures should be worked out to minimise or eliminate the possible damage of a stoppage in production.[5]
6. A careful plan of preventive maintenance during shutdown periods needs to be drawn up.
7. In all cases, and especially with consumable bio-products, a 'standard' quality must be maintained: inspection must be highly efficient and quality control stringent. Highly paid technical staff may be required to do this work.
8. Purchasing has to be carefully controlled: raw materials of the required specifications and quality must always be available.
9. There must be a careful check on all inputs and outputs, and their costs. All scrap or wastage must be accounted for.
10. Management and supervision must be 'process' experts, and be able to monitor the performance of the equipment and the staff. The workforce will possibly be smaller than in batch production, but should be large enough to cover absentees, holidays, rest periods, etc. Present indications are that workforce numbers in

---

[5] Some processes are extremely vulnerable if they ever stop: blast furnaces and the Pilkington glass-making system, for example.

flow processes will decline in the future, as tasks are increasingly taken over by monitoring equipment serving computer systems.
11. Full utilisation of the specialist equipment and machinery brings large savings. Largest costs will be the equipment; material costs will be significant, labour costs less so.

Out of factory production

Finally, to complete the list, it should be noted that one further option is available to a firm: to put out to another company the work of making components, sub-assemblies or even complete articles for which it has orders. This course of action is called 'subcontracting'.

Typical reasons for subcontracting are: lack of specialist machinery to carry out certain tasks required in production; lack of equipment capacity (all machines fully booked); lack of appropriate labour and skills; the urgency of a particular order.

Even quite large concerns may, for example, never undertake the plating of their products, and may subcontract to specialist chromium, nickel or silver platers.

Summary

1. The primary objective of a producing organisation is to make a profit (or, if state-owned or subsidised, to minimise its true loss). Profits cannot be calculated unless costs are known. Costs that are unknown cannot be controlled.
2. Profits = Sales revenue − Costs
3. A calculation to establish profits if the firm is small and makes only one product is simple. It is much more complex to analyse the profitability of large firms making different ranges of products.
4. Costing involves identifying, classifying and recording money paid out by a firm in the course of manufacture so that the total costs of production can be ascertained.
5. Costs can be classified in various ways:
    (a) Materials/labour (wages)/expenses.
    (b) Direct/indirect — *direct* being costs clearly identified as relating to the actual production of a product, *indirect* being costs which, while associated with production, cannot be clearly identified as belonging to a specific product.
    (c) A combination of (a) and (b). The total of the direct costs — materials, labour and expenses — being known as the *prime cost* and the total of the indirect costs — materials, labour and expenses — being known as the *factory overheads*.
    (d) Non-manufacturing overheads, further divided into administration costs, selling/distribution, and research and development costs.
6. The elements of cost are therefore:
    (a) *Prime costs* = Direct materials + Labour + Expenses

(b)   *Factory overheads* = Indirect materials + Labour + Expenses

(c)   *Factory costs* = Prime costs + Factory overheads

(d)   *Total costs* = Factory costs + Non-manufacturing overheads

7. When total costs are subtracted from total sales revenue, the firm's profits are revealed.

8. Individual products can be costed. However, while the *direct* costs of a product can easily be calculated, the extra added to the prime costs to cover part of the rest of the firm's costs (i.e. fixed costs or overheads) is allocated in a fairly arbitrary way.

9. Making comparisons, using total product costs, between one product and another (in respect of profitability) is difficult. A different solution is to use the contribution a product makes to overheads and profit as a basis for comparison.

10. Using this method costs are divided into variable (e.g. prime costs) and fixed costs. Once these are calculated, the following formula is applied:

Contribution = Sales revenue − Variable costs

11. The contribution method of comparison can clearly show that a product, X, which seemingly is made 'at a loss' from a traditional costing point of view, does make a significant contribution to the firm's prosperity.

12. Production systems can be divided into three major categories:

(a)   job/small batch (one-off, specialist, small-run jobs);

(b)   large batch/mass production (a wide category covering the manufacture of large batches of components, and production approaching the continuous flow system);

(c)   flow/process production (a continuous process of manufacture, e.g. assembly line, the brewing process).

13. Each system has its own characteristics: in job/small batch the product remains stationary and materials, tools, etc. are brought to the product. In large batch/mass production each product passes through the various stages of manufacture in sequence. There can, however, be queuing and delay between stages. In a flow process system the sequence of stages is very precisely laid down: each product goes through the sequence in a continuous, uninterrupted flow.

Questions

Review questions

4.1   What is meant by 'profit'? Why are profits important?

4.2   Explain what is meant by 'costs' and why we should attempt to calculate them.

4.3   Distinguish between:

(a)   materials and labour costs;

(b)   direct and indirect costs;

(c)   factory overheads and non-manufacturing overheads;

(d)   fixed and variable costs;

(e)   prime costs and factory costs.

4.4   Define 'total costs'.

4.5   State the formula and method for calculating the 'contribution'. Why is contribution so called?

4.6   What are the three basic production systems as adopted by Joan Woodward?

4.7   Define 'job production'. In this production system is the use of each piece of plant and equipment less than, equal to, or more than that of flow production? Why?

4.8   What type of production would you expect to find used in the manufacture of the following items:
  (a)   formula 1 racing cars;
  (b)   television sets (popular models);
  (c)   jeans;
  (d)   car exhaust systems;
  (e)   shoes;
  (f)   jump jets?

Discussion topics

4.9   Is it really important to know the precise contributions of each individual product made by a firm? Surely if the company makes a reasonable profit and there is work for all, there is no need to spend time on unnecessary paperwork. Discuss.

4.10 Do you agree that Joan Woodward's production system classification into three categories is realistic? Can you suggest an alternative scheme?

Assignment

4.11 Each student should compile a list of at least *two* firms in each of the three production systems discussed, obtaining the information from class visits, individual visits during holidays, class members' experience, or after discussion with colleagues at work. In a short report (to include the list) comment on any difficulties encountered in putting organisations into one or other of the categories. Are there any special cases?

Case study

4.12 Ivor Burden, the Works Manager of Acme Engineering, was wondering whether to accept an order from Gadgets Ltd for a large batch of electric motors. The recession meant that every order was needed to ensure the company's survival. Now the answer to his prayers was on his desk.

The problem was that the order was conditional on a firm promise to deliver within one month, but success with the order could lead to more business in the future. However, due to redundancies, labour was already fully committed. Should he refuse the order, take it on with some overtime, or subcontract?

Ivor had the following information on costs:

	Day work	Overtime
Expected sales revenue	37 500	37 500
Direct labour	12 500	15 000
Direct materials	9 450	9 450
Contribution	£15 550	£13 050

Quickmake Ltd quoted £23 900 for the work, delivery promised in 14 days.

(a) What course of action would you advise Ivor to take on the information given?
(b) Is there any more information you would like in front of you before *you* make a similar decision?
(c) What are the relative merits of the courses of action you have *not* recommended?

5
Value Analysis, Value Engineering and Cost Effectiveness

In this chapter the notions of value analysis and value engineering are introduced and the terms 'standardisation', 'specialisation' and 'simplification' are explained. The concept of cost effectiveness is considered: its application to the use of different processes, and its relationship to product volume.

5.1 Value analysis

Some years ago an employee of a car component manufacturers watched goods from his own company being brought into the stores of one of the big car manufacturers. He was fascinated to see one particular component unwrapped: outer cartons were ripped open and discarded, inner packages were similarly treated, protective paper wrapped round each component was thrown away, and finally a plastic thread protector was removed from a screwed shank projecting from each component. Finally the naked items were placed in the stores bins appropriate to that product.

The incident set him thinking. Why was all that packaging necessary, and what was the purpose of fitting the thread protector? Concentrating merely on the second question saved his company a great deal of money, as he proved on his return to the company that the thread protector was unnecessary, served no useful function, and was of no value to the customer. The cost of purchasing the protectors was not great — a few pence each — but thousands of the components were supplied monthly, and a further cost was labour used in fitting them.

To an outsider, the situation described is glaringly obvious: it was not to the firms concerned. Regrettably, every day many firms spend money unnecessarily in production, making items which are over-elaborate and which contain refinements that may not be required. This is where value analysis is important.

Value analysis: definitions

Many definitions of value analysis exist. Typical of many is that given in the *Fontana Dictionary of Modern Thought*,[1] which concentrates on the major objective: cost reduction. Cost reduction is significant, but much more can be achieved by the use of value analysis. Indeed we may not be able in a particular case to reduce costs by a single penny, but we could end up with a product which has a greater (sales) appeal, an increased range of functions, or is more convenient to use: in fact, a product which is 'more value for money'.

    Value analysis, then, is that technique with which we critically and systematically examine the design of an existing product, to determine whether any or all of the following improvements can be made:

(a)   satisfaction of customers' requirements more precisely;
(b)   reduction in costs;
(c)   same or even better performance at lower cost;
(d)   use of less difficult, less complicated, more convenient methods of manufacture;
(e)   elimination or simplification of some processes;
(f)   use of less expensive (or more easily obtainable) materials;
(g)   removal of embellishments which serve no function;
(h)   greater use of standard parts;
(i)   ensuring extra costs are not expended in making components which have a much longer life expectancy than the product as a whole;
(j)   production of a more stylish, even beautiful, product, or one that is more pleasing to possess.

(Note: There are some ideas which are attractive at first sight, but are not within a true value analysis approach: eliminating special finishes from the hidden parts of products is an example. Indeed car manufacturers are now coming round to the view that whole-car anti-rust treatment is a good selling point.)

    An illustration of this process was a decision made by a firm some years ago to change from making the outer 'box' of some car heaters out of metal to making it out of plastic. The metal version was complicated to make. Various sections of a complex shape were pressed out and then assembled with nuts and bolts or spot welds. Painting took place in a purpose-built plant. Inspection was necessary at every stage. Now the plastic injection moulding method automatically produces the complete complex shape in two halves, ready coloured. The final product is also rust-proof.

Value engineering

Value analysis is the technique applied to *existing* products. Value engineering is the same technique applied to the design right from the start of *new* products.

---

[1] Bullock, Lord and Stallybrass, O. (1977) *Fontana Dictionary of Modern Thought*. London: Fontana.

Value

A prime objective of a value analysis approach is to give value to the customer — 'value for money'. This value can be analysed under three headings:

1. Economic value. No matter how wonderful a product is, whatever its technical superiority, if it is not offered at a cost acceptable to prospective buyers it will not sell. Thus, the cheaper the product the more economic value it has (except where a high price in itself is attractive to certain people).
2. Use value. A product must be able to perform the essential functions expected of it. Cheaper alternative methods of production are fine, provided the new version performs at least as effectively as the old.
3. Esteem value. The extent to which a product is attractive to buyers or users, the prestige attached to ownership (Rolls-Royce cars), or the general respect an article is given (Concorde, a Victoria Cross, the Flying Scotsman) is a product's esteem value.

In the process of value analysis, cost reductions should be attempted if, and only if, both use and esteem values remain intact, or are enhanced.

Product specification

It is to be hoped that the time spent on designing a product will not be wasted and the product will have a fair chance of being produced and sold. Products are designed for a market, and firms are increasingly coming to realise that the design, manufacture and marketing of a product are but three elements of a single project. Thus the design team will need to work with purchasing and production, sales and marketing. This means that the eventual product specification will be affected by such matters as the raw materials, the tools and equipment available, the customers' requirements (their specifications), and the current state of production technology.

A product specification is basically a document or set of documents and/or drawings giving a detailed description of the product, with the dimensions, materials and quality of the work, together with the directions to be followed in making the product. To arrive at the final list of specifications, the end product as made and sold is taken as the objective. The design team work backwards, splitting the product into its component parts. Each sub-assembly or piece part is identified and described, with its material and such qualities as strength, weight, cost, appearance and quantity listed. In turn this leads back to the raw materials or bought-in components from which the sub-assemblies are made, and for which similar specific requirements are laid down.

In fact conventions have arisen specifying, for example, machined parts. The Opitz system, developed in Germany, uses a five-digit code to describe the *shape* of the component, internal and external, and a supplementary code to deal with miscellaneous details such as the shape of the original materials used and the qualities of size and accuracy. The Vuoso coding method — Czechoslovakian in origin — is a simpler, four-digit code dealing with major headings of kind, class, group and materials.

In addition, designers specify such matters as general machining tolerances, types of finishes and thread sizes. Of particular importance are health and safety regulations and specific government instructions or regulations, such as those applying to colour codes for electrical wiring.

Regrettably, experience shows that no manufacturing process or procedure ever follows completely the specifications laid down. Some variations will arrive accidentally, others by the deliberate choice of a factory supervisor or operator at the bench. It is, of course, important for the design team to be aware of any such changes, as problems can arise from unauthorised changes. Any design variations must be approved by the design team. Production difficulties can also lead to occasional design specification modifications, but a good design team should be able to produce a design which neither has specifications that are tighter than they need be, nor results in final assembly tasks which might tax operators unduly.

Products, sub-assemblies and components

As indicated in the previous section, a product can be broken down into its constituent parts. Using the terminology of Chapter 3, a product can be seen as a system and its constituent parts as sub-systems, but the sub-systems themselves can be further divided into *sub-assemblies* and *components*.

Components are the basic items from which a product is constructed. In the case of a standard three-pin, fused, 250V, 13 amp. plug, the components would be:

(a)   body (in two parts), in plastic or other non-conducting material;
(b)   flex/cord grip, in fibre, one;
(c)   screws, pin, three;
(d)   screws, cord grip, two;
(e)   screw, body-holding, one;
(f)   terminals, brass, three;
(g)   live wire/fuse connector, one;
(h)   fuse, one.

Further examination shows that two of the terminals have screws already fitted; each terminal–screw combination is a sub-assembly. Similarly the third terminal, fuse and live wire connection and screw, could also be regarded as a sub-assembly.

Thus the basic items are components, combinations of components smaller than the complete product are sub-assemblies, and the total assembly is the complete product.

Standardisation, specialisation and simplification

These three ideas are closely related to value analysis.

Standardisation.   The *Oxford Advanced Learners Dictionary* defines 'standardisation' as 'to make of one size, shape, quality etc., according to fixed standards'. From a production point of view the process of standardisation is the activity of trying to remove unnecessary extras or variations which might exist in the manufacture of a product — in materials used, the composition of materials, or methods or processes used in inspection or final testing.

A basic objective of standardisation would be to promote the use of parts and components over many ranges of products (e.g. the same speedometer in all models produced by a manufacturer). Indeed, an organisation has been set up to promote standardisation throughout industry — the British Standards Institution. It is the recognised body for the preparation and issue of national standards to include definitions, quantities, units and symbols, methods of test, and guidelines on quality and safety. Over 8000 standards have been issued.

Some advantages of standardisation are:

1. Production is limited to smaller ranges of products or components, enabling longer runs to be made and costs reduced.
2. Fewer machines are needed and the organisation can use specialist equipment, both of which reduce costs.
3. Smaller ranges of stocks (parts, sub-assemblies, components) are required, resulting in lower total stocks. This reduces overheads.
4. The same parts can be used on different models.
5. The whole production process is easier to plan, control and manage with fewer setting up operations and production interruptions; quality will tend to be more consistent.
6. Customers can benefit from lower prices and greater product availability.

Against these advantages, designs could suffer from over-standardisation, and customers have fewer choices of product. Trends show that customers demand varied choices: not only in clothing do fashions change quickly. Standardisation has also increasingly resulted in redundancies.

In conclusion, standardisation can be seen to apply in four major areas:

1. *Complete products.* The ideal situation here would be to make one version only of each different line produced. The advantages would be: longer production runs, better machine utilisation, less work in progress and cheaper production costs. Store keeping would be easier and the training of labour would be made simpler. However, the demands of the market usually mean alternative finishes and thread sizes, and other minor modifications. Thus there is a compromise between total standardisation and the requirements of customers (esoteric variations are not provided). Such an arrangement enables most of the advantages of specialisation to be gained without restricting customer choice too severely.
2. *Sub-assemblies and component parts.* The aim here is to use the same components and/or sub-assemblies in a range of similar products. For example, the same electric motors might be used in the manufacture of a range of model railway locomotives, with differing outlines. Similar standardisation could be using the same bogies, wheels or couplings on various models. As with complete products, the resulting advantages centre on the reduction of overall production costs, as universal interchangeability of parts means simpler stock-keeping, less work in progress and the economies of scale. Problems arise, however, when the standard part does not quite fit in with the overall design, or provide the durability or reliability required of an item at the more expensive end of the range.
3. *Production material.* The emphasis, again, is standardisation through variety reduction — reducing to a minimum the types of material ordered, the forms in which it is obtained (i.e. as coils, blanks, sheets, etc.) and the sizes used. If

standardisation is practised at the design stage, standardisation of materials used will follow naturally. Again the benefits are smaller stock holdings, standardisation of materials holding equipment (bins, etc.) and of materials handling equipment, and general cost reduction through increased bulk buying of a smaller range of materials. (Similar considerations apply to consumable stores, stationery, etc.)

4. *Production equipment.* All too often a machine shop or a production area will contain equipment of varying age and sophistication and from different places of manufacture. Servicing a motley variety of plant presents considerable difficulties — special tools for each machine, different methods of adjustment, and the possible difficulties of ordering individual spare parts. To standardise on one manufacturer's range wherever possible means that servicing becomes simpler, as some parts can be held in stock and work and tools can be passed from one piece of equipment to another. Training of operators also becomes simpler.

Specialisation.   To specialise is to 'make narrower and more intense' (*OED*). The concept of specialisation was first applied to labour: in 1776 Adam Smith described specialisation (or division of labour, as he called it) in terms of pin manufacture. A single worker making pins could perhaps turn out twenty pins per day. Split the eighteen operations involved in pin making among ten specialised workers, and production rises to 48 000 per day! Skills are enhanced by specialising in one task.

   Applied to machinery, specialisation entails purpose-built equipment with high initial costs, but the benefits of high output levels ensure a plentiful supply at a lower cost. Practised throughout a firm, it could lead to a decision to restrict production to supplying a very narrow market. A serious problem is not only changing fashion, but also rapid changes in technology which could lead to the disappearance of markets and out-of-date specialist equipment lying idle. Firms are finding that flexibility is essential to survive in a recession.

Simplification.   A similar concept to the previous two, simplification means making a product less complicated. Compare the simplicity of a modern desk-top computer with its cumbersome ancestor. Simplification is also used to describe the restriction and pruning of the variety of product ranges, or products within a range, or of the types of outlet in which goods are offered for sale. Variety reduction, as simplification is sometimes called, has similar virtues to the previous two ideas: longer batch runs, less setting-up time, lower unit costs, for example. Customers may be annoyed to find lines no longer available, but provided care is taken to delete the least popular lines inconvenience to customers can be relatively unimportant.

5.2 The process of value analysis

Having considered the objectives and use of value analysis, we must now look at the actual process of value analysis.

The value analysis project group

Value analysis can be carried out by one highly skilled individual, but the best results are obtained by teamwork. In a team, each member can offer to the rest his or her own experience, expertise and skills, in an effort to improve a product.

Team membership will vary with the type and size of the organisation involved, but normally the total group size should not exceed six. This does not prevent specialists from other departments or organisations being co-opted for help with particular problems.

The following departmental functions can be found represented in project groups: design, purchasing, production/production planning, research, work study, quality control, marketing, estimating and accounting/finance.

The value analysis programme

Once the project to be tackled next is agreed, it is usual to proceed with a schedule of meetings, with suitable gaps between during which suggestions can be explored in an experimental department, or even on the shop floor: pilot trials, in fact. The normal stages of a project are outlined below; in particular cases (e.g. in times of emergency) some stages may be cut short or omitted.

A chairperson or project co-ordinator is required: a value analyst in a large company, or in smaller firms someone from work study or research and development.

The basic stages

There are seven basic stages in a value analysis exercise.

Defining the problem/selecting a product for study.   A topic is chosen because it is a problem to be solved either by the design of a completely new product (value engineering) or by the re-appraisal of an existing product (value analysis). If the latter, greater savings can be made by choosing to look at a product which is costly or complex to make, and which is still selling well.

Collecting the facts.   Everything known about a product (potential or existing) is obtained and circulated to the team. Included would be drawings, methods of manufacture, samples, costs, marketing information (including customers' reactions or complaints) and material or production problems. In fact, anything which can throw light upon the economic, use and esteem values of the product is welcome.

The critical examination.   The critical examination procedure is not new. It was developed and refined for use in work study (see Chapter 12), but slightly modified for use in value analysis. The procedure is a ruthless, searching examination of every single aspect of the product — size, shape, finish, materials used, customers' needs, etc. By adopting a standardised method of examination the temptation to jump to quick conclusions is eliminated.

Six important question words are used frequently during the process: who, what, where, when, how and why. Examples could be:

1.   *What* is the purpose of the highly polished finish? (Perhaps a cheaper, duller finish would do.)
2.   *When* is the component acid-dipped? Why then? (This may lead to a re-sequencing of the production operations.)

Figure 5.1 is the kind of useful checklist which a value analysis team will draw up to assist its product review.

Figure 5.1   *Sample value analysis questionnaire.*

Value Analysis Critical Examination

Sheet: _____   Product: _____   Ref: _____

Area of Inquiry	Primary Questions	Supplementary Questions/suggestions	Notes
A Product use	1. What are the product's: (a) basic functions? (b) secondary functions?	Are these functions: essential? important? desirable? optional? unnecessary? Why? Could they be: enhanced? increased? modified? combined? transferred to another product? eliminated? Why? How?	

B Product materials	2. What is:
	(a) The original material
	  specification?
	(b) the material now
	  used?
		Is the specification over-elaborate? Are dimensions excessive, material weights high? Why?
		Has specification been departed from? Why?	

	3. What is the quality of material used/ to be used?	Has account been taken of alternative materials, newly developed materials? Could material be purchased ready-made or purpose-finished at reasonable cost?	

				Can quality be relaxed by alternative specification or designs? Can alternative qualities perform the same functions? Which?
C	Manufacturing processes	4.	What are the processes used/to be used?	Are these processes/operations: essential? important? desirable? optional? unnecessary? Why?
		5.	What are the operations used/ to be used?	Could they be: modified? simplified? standarised? reduced? combined? eliminated? Why? How? Are dimensions/ tolerances/finishing standards too strict? Can standard parts be used?
D	Product labour	6.	What kind of labour is used/to be used? (a) skilled? (b) semi-skilled? (c) unskilled?	Why is a particular category of labour used? Could it be of another category? Is labour used to best advantage? Are labour costs relatively high? Could new equipment reduce costs?
E	Economic	7.	What does the product cost?	Is the item high/low cost? Do labour or material costs take larger share of prime costs? Is this satisfactory?
		8.	Does it/would it make a reasonable contribution?	How does contribution compare with other products? Should product be eliminated? Is the selling price competitive?
F	Esteem	9.	What esteem value does the product have?	Does product offer what customers need, want? Do other products have similar values? Can esteem value be easily increased? How?

Speculation.   This stage often goes hand in hand with the critical examination. By the use of idea development techniques, a large number of possible solutions or proposals can be considered in answer to the questions posed during the questioning stage. This generation of ideas is a version of *brainstorming*, which was developed by A.F. Osborne in 1941, and is most effective in a group.

The rules are as follows:

1.   Ideas and suggestions are offered by group members, without criticism of any kind. Every idea is welcome at this stage, no matter how futuristic.
2.   Group members can enlarge on the ideas of others.
3.   There is a certain formality, with a chairperson to run the discussion, and someone to record the ideas.
4.   Sessions should not last for more than 15–20 minutes.

The major objective is to generate alternative ideas for their own sake.

Analysis and evaluation.   Each idea put forward is then carefully analysed and evaluated for feasibility and cost. This stage could take place between meetings, during which time ideas can be looked at by production staff, priced by the cost office and investigated by work study.

Choosing and recommending.   Choices now have to be made from the alternatives considered and priced. The chairperson's aim would be to get general agreement (consensus) among the group. The best result would be if all decided on changes which would reduce costs and production inconvenience, while preserving the functional and esteem values.

Clearance to proceed further will be needed from a senior executive, say the works director, or even the board. Thus it will be necessary to produce a report to management which will:

(a)   summarise the progress of each project;
(b)   list the favoured suggestions;
(c)   consider the financial (cost) implications of the suggestions;
(d)   assess the other implications (changes in working methods, shift systems, material stocks, etc.), including the industrial relations questions which could arise;
(e)   make firm, final recommendations.

Implementation.   This is the final stage. Careful thought is necessary before changes are made. The objective here is to obtain the benefits of the new methods, materials, etc. with the minimum of disruption to production as a whole. Consultation with the staff involved at every level, and with the unions, is vital.

5.3 Value analysis in use

Properly used, in a systematic way, value analysis can help firms to remain competitive in difficult times.

Applied to the example quoted at the start of this chapter, value analysis showed immediate results in the elimination of a bought-out component. Carried further, the results could have caused a complete re-appraisal of the over-elaborate method of packing.

In the second example the change to a plastic version of the car heater 'box' had the virtues of a considerable simplification of a complex production process. The function value was increased (it was now rustless and much lighter), and the costs of production were reduced.

A final example can be seen in the record industry. The gramophone record (made from a shellac base) had been fully refined by the mid-1940s. Major advances included variable pitch recording and a reduction in needle hiss. However, Columbia Records undertook a value analysis review; they wanted records with longer playing times (to avoid breaks in long classical pieces), and to increase the volume range.

The first objective was obtained by reducing the recording speed from 78 r.p.m to 33⅓ r.p.m. More than twice as much playing time was now available. The groove width was reduced (and therefore needed a new-shaped stylus), which doubled possible recording time.

A change to polymerised vinyls (plus lamp-black) from the shellac-based material entailed less friction in playing, reduced surface noise and enabled a greater extension to be made to the volume range. Variable pitch recording was still possible and surface hiss was greatly reduced. An extra bonus was that vinyl records were much stronger and less brittle.

Many of the advantages of value analysis can be seen here: a more appropriate product was now made, its quality was maintained and in several areas enhanced, costs were kept down, and the product became much more attractive to the buying public.

5.4 Cost effectiveness

Cost effectiveness is an important idea related to that of value analysis. In general terms it means getting at least an adequate (if not better) return from a product or service compared with the time, money or effort spent on it. It is more often used as a comparison between two products, processes or services: to say that one method of doing things is more cost effective than another is to say that it gives more value for money.

To train twenty students at one time, in one classroom, is more cost effective to the community than to train each of them individually. (The latter method is not only more costly but also more time-consuming.) In a production situation Adam Smith demonstrated 200 years ago that it was more cost effective to make pins by mass production than individually by hand.

In the next section comparisons are made between the cost effectiveness of several processes, and even versions of the same process. It will soon become clear that the choice of any one particular process (as being more cost effective in the circumstances) depends a great deal on product volume.

5.5 Process comparison

While the examples in this section are taken from the engineering industry, similar comparisons can be made in other production industries. Within engineering we shall concentrate on primary forming processes and welding, as used with metal and plastics.

Basic raw materials — usually in billets, slabs, ingots or blanks — are of little use; work has to be carried out on them so that they can be of more use in production. Such processes as casting and forging are typical.

Casting

Casting is a process in the metal or plastics industries in which molten material is poured or forced into a mould and allowed to harden.

Sand casting.   This is the version in which metal is poured into a mould or cavity formed in a special sand. The pouring technique is a special skill and the pattern must be carefully removed from the sand mould so that metal can be poured in. To increase precision, two-part or even more expensive multi-moulds can be used.

The full process is too complex to describe here; suffice it to say that successful work depends upon the training, skill and experience of the moulders. Disadvantages of the system are blowholes (gas bubbles in the metal), sand getting to the body of the metal, casting distortions, and misplaced cores resulting in castings with non-uniform thicknesses. Finishes are usually quite poor. The process in general is a slow one. However, where only small quantities are required sand casting is cost effective, as capital costs (i.e. the equipment costs) are negligible.

Pressure die casting.   This is a process in which metal is injected under pressure into water-cooled steel dies. Metallic moulds (dies) are used, into which the metal is forced by special equipment. Careful design of the dies is required; there are difficulties with extracting castings of awkward shapes, and narrow projections in dies can be fragile.

This process is suitable and cost effective for large quantities of precision castings. True, the dies are costly to make, and the pressure-producing equipment even more so, but once begun the process is quick, and the dies last a long time. (Note, though, that only metals with fairly low melting temperatures, e.g. aluminium, are suitable for this process.)

Investment casting.   This is used to manufacture very precise and complex shapes: metals of high melting points can safely be used. In brief, a wax pattern is prepared for each casting and attached to a base plate. Steadily a shell of heat-resistant material is built up round the wax pattern, and the whole heated to melt the wax, which is allowed to run away (hence the term lost wax casting, sometimes used). The hardened mould, pre-heated, receives the molten metal, which is allowed to cool before the mould is broken.

Whilst this is an expensive and rather slow process, a very high degree of accuracy of shape and dimensions is achieved and the amount of machining or finishing off is minimal. Very difficult and awkward shapes can be handled and for this type of work investment castings are very cost effective.

Plastic injection moulding.   This is now the most popular process for producing components in plastics. The raw granules are heated to melt the material, which is forced into a mould cavity in the equipment, where it solidifies. The mould then opens and the moulding is ejected. Production times are very short and large quantities are produced in a day.

The injection moulding machines are very expensive, as are the design and manufacture of the mould cavities. Production only becomes cost effective if there is steady demand for large batches. A slight drawback is the need to remove manually odd 'sprues' from components fresh from the mould.

Forging

Forging is a process in which metal is heated and then subjected to compressure force (e.g. hammering) to form the metal into the required shape. The craft of the blacksmith or farrier is an ancient one, still used because of its advantages which include the economy of material, the increase in strength of the finished item (grain flow helps toughness), and the relatively simple tools that are required. It is very useful for making small quantities of individual items and for operations such as bending, or cases where the size or shape of an item would entail considerable machining if made from solid metal. (Machining time is saved and less material is needed.)

Another advantage of the forging process is related to the load-bearing properties of metals. Such materials are capable of sustaining greater loads if they are applied *along* the grain than if they are applied *across* the grain. In the manufacture of complicated fittings, with potential multi-directional loading applications, the use of the hammering/reheating process draws the grain direction of the material into the same alignment as the line of the potential loads. (Subsequent machining merely cleans up the forging and fashions the attachment or load transmission points.)

There are instances — especially in aircraft undercarriage structures — where it could be said that forging provides the most effective strength/weight ratio and the most efficient load path resolution.

A source of heat is needed (a traditional open hearth with bellows is usually necessary) to make the metal malleable, and this adds to costs.

Welding

Welding is the process of joining two pieces of parent metal and a suitable filler by raising the temperature in the area of the joint by external heat to cause the melting of all three metals. Wrought iron can be joined by a blacksmith in a furnace, but odd shapes, tubes, etc. present serious difficulties. Skill is required in this slow process.

Resistance welding (or spot welding) uses an electric current and some local compression of (usually) thin sheet materials. No filler material is used and the brief passage of the current raises the temperature locally to fuse the sheets together at that point. The pressure holds the sheet together after the current is interrupted, allowing the metal to cool and solidify. A suitable rig can be safely operated by unskilled labour; the current and the duration of weld can be automatically predetermined. A short time cycle means a large number of products can be welded in a day.

Arc welding uses the heat generated by an electric arc created between an electrode and the work. Special face shields are needed and the process requires some skill on the operator's part. Very large jobs can be handled with this method.

Welding is an extensively used process in the manufacture of bridges, pressure vessels, piping, ships, aircraft and cryogenic equipment.

Some conclusions

It is difficult to lay down precise relationships between particular production methods and product volume: the job itself, the size and shape of the product, and the materials used could all affect choices. Components in cast iron are only suitable where stresses are low (e.g. car cylinder blocks); steel, however, can be forged to advantage.

We can say that job/small batch production could well use sand casting or forging to advantage, but if great accuracy and precision of shape are needed, investment castings could be the only answer. Once the item being produced goes beyond casting capabilities, fabrication by welding would be used.

Large batch production is more likely to use die casting (particularly with metals of relatively low melting points) where large quantities are economic. Flow production (e.g. car assembly) would use spot welding extensively.

The same considerations can be given to other materials (ceramics, glass, nylon, etc.) and other production methods such as pressing, piercing, milling, extracting, draining and manually controlled and computer-controlled machinery.

Summary

1. Value analysis is that technique with which we critically and systematically examine the design of an existing product to determine whether improvements can be made to it.
2. Improvements could include meeting customers' needs more closely, reducing costs, enhancing performance, using simpler methods of manufacture, eliminating or combining processes and increasing standardisation.

3. Value engineering is the same approach and general set of principles applied to the design of new products.
4. Value can be broken down into three component ideas: *economic value*, the product's price acceptability; *use value*, its fitness for its intended purpose; and *esteem value*, its attractiveness or pleasing appearance to buyers, or its prestige in the eyes of the purchaser.
5. A product specification is basically a document or set of documents/drawings giving a detailed description of a product — the dimensions, the materials used and the quality of the work. Each component part and sub-assembly is so specified, as are the raw materials and components purchased.
6. Coding methods can be used (such as the Opitz or Vuoso methods) to simplify and standardise the presentation of information.
7. A product is composed of:
   (a) basic components;
   (b) sub-assemblies (several components assembled);
   (c) complete assembly (the total product of all components and sub-assemblies).
8. Standardisation is the activity of attempting to remove anomalies, unnecessary extras, or varieties which might exist in materials, methods or processes used in production. Specialisation means concentrating activities into a narrow area, whether this be the market for products or the use of purpose-built machinery. Finally, simplification is the process of making a product less complicated.
9. Standardisation applies to:
   (a) complete products (where the range is kept to an absolute minimum);
   (b) assemblies and component parts (products incorporate standard assemblies and components wherever possible);
   (c) production material (the use of as few types of raw materials as possible);
   (d) production equipment (the use of machines similar in type and source wherever possible).
10. Value analysis is best regarded as a group activity. Any group engaged in value analysis should be relatively small, but have representatives from diverse functions in the organisation. A chairperson or co-ordinator is required.
11. The basic stages in value analysis are:
    (a) defining the problem and selecting a product for study;
    (b) collection of all relevant facts and data;
    (c) the critical examination, being a fundamental appraisal of the product/proposed product; areas which are examined will include the product use, the materials involved, the manufacturing processes adopted, the labour employed and the economic and esteem values of the product;
    (d) the speculation stage, at which alternative ideas and methods are discussed and solutions to problems are offered; alternative ideas are generated for their own sake;
    (e) the analysis and evaluation of the speculative ideas;
    (f) choosing the most appropriate suggestions, and recommending them to the decision-makers in the organisation;
    (g) implementation — putting the successful recommendations into practice.
12. Value analysis is now a commonly accepted technique, used in a variety of industries.

13.   Cost effectiveness is a method of judging whether the best way of performing a task has been chosen: a comparison is made between the economic and time outlay and the return obtained. To be cost effective a method must give an adequate return on the investment of time and money.

14.   A variety of basic processes exist in manufacture. The choice of any particular process in the making of a product will depend on many factors — size, shape, materials used, for example — but *product volume* is an extremely significant element in such a choice.

Questions

Review questions

5.1   What is meant by value analysis? In what way does it differ from value engineering?

5.2   What is the use value of a product? Account for the fact that some customers are willing to pay a very high price for a particular model (e.g. Rolls-Royce) which has a basic use value similar to other cars.

5.3   Define standardisation. Name three advantages standardisation could bring. Is it *always* desirable?

5.4   What is a value analysis project group? Why is a team approach favoured for value analysis?

5.5   Describe the critical examination process.

5.6   What is brainstorming and how is it useful in value analysis?

5.7   Explain the term 'cost effective' and compare the cost effectiveness of making six special shelf brackets by die casting and forging.

Discussion topics

5.8   Discuss the view that, because the striking achievements of the Industrial Revolution were made without the use of value analysis groups, the whole value analysis idea is irrelevant and a waste of time.

5.9   Is the seven-step sequence of value analysis the best way of proceeding? Suggest other ways of carrying out a value analysis inquiry.

5.10   'Value analysis is just a cost-saving exercise.' Discuss.

Assignments

5.11   The class should divide into groups of six. Each group becomes a value analysis team to consider *either* a product/component well known to the class *or* one of the following: a particular model of fountain pen, a bulldog clip, a pair of stereo headphones, a cricket bat, a knife, or a box of chocolates. A session of 15 minutes is suggested.

       Each group is to subject the chosen item to the standard procedure, as far as practicable. In particular they should try to establish what use value the product has to customers: is performance, durability, appearance or prestige more important? Examine the materials used: could there be (cheaper) substitutes and would their use make the product less desirable or useful? Could the product be made in another shape or simplified in any way?

After discussion, the groups' ideas could be compared.

5.12 Using the same arrangements as for Assignment 5.11, the groups are to consider a selection of three-pin plugs (both round-pin and flat-pin types) dating from post-war to present times. The groups are to identify the design changes over the period. Are the most modern plugs better value? Consider the material changes and the amount of simplification that has taken place. Consider safety implications.

6
Process Planning

In this chapter the principles of process planning are outlined, and differences in planning methods between industries are noted. Next the job of the process planner is examined, as well as the work of both the jig and tool department, and the toolroom.

The influence of quantity on process planning is then considered, followed by a comparison of processes for orders of differing quantity for a turned component. Finally, the effect of current trends in machine tool design is discussed.

6.1 The principles of process planning

The principles of process planning are simple and straightforward: the product must be manufactured to the necessary design standards commensurate with the customer's requirements of accuracy and reliability, at minimum cost to both the customer and the manufacturer.

Process planning differs within different industries. Large chemical plants and food processing plants, for example, are designed and laid out to suit only those industries and, once established, function for long periods with only small (but usually very important) revisions to packaging or wrapping operations, with the bulk of the process remaining stable.

In engineering concerns the business of planning the method (and hence controlling the production, in respect of both meeting delivery dates and operating within cost budgets) varies with the quantity required, the materials available (in regard to both physical shape and properties), the type and capacity of machine tools available (either existing within the company or newly designed by the machine tool manufacturer), the quality of the labour force (skilled/semi-skilled/unskilled) already employed or locally available and, sometimes, the availability of floor space/stores/storage racks. The question of storage racks arises where quantities of parts are 'in work' or 'between operations' and there is a need to protect them from damage since they represent a large amount of invested capital in the form of the material and the work already carried out on them. The problem of accommodating the work satisfactorily, either within the capacity of the machine tools or within the production system generally, may well highlight the need to investigate the ability of specialist manufacturers to supply components to the required quality and the necessary usage rate. This approach is often adopted in order to obviate the need to purchase special-purpose machinery, which is often expensive and difficult to absorb into the selling price of the product unless substantial numbers are made. Such components would be referred to as 'bought-out' parts and may be completely, or partly, finished items.

Although the process of manufacture is planned to suit the design of a component, it may well be expedient to change the design very slightly, with the approval of the designer, to suit some standard practice well established and followed in the manufacturing system. Also the process should be adapted, where possible, to take advantage of analyses carried out by the work study department (even though the function of such a department might be to check the method of applying the process and to establish that the workforce is not becoming disenchanted with the sequence of operations, which may be affecting their earnings).

An important use of process planning, apart from in the actual manufacture of particular components, is that made by the estimating department when pricing new work. Quite often the customer may require a quotation for a product which is similar to current products and it is advantageous for the estimating department to have evidence of the cost of the latest processes, since the question of whether the company makes a profit depends on the ability of the estimator to give a practical estimate of the price.

Process planning also enables the production control department to plan ahead with regard to machine loading capacity. This aspect could also operate in reverse, provided costs are not affected, since the production department could well advise the planning department of possible shortcomings in a particular process which may lead to a bottleneck in production and which could be avoided by a slight change of operation or operation sequence.

The information contained in a process plan may be used in the setting up of standard costs for a product, since it usually provides an accurate statement of the time required for each operation, while the method of production would indicate the quality of operator needed and hence the rate of pay involved.

The design and manufacture of the necessary manufacturing jigs, fixtures and cutting tools would arise from the planning of a manufacturing process, since most of the components made in engineering factories are formed from standard-size sheet, bar or tubular materials and specific castings and forgings which need to be cut or formed (forced) into the design shape and size. Such operations require the application of considerable forces and so fixtures and jigs must be designed to resist the cutting/forming forces and as necessary to hold the work, presenting it to the tool in the correct position — a function performed by the jig and tool design department in conjunction with the planning department.

6.2 The process planner or planning engineer

The process planner or planning engineer occupies a very powerful and responsible position within a company since his or her interpretation of how a job should be carried out, or how a component should be manufactured, will have considerable direct influence on manufacturing costs and hence indirectly on company profit. The type of person best suited for this exacting work is someone who has an intimate knowledge of the basic processes employed for manufacture in the particular company. For example, a person experienced in practical watch or instrument manufacture will find this experience rather wasted in a marine-engine manufacturing organisation. A prerequisite for this position is considerable practical ability and experience of the appropriate manufacturing processes coupled with a good academic standard such as that represented by ONC or BTEC Certificate, or better. In short, the process planner should be able to do the job him or herself to the standard required and should also be capable of communicating his or her requirements to the person actually doing the job. As we saw in the previous section, the work of the process planner is the basis of much of the day-to-day information necessary to the satisfactory operation of a manufacturing organisation. However, the process planner should keep up to date with the development in materials, machine tools and equipment in his or her particular discipline (and also associated disciplines) in the present fast-moving age of technology. As suggested above, the process planner requires an intimate knowledge of the plant within the factory, but in addition needs to know about any updating of the equipment such as the purchase and fitment of additional extra-operation/labour-saving accessories as well as the present state of the machines regarding wear in bearings (with their consequent effect on speeds, feeds and accuracy). A good deal of such information can be obtained from investigating the maintenance department history-card system, which should give accounts of repairs, breakdowns, replacements, accessories and preventive maintenance of the equipment or, failing that, much information can be obtained from inspection records of scrap, such as how and who produced, which machine, etc. The gathering of such information will enable the process planner to advise the management, through his or her superior, of the deterioration. He or she could also possibly offer recommendations about replacement by more advanced machines.

In order to carry out the planning of a particular process, the planner requires:

(a)   a drawing, or drawings, or some detailed description, of the component to be made;
(b)   information regarding the quantity to be made;
(c)   information on whether an estimated cost of manufacture has been given and how much it is.

When the process planner has the estimated cost a general analysis of the requirements can be made. Which machines can be used? Would it be better to make the component within the factory or to subcontract it? If it is decided to manufacture in-house then the process planner must decide on the raw material, which machines will be used, what the sequence of operations will be and whether any special jigs or fixtures are required or whether there are existing tools which can be easily adapted. (The process planner has often graduated from the jig and tool design department.) He or she will also contact the production control department to find out what their shop-loading position is with regard to the machines to be used.

When all the required information has been obtained and the process planner is satisfied that the product can be made within the estimated price, then he or she will prepare a process planning layout or operations sheet, which will carry such information as:

(a) a description of the component and drawing/part number and number off;
(b) assembly drawing number;
(c) raw material, specification and size and possibly an alternative;
(d) contract/works order number;
(e) list of operations with time for each;
(f) machine/workshop and tooling for each operation;
(g) layout issue number and date.

The information is duplicated and various forms printed so that departments concerned with scrap, job costs, material requisitions and identification labels can enter or extract the information pertaining to the job as it passes through the shops to the finished part store.

6.3. The jig and tool design department

In most engineering situations jigs and fixtures are necessary to hold components in the correct position for a particular operation to be carried on accurately and positively. This necessity occurs in every type of engineering production from jobbing, through batch and mass to flow. Of course, the manufacture of jigs and fixtures can be costly, so the facility is not usually provided in a jobbing shop by the official process layout and any that are made are purely functional and are due to the individual initiative of the skilled operator performing the work.

For mass production, the initial cost of jigs and fixtures is less important than the time and effort expended by the operator (usually semi-skilled) and so the tooling has to be designed to be easily, yet effectively, used in repetitive production for periods of, say, three years or more.

Production of some batches would also justify inexpensive and simple tooling derived from the many standard unit tooling parts manufactured by specialist tooling concerns and carried as stock items by many batch manufacturers. Such tools could comprise parts cannibalised from disused or outmoded tooling from previous production runs. Certainly every attempt is made to utilise a jig or fixture for as many basically similar components as possible by perhaps changing drill bushes around, especially where a component may be right-handed or left-handed.

The tool designer has the task of making the manufacturing drawings of the tooling requirements for a process and sometimes the very act of producing the drawings leads to the combination of separate operations, or, alternatively, the drawings may indicate that single operations may be better or easier when fragmented.

During the drawing process an outline of the component in each of the various manufacturing modes will enable a study to be made of the cutting forces to be applied at any stage and thus the clamping and support arrangements can be made to accommodate them. Also, if the manufacturing process is complicated then these drawings can be cleaned up and used in conjunction with the operations layout sheet to provide the operator with an authentic picture of the component profile at a particular stage and so perhaps avoid misunderstanding and consequent scrap.

It may be necessary to modify the design, temporarily, of the component by leaving extra lugs on it in specified positions to facilitate location in jigs and fixtures while carrying out early operations (these lugs would be removed at a later stage in the manufacture). So the process sheet for the component would carry additional operations to fashion the lugs in the first place and then, subsequently, to remove them. All machining drawings so affected would also be modified to show the lugs.

Having decided the form of the component tooling the tool designer will produce detail drawings, using standard parts where possible, supplemented by special parts as the need arises. The tool designer takes just as much pride in tool design as does his or her counterpart in the component design office, since both designers are producing an article to perform a specific task.

The next stage will be for the original process planner or perhaps a tooling process planner (another specialist) to compile and issue an operations layout for the toolroom to manufacture the tools.

6.4. The toolroom

The toolroom manufactures the 'in-house' tooling and a tooling process planning layout or operations sheet is also prepared and issued to the toolroom calling up all the necessary materials but, since the standard of skill is so high in this department, the amount of detailed instruction is much less. There is a system whereby the tooling produced is operated by an independent member of the toolroom staff to ensure correct functioning in subsequent production use.

The toolroom functions as a self-contained production unit with its own turning, milling and grinding equipment as well as the traditional surface tables and high-class measuring and marking-out equipment. It has an extremely capable and highly-skilled toolroom staff including independent inspectors, on whom the production staff rely implicitly.

A first-class toolroom may be expensive to set up and run but it does give the product manufacturing system the best of support.

6.5. The influence of quantities on process planning

In section 4.7 reference was made to various types of production (job, batch, mass and flow). While no figures were actually quoted, job implies a one-off order, batch may imply 2–100 off, depending on circumstances, mass may imply 101–1000 perhaps, and flow implies continuous production.

Figures 6.1 and 6.2 show that, in certain circumstances, production of some components by hand would be the cheapest method. However, as the number off increases so the cost per piece reduces for each machine, but not for those made by

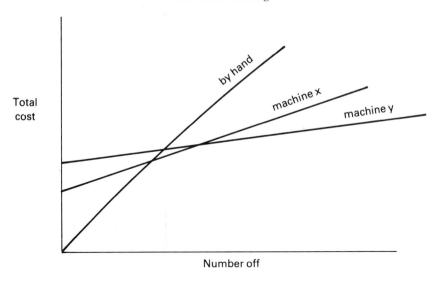

Figure 6.1 *Total cost comparisons for different manufacturing methods.*

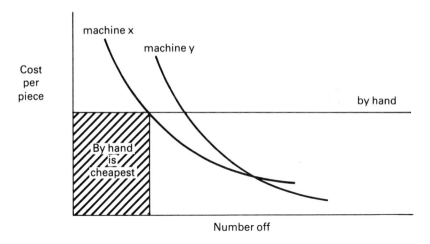

Figure 6.2 *Cost per piece comparisons for different manufacturing methods.*

hand. With quantity production, if all turning operations were carried out on a centre lathe, the cost of production would be astronomical compared with similar production on a capstan lathe. The operator for the centre lathe would need to be highly skilled and the number of different operations which could be carried out without resetting the tools would be limited to perhaps four or five at the most. On a capstan lathe, however, the operator could be semi-skilled, perhaps even unskilled, and the number of different operations could be as many as eleven without resetting the tools. The difference between the two methods is that whereas skilled turners would set up their own centre lathe, semi-skilled operators would have the tools and stops set up for them and if it were a bar-feed capstan with a collet chuck, the operators would merely have to learn the sequence of turret and cross-slide movements in conjunction with specific speed changes for each. Apart from the initial tool costs and setting-up costs the cost per piece using such a system would be much less in terms of time and labour since less time would be spent in changing and resetting tools compared with the centre lathe production system.

The production of a large number of corner brackets or cleats from sheet material (see Figure 6.3) would be a long and laborious exercise if they were marked out, drilled, cut out, rough filed, draw-filed and deburred and bent up on bend bars on an individual basis. For a batch quantity we may well make a small hardened template of the developed shape and size of the cleat and perhaps drill and bolt five or six thicknesses to the template and cut round the template on a bandsaw and finally clean up the developed plates and bend them on bend bars. If we had a mass-production or flow-production order then we would probably consider a pierce, blank and form punch and die tool which is 'strip fed' and could turn out hundreds of these cleats at minimal cost.

Circumstances alter cases and provided the production quantity is high enough then the cost of simplifying the production of components can be reduced to insignificant proportions.

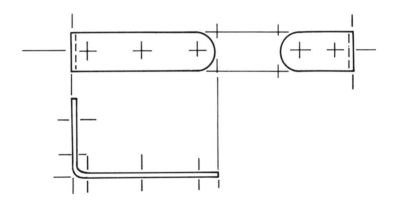

Figure 6.3   *Production of corner brackets from sheet material.*

6.6 A comparison of processes for a turned component

Consider the pivot shown in Figure 6.4. It has to be manufactured from En 5 32 mm diameter bar to a drawing tolerance of ± 0.1 mm all dimensions. If a centre lathe were to be used to produce it on a one-off basis for a small batch, then the procedure might well be:

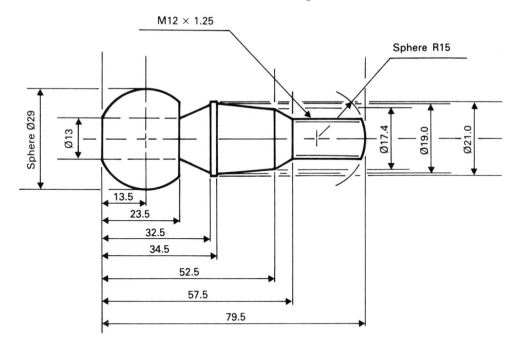

Figure 6.4 *Pivot.*

1. Set up centre lathe using three-jaw chuck plus tailstock 'dead centre' support.
2. Cut bar to length (allow 8 mm chuck face clearance, plus 20 mm chucking length, plus 8 mm centre-drill allowance at threaded end of workpiece = +36 mm on drawing overall length).
3. Place bar 20 mm into chuck, centralise and tighten chuck.
4. Face and centre-drill end of bar (60° cone 4 mm deep) at about 360 rev/min.
5. Fit 'dead centre' to tailstock, bring up to workpiece and lock tailstock in position.
6. Scribe datum at 53 mm from faced end to locate right-hand edge of the collar.
7. Rough turn 12 mm diameter down to +0.25 mm at right-hand end of workpiece at about 260 rev/min, carriage feed 0.15 mm/rev depth of cut 2.5 mm maximum, using RH 60° oblique roughing tool.
8. Finish turn 12 mm diameter down to drawing tolerance at about 500 rev/min. using RH 90° (orthogonal) finishing tool, carriage feed 0.05 mm/rev depth of cut 0.1 mm.
9. Rough turn 19 mm diameter down to +0.25 mm, parallel to centre-line of lathe, to 53 mm datum line, using RH 60° oblique roughing tool, feed 0.15 mm/rev depth of cut 2.5 mm maximum, at a speed of about 225 rev/min.
10. Attach taper-turning dovetail slide between lathe bed and cross-slide, releasing set-screw to disengage cross-slide screw from its nut; set taper turning slide to 2.54° and lock. Set centre-line of compound slide square to centre-line of lathe

and turn 18 mm long taper at 50 rev/min using RH 90° (orthogonal) finishing tool, carriage feed 0.05 mm/rev, depth of cut 1 mm maximum at start of 19 mm diameter.

11. Remove taper-turning dovetail slide and re-engage cross-slide screw and nut and tighten set-screw.
12. Set centre-line of compound slide at 27.08° to normal 'square' position and radial-cut to finish turn 5 mm long taper down to 12 mm diameter. Speed 50 rev/min, hand feed along compound slide, using a squared-cutting-edge 'parting-off' tool or a straight recessing tool.
13. Turn RH screw thread M12 × 1.25 at 50 rev/min, using metric thread form tool.
14. Turn 9 mm wide recess, using special front-cutting form tool at 50 rev/min, hand feed radially.
15. Turn 21 mm diameter using front roughing tool at 216 rev/min, hand feed.
16. Remove tailstock 'dead centre' support, reduce length of and radius end of 12 mm diameter screw thread to 45 mm dimension using 15 mm radius form tool, hand feed radially, speed 50 rev/min.
17. Turn 29 mm diameter spherical and, using special form tool, hand feed radially, speed 50 rev/min.
18. Part off at 50 rev/min.

When issued from the planning department as a process sheet the above procedure will not contain all the details since the centre lathe operator will have most of the knowledge at his or her finger-tips or will know where to find or how to calculate missing values. Nevertheless sufficient information will be given as a basis on which the operator can superimpose his or her considerable skills.

The procedure for the manufacture of the pivot on a centre lathe may thus appear as is laid out in Figure 6.5.

When the procedure is issued as a planning process sheet for larger quantities, the instructions are modified to take account of the special tooling which has been prepared for the production of components by semi-skilled or unskilled operators using capstan lathes. These lathes have numerous additional tool-holding devices compared with the usual four-tool front tool post of the centre lathe; the capstan lathe also has a rear tool post (usually reserved for parting-off operations) and at least a six-position turret tool-holder.

The capstan lathe also has a series of automatically indexing stops which align with front-tool-post positions and a further set which align with the turret tool holder positions. The lathe is set up by a skilled operator who 'proves' the machine by producing one or two components. Once these first offs are approved the machine is available to the semi-skilled or unskilled operators.

The planning process sheet for the pivot manufacture using a capstan lathe as shown in Figure 6.6 (i.e. quantity production) may well be as laid out in Figure 6.7.

6.7 Effect of current trends in machine tool design

In planning the sequence of operations the planning engineer has to take into account all those necessary movements carried out by the operator in connection with the

Drawing number	Number off	Material and size	Shop	Finish	Planner	Date
237	1	En 5 × 32 mm diameter	Machine	Natural, deburred	A.N. Other	25.7.83

Operation and number	Machine	Speed (rev/min)	Feed (mm/rev)	Tooling
1. Chuck bar	Centre lathe number 15	–	–	–
2. Face and centre drill end	"	360	Hand	Facing tool, centre drill
3. Rough turn 12 mm diameter	"	260	0.15	RH 60° oblique roughing tool
4. Finish turn 12 mm diameter	"	500	0.05	RH 90° finishing tool
5. Rough turn 19 mm diameter parallel to spindle	"	225	0.15	RH 60° oblique roughing tool
6. Taper turn 18 mm long taper at 2.54°	"	50	0.05	Taper turning attachment and RH 90° finishing tool
7. Taper turn 5 mm long taper at 27.08°	"	50	Hand	Compound slide and straight recessing tool
8. Turn RH screw thread M12 × 1.25	"	50	Lead	Metric thread form tool
9. Turn 9 mm wide recess	"	50	Hand	Special front-cutting tool
10. Turn 21 mm diameter	"	216	Hand	Front roughing tool
11. Reduce 12 mm to length and radius end	"	50	Hand	15 mm radius form tool
12. Turn 29 mm diameter spherical end	"	50	Hand	Special form tool
13. Part off	"	50	Hand	Parting-off tool

Figure 6.5 *Planning process sheet: pivot 'one-off' manufacture.*

process, yet which are not recorded in the layout. When the work has to be done by a mechanical system in place of the human system then instructions for such movements have to be specific and there must be a feedback system in order to monitor such activities in order to equal or better the production repeatability achieved by the competent operator.

However, it must eventually occur that the machine, having been fashioned to mimic the human system, will substantially improve on human ability to the point

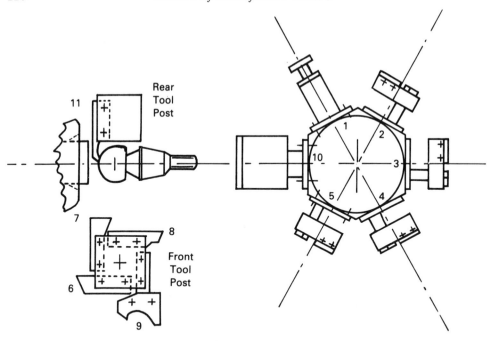

Figure 6.6   *Pivot manufacture using a capstan lathe.*

where mechanical systems, aided by electronics, will perform with tireless and relentless efficiency, punctuated by the occasional cutting-tool or bearing failure due to overheating (unless such an event has already been anticipated and catered for in the mechanical system).

Such a view of the future manufacturing system could be pessimistic since it assumes that manufacturing concerns will be able to accommodate the high capital costs of such equipment in the price of their products. Yet the desire to stay in business may well dictate some adoption of machine systems capable of working to predictable standards of accuracy by offsetting the costs against the more efficient use of the labour force. Certainly the current interest in machining centres, flexible manufacturing systems, numerical control, computer numerical control and direct numerical control, to say nothing of programmable transfer systems and in-situ gauging of components, using binary coded decimal systems, suggests that ultimately the manufacture of a product may be accomplished by the use of computer programs controlling various machines from drawing-office design work, through process planning, to actual manufacture of the component with very little human involvement.

Drawing number	Number off	Material and size	Shop	Finish	Planner	Date
237	100	En 5 × 32 mm diameter	Machine	Natural, deburred	A.N. Other	25.7.83

Machine: Capstan lathe number 20

Operation and number	Tooling	Turret FTP RTP	Speed (rev/min)	Feed (mm/rev)
1. Feed bar to stop	Adjustable stop	Turret 1	–	–
2. Turn 12 mm diameter	Roller-steady box tool	Turret 2	1000	0.25
3. Turn 19 mm diameter	Roller-steady box tool	Turret 3	450	0.25
4. Turn 21 mm diameter	Roller-steady box tool	Turret 4	450	0.25
5. Radius (15 mm) end face	Roller-steady ending tool	Turret 5	450	Hand
6. Turn 5 mm taper	Form tool	FTP 1	100	Hand
7. Turn 18 mm taper	Form tool	FTP 2	100	Hand
8. Turn 9 mm recess	Form tool	FTP 3	100	Hand
9. Turn 29 mm diameter spherical end	Form tool	FTP 4	100	Hand
10. Rough die thread M12 × 1.25	Coventry die head	Turret 6	250	1.25
11. Finish die thread M12 × 1.25	Coventry die head	Turret 6 (Reset die head)	250	1.25
12. Part off	Parting-off tool	RTP	250	Hand

Figure 6.7 *Planning process sheet: pivot 'batch' production.*

The job of planning engineers would change from that of planning the method of manufacture to be communicated directly to the operators, for they would now need the services of part-programmers to translate their specific instructions, along with their implied instructions, into a language understood by the machines. Ultimately the design engineer may well have to design and plan the process, and write the program for a particular component.

There are many good books on Manufacturing Technology levels 3 and 4 which carry details of such programs to which the student should refer.

Summary

1. Process planning aims to ensure a product is manufactured to the necessary design standards (in accordance with the customer's requirements of accuracy and reliability), and at the minimum cost.

2. Process plans drawn up in flow-production organisations, once completed, can remain (with minor amendments as required) virtually unchanged over long periods. However, in engineering concerns — particularly those with a job/small batch output — process plans will mainly vary with the quantity of items required, the materials and plant available, the quality of the local labour force, and, often, the amount of storage space available.

3. At times these latter considerations would even raise the question as to whether items ordered should be purchased from other firms (bought out), either as partly finished or even completely finished items.

4. Process planners, in the interests of following well-established practice, may influence minor aspects of a product's design, and, in turn, may be influenced by analyses carried out by the work study department.

5. Process planners can assist in the pricing of work prior to quotations being sent out to potential customers, can help the production planning and control department to plan machine loading capacity, and, finally, the information contained in a process plan can be used to help prepare the standard cost of a product.

6. The design and production of manufacturing jigs, fixtures and cutting tools can be derived from process planning in so far as such planning usually specifies the use of standard materials, cut to shape.

7. The important post of process planner (or planning engineer) is best filled by a practical person not only versed in the basic processes used in the organisation employing him or her, but also possessing a sound technical academic background and good communication skills.

8. The process planner needs to keep abreast of all new developments in materials, plant and equipment, and to keep a close watch on the performance, reliability and capabilities of existing plant and equipment. He or she is then in a position to advise on replacement equipment as necessary.

9. When planning a particular process, the planner requires a drawing or some detailed description of the item to be made, details of the quantity involved, and the estimated cost of manufacture (when this is known).

10. Next he or she proceeds to decide (on the basis of plant/equipment available) whether to 'buy out' or have the items required made in the factory.

11. Provided the work is not subcontracted, further decisions are then made about:
    (a)   the raw materials to be used in production:
    (b)   the plant/equipment to be used, and the sequence of operations;
    (c)   the special jigs and fixtures required.
    (These decisions are made in consultation with production planning and control.)

12. When the process planner is satisfied that the product can be made within the estimated cost, a process planning layout (or operations sheet) is prepared for circulation. It contains:
    (a) component description, part number, quantity needed;
    (b) assembly drawing number, order number and other references;
    (c) material specifications;
    (d) list of operations, timed;
    (e) location of work and tooling for each operation.
13. Jigs and fixtures (to hold components in position while being worked upon) are required in most (engineering) manufacturing contexts. In a small batch/jobbing area, such fixtures are often made through the initiative of individual operators; in mass production the initial high cost is easily recoverable over the large quantities made, and tooling is designed for the purpose. In any event, for a new order, care is needed to make the best use of existing fixtures (even if modifications are needed). The process of tool design can lead to operations being combined or, alternatively, fragmented.
14. The tool designer designs the fixtures, tools, etc. from studying the cutting forces to be applied at any stage. (He or she may influence minor changes in component design by specifying that holding lugs are to be available at certain stages in manufacture.) The process planner then compiles and issues (to the toolroom) a tooling operations layout.
15. The toolroom is a self-contained production unit employing highly skilled staff, and with its own independent inspection system.
16. The quantities involved in a particular order for components can influence significantly the work of process planning. For example, smaller quantities of components could well be more cheaply (and more quickly) made by hand. Larger quantities could be produced more economically on a simple general-purpose machine used by a skilled operator. Larger quantities still could perhaps best be handled using a more sophisticated machine needing a less highly skilled operator.
    Similar considerations apply to mass or flow production, where special tools can be used to good effect.
17. These changes in production methods are reflected in the process planning sheets issued, and the types of instructions contained therein. (See the detailed example of pivot manufacture in the main text.)
18. Process planners, when preparing process documentation where human operations are involved, need to take into account operators' movements. However, as total mechanical and electronic manufacturing systems are developed, instructions to machines need to be precise and specific, with provision for feedback monitoring systems.
19. The current interest in robotics and computer-assisted equipment could even lead to the manufacture of products being completely computer-controlled from start to finish. In turn this could entail process planning becoming a computer-programming exercise.

Questions

Review questions

6.1 What are the aims of process planning in respect of any particular product?

6.2 Why does process planning differ from one industry to another (for example between a small joinery works and a brewery)?

6.3 What factors affect the planning of manufacturing methods and processes in engineering works?

6.4 Why do manufacturers sometimes choose to have products ordered from them made by other suppliers (i.e. 'bought out') rather than making such products in their own factories?

6.5 Describe the contribution that process planning can make to:
    (a)   the preparation of estimates to customers;
    (b)   the work of production control;
    (c)   the standard costing of a product.

6.6 What kind of person is best qualified as a process planner? List the kind of knowledge he or she should have of the organisation in which he or she works, particularly associated with the manufacturing and ancillary functions.

6.7 What information does a process planner require when carrying out the planning for a particular process?

6.8 What kinds of information are contained in a process planning layout or operations sheet?

6.9 State the uses of jigs and fixtures.

6.10 Jigs and fixtures can be expensive to make. Why is the use of specially designed and made equipment of this kind justified in mass or flow production?

6.11 In what way could the use of jigs and fixtures temporarily affect the design of a component?

6.12 Describe the facilities a toolroom normally has.

6.13 Explain the influence the *quantity ordered* of a particular product can have on process planning.

6.14 In the future, how might the job of process planning change in view of current trends in machine tool design?

Case studies

6.15 Crescent Bakery, run by Ms Goodbody, was a busy village business making a standard range of rolls, loaves and cakes. One day a TV company who were filming in the district asked Ms Goodbody to make them a special birthday cake (for use in the film) one metre in diameter—they were willing to pay any reasonable price.

Ms Goodbody was reluctant to turn the order down. 'I could buy one of those new large electric ovens,' she mused, 'or perhaps pass the order on to Monumental Foods to do it for me.'

Discuss what factors (including that of cost) Ms Goodbody might take into account in reaching a decision to make or buy.

6.16 Prestige Leatherworks were proud of the high quality of their product. It was a matter, then, of some concern when in one of their special lines, trouble was experienced in getting complete adhesion between the leather and a canvas liner. The process engineer was pleased when he overcame the trouble by specifying a new adhesive, the method of application, and drying time. He also instructed that adhesion could be improved by scratching the leather surface and roughing it up.

However, within a week new problems arose. Different operators had their own ideas about how much surface scratching was necessary, and it was difficult to establish a rate for the job. The work study department were called in and by experiment found twelve strokes of a wire brush were adequate. Dolly Bright, the chargehand, commented that the job was less tiring now, and her team were confident that they were doing it right.

Discuss why the original problem could have arisen, why the second crop of problems came about, and how the confusion might have been avoided.

Assignment

6.17 You are required to examine the pivot illustrated in Figure 6.4. Compare the two planning process sheets for one-off and batch production and list as many differences between the two methods of manufacture as you can find.

7

Capacity Planning and Demand Forecasting

This chapter reintroduces the notions of controlling and budgeting (see Chapter 1) and examines the two basic approaches of demand forecasting, the analytic and the synthetic, and concludes by mentioning a few considerations that need to be borne in mind when generating a capacity plan.

7.1 Budgeting and forecasting

Every manufacturing unit, large or small, needs to plan its production ahead. It possesses buildings, machinery, tools and stocks of materials ready for use. If no use, or less than optimum use, is made of these expensive resources then a less than adequate profit may result. The larger the firm the more important is the necessity to plan the use of such items further and further ahead. Basically the question to be asked about each product is how many to make.

In Chapter 1 mention was made of controlling and budgeting. Controlling deals with the adoption of objectives or targets: budgeting is the process of quantifying the targets or plans. A budget is simply a statement in financial or volume terms of what is planned or expected to happen: it is a forecast.

To become, and remain, efficient a firm needs to budget for the immediate future (short term) and for much further ahead (long term). Short-term budget forecasts provide detailed information on expected throughputs, for machine and process scheduling and the ordering of materials. Long-term forecasting provides guidance on such matters as the redeployment or purchase of plant and machinery, the revision of production methods, and forward planning for future production.

The more accurate the forecasts are, the more useful and reliable are budgets derived from them. Capacity planning can only be as good as the supporting forecasts.

7.2 Demand forecasting: information sources

Budgets are usually prepared ahead for a specific period (e.g. one year, six months). Figure 7.1 illustrates the flow of information involved in the demand forecasting and budgeting process for Acme Engineering Ltd. It is assumed, in the period concerned, that the company will continue to manufacture three existing products (A, B and C) and start producing two new products (X and Y).

The total information available is derived from the following sources:

(a) those internal to the company;
(b) marketing/sales;
(c) those external to the company.

From this information both the financial and the volume budgets are prepared. Financial budgeting is dealt with in Chapter 14: this chapter concentrates on the volume aspect.

Internal information

This information would include the following:

1. Existing definite orders on the books relating to the budget period (very firm information).
2. Records of actual sales of products A, B and C over previous periods. These figures can be analysed to reveal sales trends (up, down, steady demand) and seasonal surges or declines (useful information as a guide).
3. Knowledge of progress in the development of new products X and Y and their expected launch dates (production will need to be put in hand before the launches) (fairly firm information).
4. Knowledge of the state and capacity of all existing plant and machinery and what new items/processes are likely to be brought into use before or during the forecast period (fairly firm information).

Marketing/sales information

Information of varying reliability can be obtained from this source:

1. Market research staff will provide ideas about the state of the market, and included would be estimates of sales of products X and Y, and the possible effects of competition on sales.
2. Advertising staff will be able to advise which products will be heavily advertised and give some idea of increased demand.
3. Home and export sales staff or agents will provide their estimates of the sales likely to be achieved for each product.

This is rather speculative information, and will need to be carefully reviewed by the marketing or sales manager: the final figures must be realistic.

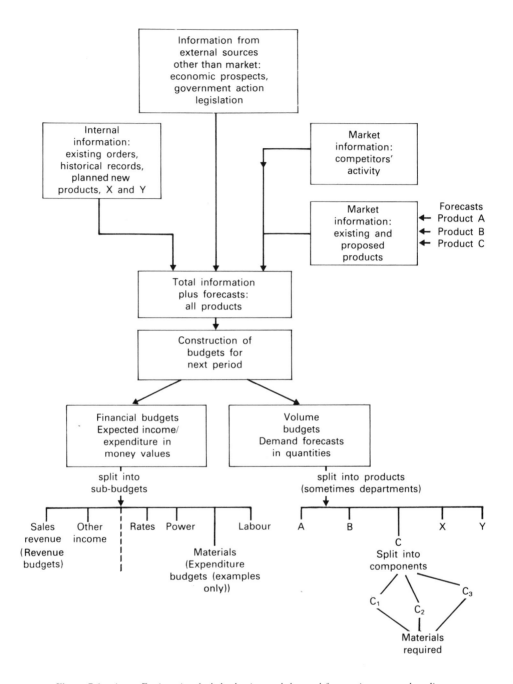

Figure 7.1 *Acme Engineering Ltd, budgeting and demand forecasting, general outline.*

External information

This would be obtained from government sources, published reports, the CBI, newspapers, TV, etc. It would include:

1. Economic predictions about how the national economy will behave (boom or recession), the prospects for various industries, and rates of inflation.
2. Tax changes, HP rates, current and possible future interest rates.
3. Government intervention, such as assistance to industry (e.g. to ship-building), or new legislation which could affect demand for products (e.g. compulsory seat-belts).
4. The industrial relations climate.

Collating information from all sources

All the information will be collated and eventually final figures will be prepared. Great care and skill are required at this stage, as no one source is likely to give a trustworthy or complete assessment of the future. Sales staff may offer over-optimistic expectations without regard to internal production problems or external economic factors. However, provided possible future circumstances are taken into account, and the market research and statistical techniques considered in the next sections are used, the opinions of the sales staff (particularly outside representatives) could be useful.

7.3 Classifications of demand forecasting

Demand forecasting can be classified in two quite distinct ways. The first classification is by the *methods* used (i.e. synthetic and analytic). The second is by the *time-scale* involved (long-term and short-term). In this section both types of classification are examined.

Synthetic forecasting

The verb 'to synthesise'—from which synthetic is derived—means basically to combine separate items into a whole. In synthetic forecasting, then, demand forecasts are built up by taking information from a variety of sources. Acme Engineering Ltd will want to consider the state of the economy and international trade, possible government intervention, market research to assess market trends (changes in fashion), market share and those of competitors, reports from sales staff, and predictions about the performance of new products.

Synthetic forecasting is thus based on mostly external information, is speculative and is not often based on hard fact. While people would always like to work on sure and certain data, if the business (such as Acme Engineering) depends on large orders for a few products, the synthetic method is probably more effective.

Analytic forecasting

This form of forecasting is essentially making predictions about future demand based on past data on demand. The various techniques for doing this all rely on obtaining precise information from records on past sales and outputs, and identifying trends which are projected into the future. On the face of it this is a scientific approach to forecasting, but there are two significant drawbacks. First, the process assumes that the outside (marketing) environment and other conditions under which products are sold will not change much in the future (a dangerous assumption to make).

Second, it is normally true in statistics that the more data available (e.g. in a sample), the more accurate will be the predictions made from those data. Unfortunately, the more data used in analytic forecasts the further back in time one must go, and therefore use data which are more and more out of date.

Analytic forecasting methods

To enable the different methods examined here to be grasped more easily, and to enable comparisons to be made of the results obtained, the data in Table 7.1 will be used throughout.

Table 7.1 *Acme Engineering Ltd: Sales of product B, in 000s.*

Month	Year 1	Year 2	
Jan.	22	22	
Feb.	24	26	
Mar.	20	24	
Apr.	18	20	
May	24	28	*Note:* Average monthly sale prior to records here was
Jun.	18	20	19 000.
Jul.	25	26	
Aug.	16	18	
Sep.	14	20	
Oct.	26	26	
Nov.	21	22	
Dec.	24	26	

Method 1: moving averages (past arithmetic average). By taking a sufficient number (say six) of previous periods (in our case months) and averaging the total, we predict the next period's (month's) demand. Using the figures in Table 7.1, the following result is obtained from July to December in Year 1.

This method has failed to cope with wide monthly fluctuations and the tendency for sales to drop in mid-year. Predictions based on mid-year figures will tend to be out when applied to year-end figures.

Month	Actual sales (000s)	Forecast	Error (000s)
Jul.	25	21 (Jan.–Jun.)	+4.00
Aug.	16	21.5 (Feb.–Jul.)	−5.50
Sept.	14	20.16 (Mar.–Aug.)	−6.16
Oct.	26	19.16 (Apr.–Sep.)	+6.84
Nov.	21	20.5 (May–Oct.)	+0.50
Dec.	24	20 (Jun.–Nov.)	+4.00
		Total	+3.68

By 'error' is meant the extent by which sales fail to equal the forecast.

Method 2: quarterly moving averages. A way of smoothing out this fluctuation is to take averages of averages. By extracting from Table 7.1 the quarterly figures for the period Jan.–Mar., Apr.–Jun., etc. for both years, and then working out a four-period or quarterly moving forecast, we get the following:

Year	Quarter	Actual totals (000s)	Moving average	Error
1	1	66	—	
	2	60	—	
	3	55	—	
	4	71	—	
2	1	72	63	+9.00
	2	68	64.50	+3.50
	3	64	66.50	−2.50
	4	74	68.75	+5.25

Preparing the figures this way shows seasonal fluctuations, and averaging the averages smoothes these out. The moving average also clearly indicates the underlying trend of increased demand. However, if it is realised soon enough in Year 2 that sales are increasing at about 10 per cent over Year 1, and Year 1 figures are being used to forecast, then the moving averages could be compensated by this amount. The new figures would be as follows:

Year 2	Quarter	Moving average	+ 10 per cent	Actual	Error
	1	63	69.30	72	+2.70
	2	64.50	70.95	68	−2.95
	3	66.50	73.15	64	−9.15
	4	68.75	75.62	74	−1.62

Basing a production programme on these figures would at least have the virtue of making about 5 per cent more than immediate demand in an expanding situation.

Method 3: exponential smoothing.   This is another method to compensate for changes, but in this case by giving more weight (or emphasis) to the latest figures available, and less to the earlier figures. Another virtue is that excessive calculations (as with moving averages) are avoided.

To make a prediction for the next period in the future (P) using this method, just three items of information are needed. Two items are data from the immediately preceding period, O: the forecast originally made for O (the old forecast) and the actual demand (sales) in period O. Finally, the value of a co-efficient X—a smoothing factor—is determined.

Basically X is the amount of weight or emphasis required by the most recent figures available (i.e. period O). The value of X theoretically can vary from 0.0 to 1.0, but in practice is normally between 0.1 and 0.3. A value of $X = 0.2$ is equivalent to saying that a 20 per cent emphasis is being given to latest demand data; $X = 0.4$, a 40 per cent emphasis, etc. The formula is:

$$\text{Forecast for } P = (X)(\text{latest sales } O) + (1 - X)(\text{old forecast})$$

where P = next period, O = last period, and X = smoothing factor.

Applying the formula, for example, to the same example discussed in Method 1 (i.e. July to December, Year 1, Product B), and assuming $X = 0.2$ and the old forecast for June was 20, we obtain:

$$
\begin{aligned}
\text{Forecast for July} &= (X)(\text{latest sales } O)+ (1 - X)(\text{old forecast}) \\
&= (0.2 \times 18) \quad\quad + (0.8 \times 20) \\
&= 3.6 \quad\quad\quad\quad\; + 16 \\
&= 19.6
\end{aligned}
$$

Carrying on the calculations for the whole six months, the following figures are obtained:

Period	Sales	Old forecast	Previous sales	New forecast	Error
Jul.	25	20	18	19.6	+5.4
Aug.	16	19.6	25	20.7	−4.7
Sep.	14	20.7	16	19.8	−5.8
Oct.	26	19.8	14	18.6	+7.4
Nov.	21	18.6	26	20.1	+0.9
Dec.	24	20.1	21	20.3	+3.7
					+6.9

Other methods.   Other methods of prediction/forecasting include *graphs* from which various fluctuations (seasonal or cyclical) can be identified, or trends determined, such as a slow decline in sales. Also graphical is the *cumulative sum technique,* which is the plotting of the cumulative totals of the differences from a predetermined mean level of sales for each period considered. Upward or downward trends are clearly identified by this method.

Long-term forecasting

Forecasts looking ahead for a year or more are known as long-term. Long-term forecasts will tend to be more synthetic than analytic, the more so the further ahead the predictions are made (e.g. five, ten years ahead). Large firms such as ICI or BP could well forecast ahead as far as twenty years.

Short-term forecasting

Forecasts made on a weekly, monthly or quarterly basis are short-term. As synthetic forecasting needs a great deal of research it cannot be implemented at frequent intervals, so short-term forecasting is likely to be analytic.

7.4 Demand forecasting: final comments

It has been said that forecasting is an art, not a science. A review of the methods considered here shows that synthetic forecasting has an increasing air of uncertainty about it the further ahead projections are made, and that analytic methods do not produce spot on predictions every time. Any method, or combination of methods chosen by a firm must be updated and modified in the light of experience to produce the best results.

7.5 Capacity planning: final stages

Once all the information (internal, marketing and external) has been collated, an overall budget for the company can be prepared (see Figure 7.1). As we have seen, the likely demands for individual products can be estimated for a coming period. From this data a production budget can be prepared.

Such a budget may not precisely follow the demand forecasts: problems with plant or machinery and alterations to layouts may reduce capacity potential, and budgets may have to be prepared at a lower rate than expected demand. In such cases decisions such as make or buy will have to be taken. Again it may be decided to make for stock as well as against expected immediate demand, particularly where stocks have fallen low.

Having taken all these points into account the actual quantified planning can begin.

Summary

1. Every organisation, whatever its size, needs to plan its production ahead, so that the best use can be made of the plant, machinery, and materials available: it needs to be controlled.
2. Budgeting, or forecasting, is an essential part of the control function, as it translates broad objectives or targets into precise financial or volume quantities.
3. Demand forecasting is based on information from three sources:
    (a) *internal* (existing orders, historical records of past sales, knowledge of new products and knowledge of the state and capacity of plant);
    (b) *marketing/sales* (the existing state of the market, estimates on performance of each product in the next period and the effects of advertising and competition on sales);
    (c) *external* to the company (economic predictions, fiscal or tax changes, interest rates, the rate of inflation, possible or known government intervention and industrial relations).
4. Information is collated (the budgeting process) and final figures prepared.
5. Demand forecasting can be classified into:
    (a) *synthetic forecasting* (building up a forecast by considering external sources of information, and marketing/sales forecasts);
    (b) *analytic forecasting* (based mainly on internal information: historical sales records, and any modifications made to figures in the light of marketing/ external information).
6. Analytic forecasting methods include:
    (a) *moving average* methods—these would normally be on a four- or six-monthly moving average (though some firms use a twelve-month system);
    (b) *exponential smoothing*—this method (applied to moving average methods) aims to give more emphasis to the very latest figures. The amount of emphasis is usually between 10 per cent and 30 per cent. (i.e. the coefficient $X = 0.1$ to 0.3); the basic formula is:

    $$\text{Forecast for } P = (X)(\text{latest sales } O) + (1 - X)(\text{old forecast})$$

    where P = next period, O = last period and X = smoothing factor;
    (c) *other methods*—visual sales graphs of historic data are projected forward; another variation is the cumulative sum technique involving plotting of cumulative totals of differences from an assumed mean of sales.
7. The remaining classifications of demand forecasting methods are:
    (a) *long-term forecasting* (deals with periods in excess of one year ahead—more synthetic than analytic);
    (b) *short-term forecasting* (deals with weeks or months ahead, with the emphasis more on the use of analytic methods).
8. Forecasting demand is not an exact science. The particular methods adopted by a company (probably a mixture of synthetic and analytic) will be evolved through experience.
9. The final capacity budget will not only take into account the demand forecasts, but will also incorporate what it is possible to do. (Some demands may not be capable of being met.) Other policy decisions (such as building up stocks of finished goods) may affect the final result.

Questions

Review questions

7.1 What is a budget?

7.2 Describe the overall budget-making process.

7.3 What are the sources of information from which demand forecasts can be made?

7.4 What kinds of information useful for demand forecasting can be obtained from:
  (a) historical records of the company;
  (b) the marketing department?

7.5 Are budgets/forecasts built up entirely from one source of information? Explain your answer.

7.6 What are the four classifications of demand forecasting?

7.7 Explain the exponential smoothing method, and the justification for adopting it.

7.8 Describe the quarterly moving average method.

7.9 Why might the final capacity plan not *exactly* match the carefully calculated forecasts?

Discussion topics

7.10 Comment on the statement 'Forecasting is only crystal-ball gazing, and companies might just as well engage a fortune teller to help them with demand forecasting'.

7.11 Discuss the following 'If all the work-hours spent in working out budgets and demand forecasts were used in actually making more products, firms would become much more efficient'.

7.12 With regard to any firm or organisation known to class members discuss the most appropriate methods of demand forecasting: synthetic, analytic or a combination of both.

Assignments

7.13 Using the data in Table 7.1, and in the text:
  (a) Prepare, using the exponential smoothing method ($X = 0.2$), forecasts for the first six months of Year 2 for Product B.
  (b) Comment on the amount of error achieved between forecasts and sales. Is this limit of error acceptable?

7.14 The company for which you work, Acme Engineering Ltd, is considering using demand forecasting methods *for the first time*. (Previously a fixed number of each product was made each month, irrespective of demand.) Write a *short* report (one side of A4), explaining to Mr. Will Tappit, the works manager, the value of demand forecasting to Acme Engineering Ltd.

Case study

7.15 Phil Sellars, marketing manager of Marinecraft Ltd, rushed into the office of Bill Shepherd, the works manager, at 8.15 a.m. last Monday morning. 'It's fantastic,' he exclaimed. 'We've had a bumper week at the Boat Show—the old *Velocity* class was still in great demand. I have twenty firm orders in my pocket. The main thing I want to tell you about is the tremendous interest in our new boat, the *Lightning*! I had forty inquiries each day, and all the well-known yachtsmen and women praised her. I want you to lay down a production line of ten per month straight away—we mustn't be caught out when the rush starts!' At that Phil swept out to tell the glad tidings to the managing director. Bill looked thoughtful.

(a)   What should Bill do? Act at 'lightning' speed to plan the new production line, purchase the new equipment and materials needed and redeploy labour and shop space? Explain your answer.

(b)   What other matter must Bill attend to quickly?

8
Maintenance and Maintenance Policies

This chapter deals with the definition of maintainability and maintenance, and describes the relationship of maintenance to the control function. The justification for having a definite commitment to a maintenance policy is also discussed. After considering the objectives of maintenance policies, and the efficacy of various alternative maintenance strategies, a case is made for preventive maintenance. Finally, there is a brief introduction to terotechnology.

8.1 Maintainability and maintenance: definitions

The basic ideas behind the word 'maintenance' (see the *Oxford English Dictionary*) are 'sustaining, preserving unimpaired, keeping in being, keeping going, keeping in good order'. Applied to the production function, maintenance can be said to be:

> that set of activities, the aim of which is to ensure that the buildings, plant and machinery of an organisation are kept in such a condition (or restored to such a condition) that they can continue to carry out their required functions satisfactorily.

Definitions of the various maintenance strategies are given as they arise.

Many products are designed in ways which make it inevitable that action will be needed either to offset wear and tear (e.g. reboring a cylinder), or to replace parts (e.g. gaskets, filters, etc.) during the products' lifetimes. The degree to which such work can be carried out with the minimum of problems is known as the maintainability of a product. Obviously products with a high degree of maintainability will be attractive to customers.

8.2 Maintenance and control

Controlling, as has been previously noted, is the process of setting targets or laying down standards and preparing budgets, and then ensuring that what was planned to happen actually does happen (as far as is possible). A major problem for production management is that so many things can go wrong and upset plans: material may not be delivered, customers may change their minds, workers may strike, etc. If, however, management can rely on plant and equipment to function when it is needed then the job of production control is made that much easier.

8.3 The need for maintenance

Until the late 1960s maintenance was seen as a poor relation of the production department. Management saw maintenance as a necessary (but expensive) evil and factory supervisors often resented and resisted attempts to overhaul their machinery, working overtime to meet the demands of the then still expanding economy. In recent times a substantial shift in attitudes has taken place, due in part to the following factors:

1. Government interest in maintenance,[1] and reports circulated widely throughout industry.
2. As economic conditions have worsened, firms have seen the need for increased productivity, and have realised that increased labour productivity depends heavily on investment in plant and equipment. If their equipment does not function efficiently, production and profits suffer.
3. Breakdowns when machines were mostly general or multi-purpose were less serious: one machine could be substituted for another. Now machines are tending to become more specialised, complex and sophisticated: it is less possible (due to expense) to have back-up machines available. Breakdowns are now far more significant in terms of production lost.
4. Machinery is now not only very expensive, but technological advances mean that its expected working life before it becomes outmoded is decreasing. It is vital to make the maximum use of the equipment during its lifetime.
5. Machines are now so interrelated and interdependent (e.g. in large batch/continuous flow process) that a failure in one part of one machine could have a 'knock-on' effect throughout the factory. The costs of a stoppage in such circumstances could be very high.
6. The Health and Safety at Work etc. Act 1974 imposed a duty on employers to 'maintain plant and systems of work that are, so far as is reasonably possible, safe and without risks to health'.

A strong thread running through this list is the adverse affect that breakdowns have on costs (and ultimately on profits), as well as any possible effects on the workforce, who might be injured while using inadequately maintained plant.

---

[1] For example the *Report by the Working Party on Maintenance Engineering* (1969). London: HMSO.

The costs of maintenance down time (a term used by engineers to refer to the length of time equipment remains non-effective) could include any or all of the following:

(a)   the costs of labour, and material used in completing repairs;
(b)   the wages of machine operators while machines are idle;
(c)   the costs of scrap/refurbishing of faulty parts made;
(d)   the loss of contribution from the unmade products;
(e)   the cost of accidents, including legal proceedings.

Add to this list general frustration, ill-feeling, and unhappy customers, and a formidable argument emerges for every company having a soundly based maintenance policy.

8.4 Maintenance policy objectives

The objectives of any positive maintenance policy follow naturally from the ideas considered above. In essence they should attempt first to prevent breakdowns arising at all, and second to reduce down time and other losses to the absolute minimum. More specifically, such objectives should include the following:

1.   To assist in safeguarding the firm's assets.[2] (All plant is costing more and more to replace: when it is sold off or traded in, the firm will want to get the best possible price.)
2.   To help ensure that the whole production process—buildings, plant, equipment, tools—operates at the lowest total cost. (The eventual choice of maintenance strategies will be partly influenced by which method gives the best return.)
3.   To prolong the active life of the assets, and minimise down time. A striking example (admittedly from a service industry) of how this objective is achieved is that of British Rail's high-speed trains (HSTs), which are inspected (as complete trains) every two days, at times when they are not needed for passenger duties. Appropriate running maintenance is then carried out. Only with such a constant checking programme and appropriate maintenance can trains be kept running as part of a daily, highly intensive HST service.
4.   To maximise the efficiency of the assets. (As with the HSTs, without maintenance some equipment will continue to function for a while, but with a declining efficiency rate.)
5.   To help reduce accidents which could cause damage to life, limb or property. (The legal safety obligations of employers are very great.)

---

[2] In this context 'assets' means buildings, plant, machinery, equipment, tools, etc.

8.5 Maintenance policies and strategies

A firm has a series of possible options to choose from in its attempt to fulfil its maintenance policy objectives (particularly that of minimising costs). The most cost-effective methods for that firm will be chosen.

Breakdown or emergency maintenance

Two somewhat different philosophies are given the same general title. The first (sometimes called a 'run or bust' policy) entails running plant and equipment without maintenance or repair until and unless there is a failure or breakdown.

There is some merit in this approach if the equipment is of little value and nearing the end of its useful life, or, alternatively, if the prime costs of maintenance are excessive, and down time high even for a relatively minor service. However, machinery run without proper servicing will tend to break down at shorter and shorter intervals.

Second is the policy where it is accepted—no matter what else is done—that failures and breakdowns will occur out of the blue. Provision will be made for appropriate repair equipment, spares, labour, etc. to be available.

Standby capacity

A minimum stoppage time can be achieved by having spare plant, machinery, fork-lifts, etc. available as reserves. Normally, standby capacity is unused, so it is an extremely difficult and expensive policy to sustain if plant, etc. is highly specialised and costly. It could be useful where low-cost standard equipment (e.g. electric pumps) is being used, and the repercussions from a stoppage (e.g. a lost repeat order) are high. Standby plant is often elderly.

Double track provision

Here there is a duplication (possibly even side by side) of a production line or a process. A failure in one line (or if it is shut down for routine maintenance) does not result in a complete stoppage of production. If each line normally runs below maximum capacity, the still-running line can be speeded up to make good some of the loss.

Reservoir stocks

Where large batch/continuous flow production methods are used or where final assembly lines depend upon components and sub-assemblies being fed into them, a breakdown could mean a total stoppage. A maintenance strategy can be to have reservoir or buffer stocks available at every stage. Production flow can continue while repairs or maintenance are carried out.

Preventive maintenance (PM)

The old adage 'prevention is better than cure' applies to maintenance. The aim of PM is to reduce or eliminate breakdowns and failures, and to minimise the resulting losses or damage.

The first vital step in PM is *inspection*. In some cases a visual inspection, or information from electronic monitoring equipment, will be all that is required, but all too often a complete strip-down will be necessary: internal and external parts need equally to be examined. Similarly the second step, *servicing*, can vary from oiling moving parts during a production run, to cleaning, refurbishing and changing worn parts, re-inspecting and testing.

Capricious or impulsive decisions to overhaul a milling machine, or leaving PM to the last possible moment, do not give the best results. Planned PM at fixed, regular intervals is carried out not only to ensure that *all* equipment is inspected, but also to make use of maintenance staff to spread the work as evenly as possible. Production departments can make arrangements in advance to cope with known PM arrangements for particular equipment.

Under a planned PM scheme, specific time limits, operational work hours, or mileage covered between inspections are laid down. The regularity of inspection varies according to the asset: a factory building may be inspected once or twice per year, a moving piston driving a heavy load once a week and guards on a dangerous machine before each shift.

Some PM is carried out regardless of the state of the asset (e.g. a machine oil change). Electric light bulbs may be replaced every 1000 hours and even a machine not in use may be regularly oiled and inspected.

8.6 Preventive or breakdown maintenance?

In section 8.3 the costs of maintenance down time were considered. Breakdowns will incur virtually all the costs listed, but provided maintenance can be carried out (as with the HSTs) when equipment is not in use, a considerable amount of the indirect costs can be avoided. From Figure 8.1 it will be seen that on balance there is much in favour of PM.

Relative costs

The relative costs of the two strategies can be established only if each is pursued for a period separately, and careful records kept. (In practice this could be difficult to do for all equipment: sampling could be tried.)

Consider Figures 8.2 and 8.3. Figure 8.2 illustrates (either for a company's plant as a whole or for a single item of equipment) the situation where breakdowns are few and are not expensive to repair, and where other effects are not significant. It will be seen that it is less costly to adopt BM than PM.

Figure 8.3, in contrast, shows a different story: a situation where breakdowns are many and/or costly, and where PM can make a significant reduction.

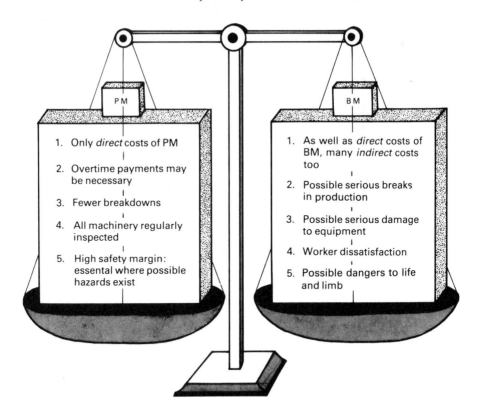

Figure 8.1   *The balance between preventive maintenance and breakdown maintenance.*

Both figures taken together, however, make two other points: the more PM is done, the greater the cost. In fact, in Figure 8.3 the point where the two curves cross is an optimum mix point: it is actually cheaper to limit PM, and retain the chances and expenses of BM. The target of 100 per cent reliability may be so expensive to achieve as to make it totally uneconomic.

8.7 Over-maintenance

There is little doubt that some organisations have moved to highly intensive maintenance programmes—more intensive than is really required. It is indeed time-consuming to identify exactly how long equipment should be left between one overhaul and the next in a PM scheme. Some work carried out in a water authority

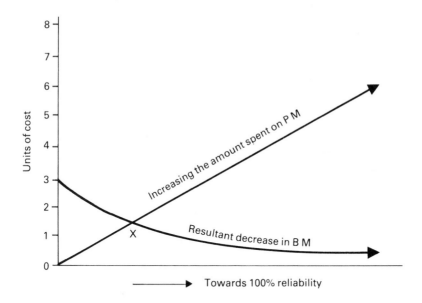

Figure 8.2 *Costs of preventive maintenance and breakdown maintenance compared when breakdowns are few and not costly.*

Notes
1. *At zero PM in this example costs are:*

BM	3.0 units
PM	0.0
Total	3.0 units

2. *At 6 units of cost of PM costs are:*

BM	0.5 units
PM	6.0 units
Total	6.5 units

Best choices strictly on cost:

(a)   *no PM*
(b)   *where lines cross at X*

recently even suggested that over-maintenance was detrimental, and caused certain parts (of pumps) to wear out more quickly. Further investigations were to proceed to establish if the degree of wear could be related to the degree of isolation noted by sensitive electronic measuring equipment. If successful, such testing would remove the need to inspect by stripping down.

Where safety is paramount, or equipment is required to be able to cope with greatly increased work loads at a moment's notice, frequent maintenance could be termed 'supermaintenance' rather than over-maintenance. A striking example was the sudden

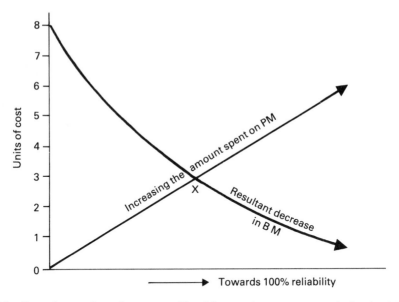

Figure 8.3 *Costs of preventive maintenance and breakdown maintenance compared when breakdowns are many and costly.*

Notes
1. *At zero PM breakdowns are most costly: 8 units.*
2. *At 6 units of cost of PM costs are:*

$$
\begin{array}{ll}
BM & 0.5\ units \\
PM & 6.0 \\
\hline
Total & \overline{6.5}\ units
\end{array}
$$

Best choice strictly on cost *is where lines cross at X.*

demands made on the RAF's VC 10s in the Falklands campaign: in a short period they made 150 long flights, carried some 3800 people and 2.8 million lb of freight.[3] Such commitments could have been fulfilled so efficiently only by aircraft highly maintained as a matter of course.

8.8 The maintenance team

There are a variety of questions concerning the maintenance team: how many, and what skills should they possess? Indeed the same question arises as with production—whether to do all maintenance (building, plant and equipment) with a firm's own staff, or to use specialist outside contractors for some work. The answers can be found only by a careful analysis of costs and skills required.

[3] *Witney Gazette* 5 August 1982.

8.9 Terotechnology

Terotechnology is a difficult-looking word when met for the first time: luckily it is not difficult to understand. Derived from a Greek root 'tereo' (caring), it means the 'technology of caring for', the caring for an organisation's capital assets, including those used in production. This caring extends to the whole life-cycle of an asset: a study of the asset from its initial conception, specification and design stages to launching, production, installation, use and maintenance, and finally to its eventual removal and replacement. The objective of such study is to make the total life-cycle as economic and cost-effective as possible.

Central to a terotechnological approach at a design stage is the desire to design plant not just for its function or use, but also for maximum reliability and maintainability. The aim here should be (even if a higher initial cost is involved) to eliminate maintenance altogether, or to reduce and simplify what maintenance will be necessary.

Plastic cladding on a factory building means some painting is eliminated. A chain running in a sealed oil bath does not need frequent inspection and oiling. A stainless steel exhaust system (admittedly at extra initial cost) eliminates the need for the fairly frequent changes required when thin-section, corrodible metal is used.

Summary

1. Maintenance is that set of activities which aim to ensure that the buildings, plant and machinery of an organisation are kept in such a condition (or restored to such a condition) that they can continue to carry out their required functions satisfactorily.
2. Maintainability is the degree of ease in which a product can be maintained.
3. Maintenance, by helping to keep production plant and equipment fit to function, aids the job of production control.
4. Government interest, the high cost of machinery, economic conditions, new sophisticated technology, the integration of machinery in complex systems, and increased awareness in safety—all have tended to highlight the need for maintenance policies.
5. The costs of breakdowns can be high, including direct repair costs, indirect costs of idle machines, scrap, loss of sales income and costs of accidents.
6. Maintenance policies aim to safeguard the firm's assets, help to minimise production costs, prolong machine-life, maximise equipment efficiency and assist in accident reduction.
7. Maintenance strategies include breakdown or emergency maintenance, the provision of a standby capacity, double or duplicate provision of production lines, reservoir stocks and preventive maintenance schemes.
8. Preventive maintenance has the advantages of minimising breakdowns and ensuring regular inspection of equipment and a higher safety margin, while breakdown maintenance may incur many indirect costs and lead to production

stoppages, damage to equipment and a greater risk of accidents. However, where few breakdowns occur BM may be the better choice. The final decision needs careful cost information.

9. Over-maintenance can occur, and may even be detrimental. However, where safety or immediate availability for extra work is involved, supermaintenance is essential.

10. Terotechnology, the approach which views the life-history of equipment *as a whole* with a view to minimising total life-time costs, affects maintenance and maintainability. It suggests that built-in maintainability and simple methods of maintenance should be considered at the design stage.

Questions

Review questions

8.1   Compare the terms 'maintenance' and 'maintainability'.
8.2   Why is maintenance important in helping to achieve control of production?
8.3   List *five* reasons why maintenance is now accepted as a useful activity.
8.4   Explain what the *two* major aims of maintenance policies are. List the *four* subsidiary objectives.
8.5   What are the following:
      (a)   a 'run or bust' policy;
      (b)   double-track provision;
      (c)   reservoir stocks?
8.6   Explain the ideas behind PM.
8.7   Contrast the relative advantages and disadvantages of PM and BM.
8.8   What is meant by terotechnology? How is it relevant to a discussion on maintenance?

Discussion topics

8.9   Discuss the view that as failures and breakdowns are inevitable, even in the best run plants, preventive maintenance is just a waste of time.
8.10 Discuss (in groups) what kind of maintenance strategies would be most appropriate for:
      (a)   fork-lift trucks;
      (b)   gas piping;
      (c)   electric light bulbs;
      (d)   standby generator;
      (e)   blast furnace.
8.11 Examine (in groups) examples of items or products available at work or in college. Discuss ways in which maintainability could have been improved at the design stage.

Assignments

8.12 Choose an item of plant or equipment used at work or college, about which there are some maintenance records and records of any breakdown repairs between PM. Write a short report on the item describing the details of its maintenance intervals between repairs, etc. and suggest any changes you believe to be beneficial.

8.13 Draw up a suitable record card for logging servicing and repair, to include dates of repair, category of maintenance, costs, etc. (You may need to do some research into existing documents of this type.)

Case study

8.14 Acme Engineering Ltd has a special flow production line for a high-value product, B. The line functions every day and normally just manages to keep up with demand without overtime being worked. Any interruption in production is serious. Charlotte Grant, the maintenance engineer, is preparing a report for the works manager, and would dearly love to have a back-up machine available.

At present Acme Engineering has a policy of only breakdown maintenance, and often makes use of an outside firm's labour (who only come in normal working hours). Charlotte wants to change the policy: she gets 'flak' from the shop supervisor each time the machine fails. She has the following information:

	Normal eight-hour day	*Outside normal day*
Repair costs per hour	£30 (contractors)	£45 (own staff)
Total down time costs per hour	£1000	Nil
Repair times (in hours)		
Breakdowns (average)	10	–
PM (estimate)	–	6
Replace machine	1	1
Cost of new machine	£35 000	

Assuming there are four breakdowns expected in the next year, and a PM scheme would ideally need two inspections/services a month, what should Charlotte recommend?

9
Facilities Layouts (Manufacturing Systems) and Materials Movement

In this chapter, after defining facilities layouts and revising types of production the following types of layout are considered: fixed position, process, product/flow and group. Finally, the methods of planning and evaluating layouts by means of charts, models and matrices are described.

9.1 Facilities layouts: definition

Facilities layout usually means the way in which production, plant, equipment, fixtures, etc. are set out or positioned.[1] There are, however, three distinct situations to which the term can be applied:

1. The way in which different departments (e.g. press and paint shops, assembly departments) are positioned in relation to each other.
2. The way in which different machines (or equipment, etc.) are positioned in relation to each other within the same department.
3. The way in which different machines, etc. are positioned in relation to others within the same working area within a department.

In this chapter we shall come across all three situations.

9.2 Types of production

It will be recalled from Chapter 4 (section 4.7) that production systems can be divided into three main categories:

(a) job/small batch (one offs, specials, small runs);

---

[1] For the rest of this chapter 'facilities' is to be taken to mean plant, equipment, tools, fixtures, etc. as appropriate.

(b) large batch/mass production (a wide category from large batches to almost continuous flow);
(c) flow/process production.

The relationship between these categories and various production layouts was mentioned in Chapter 4: in this chapter a closer examination is made of these layouts.

9.3 Fixed position layouts

This term is something of a misnomer as it is the *product* rather than the plant, equipment or tools which is fixed. Essentially this production layout involves a stationary product: materials, equipment and labour are brought, or come, to the product as required during assembly. Size is an important factor here: ships as big as the QE2 can hardly be moved from one place to another, except by launching after the major work has finished.

Buildings of all kinds, bridges, aircraft, racing and other specialist cars, many kinds of repairs—all involve construction on site or in one place. Job/small batch production is very often done in a fixed-position layout (though if facilities are spread throughout a factory even a 'special' will be put through in a standard way).

Fixed position can be found to a greater extent where *most* of a job is carried out in one place, with perhaps the final finishing process somewhere else close by. The process (called 'making through' in the garment industry) entails most of the work—for example on a dress—being carried out on one table by a single skilled operator with the garment being passed over to others to put in the finishing touches.

Common to all fixed-position layout work is a high (even excessive) degree of handling materials, so a high labour content (mostly skilled or highly skilled) is required, but a great advantage is that a wide range of products can be made in varying materials, sizes, shapes, etc. Production times can be long, depending on the complexity of the job.

9.4 Process (functional) layout

The term 'process' (or sometimes 'functional') is applied to layouts where facilities of a similar type are grouped together in a recognisably separate work area, or department.

This type of layout is well known, and widely used in engineering. The use of the term 'shop' (and sometimes 'department') in such words as 'press shop', 'welding shop' and 'machine shop' serves to indicate the grouping of similar facilities in one area. As seen in Figure 9.1, materials (in the form of, say, low-carbon steel strips) enter the press shop to be bent into two separate shapes. The next stage sees the pressings being welded (in the welding shop) and passed on to the paint shop. Inspection sees the parts off to final assembly.

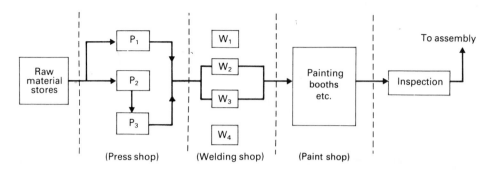

Figure 9.1 *Process layout: engineering.*

The clothing industry, with its emphasis on the basic elements of cutting, sewing and pressing also uses process layouts widely. Each element takes place in a different area. In blanket making a finished item will have gone through many different departments, especially where the raw material starts as fleeces.

Similarly, in military beret manufacture at Compton Webb (Headdress) separate areas exist for the various stages. In one area the woollen thread is prepared, and in another it is knitted on a group of machines which can produce several styles, and finally the knitted berets are joined—again a group of machines can do this task. The berets (after tidying-up operations) then pass into the felling/milling/felling process which both washes the berets and prepares them for dyeing. After being put on stretchers and dried, the linings and other fittings are added.

The need to be able to cope with orders in which quantity, size and colour can vary and successfully deliver a high-quality article on time dictates the adoption of a process layout. In whatever industry a process layout is used, the need is for *batch* production with range changes. This versatility is bought at the cost of handling and movement between operations, a considerable amount of work in progress, with queuing between departments, and frequent inspections, which can cumulatively be expensive.

However, a breakdown will not cause a total stoppage (particularly where machinery is versatile and/or duplicated) even in the department in which it occurs. Preventive maintenance is often possible within normal working hours. Less skilled labour than that used for fixed position is required, so prime costs are lower. Conversely the handling, storage and delays entail considerable increase in overhead costs.

9.5 Product (line) layout

The term 'product' (or sometimes 'line') is applied to layouts where all the facilities applicable to one product (or a related family group of products) are laid out in line, or sequence. Instead of a work area or department being concerned with (and being named after) a process, in product layouts each department is devoted to the manufacture of one product (i.e. making the majority of, if not all, the stages).

The drawbacks of the process-type layout were indicated in the previous section. Imagine the problems increasing as the size of batches increases from, say, 1000 to 100 000: handling between departments, storage and work in progress become serious and expensive matters to cope with. More and more space would be required, but, particularly in urban areas, it is not only expensive but often impossible to expand the total floor area. One answer lies in adopting better work-handling methods—conveyors, lifting tackle, quick-action work clamps, etc. Second, machines can be placed closer together, avoiding the waste of time, effort and money in trundling partly finished items round the factory. Not only is space saved, but the work in progress is greatly reduced.

If the tasks that the product line is called upon to carry out can be broken down into small separate elements (i.e. 'specialised'), each separate element can be mechanised, even down to the handling and transfer from one machine to the next. Direct labour costs will fall: fewer, less skilled workers will be required.

Consider the imaginary product line in Figure 9.2, which shows a cast-iron cylinder head going through a sequence of machining operations in one department, and which takes advantage of the benefits of the product layout. One new problem does emerge: in order to get a constant rate of production, each operation will need to take the same time: the line needs 'balancing'. Line balancing has to be tackled on two fronts. Each machine should be capable of similar output rates, and, where operators are involved, they should work at uniform rates.

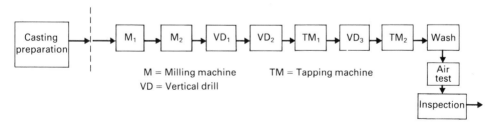

Figure 9.2 *Product layout: engineering.*

Example 1: machine balancing

Acme Engineering Ltd has product line X with five machines, 1, 2, 3, 4 and 5. They are capable of producing as follows:

Machine	1	2	3	4	5
Hourly output	200	350	150	300	300

Even with machine 3 operating at maximum capacity, total output in the line will only be 150 per hour. It could make sense to double capacity at 3 by adding another machine, or replacing 3 with a machine of at least double capacity. However, to do either focuses attention on machine 1, and so on. In the end a compromise will be reached, with some machines idle while the slowest completes a cycle, which avoids building up work-in-progress stocks.

Example 2: work balancing

Acme Engineering Ltd has a product line, Y, of five machines controlled from 8 a.m. by five operators, A, B, C, D and E. Each has control over the work on his or her machine. Expected output per hour per operator is 300. At 10 a.m. output totals are as follows:

Operator	A	B*	C	D	E
Output	900	300	600	600	590

*B is new to the work.

Reasons for discrepancies having been established, a solution to the problem would be to interchange operators A and B (assuming there is nothing wrong with their machinery). It could be acceptable to allow E to continue with a small amount of work in progress at the end of the day.

Example 1 shows that where machines alone are involved, line balancing is a question of equal division of work among operators. Example 2 shows that where workers are involved there can be variable speeds of work, and that it may be necessary to re-allocate workers, or even double up if machines are readily available, to achieve balance.

9.6 Flow layouts

The term 'flow' (or sometimes 'continuous flow') can be applied to layouts which are basically product or line layouts but where operations are, through choice or necessity, undertaken continuously, that is without any breaks in production. Examples are the assembly line with a moving track, with workers adding materials or components from the track side, the production of chemicals, particularly industrial gases, or where food is processed either from slaughtered carcasses, or from raw materials into, say, pasteurised milk.

Automation

Automation (introduced as a term in 1948) describes the control of machines by other machines, and flow layouts which have their own automatic control systems. Handling and transfer are automatic: the whole line runs with the minimum of human intervention. The virtues of this type of flow layout are high continuous output of constant quality: balancing these are the (often) vast costs of the equipment and plant, and the high degree of specialisation. Changeover to another model is a lengthy, costly and difficult operation.

Robots

Robots are used to make lines which were once operator/machine into machine only: they become automated. There is a wide range of application for robots in flow layouts: loading and unloading parts, drilling holes, welding, painting, even inspecting parts. If designed to work at human pace they can be dovetailed into other factory activities still under direct human control. The steady pace of robots' work means that line balancing is a simple matter.

9.7 Group layouts

The term 'group' (or sometimes 'cell')[2] technology is applied to layouts which attempt to combine the virtues of product layouts (economies of space, standardisation, and work in progress) with the ability to cope with batch production and its attendant varieties of range, etc.

Figure 9.3 shows a set of group layouts in a firm. A variety of products may be manufactured in batch quantities, but the engineers have been able to sort them out into groups (or families): in this case, three groups. The basis of selection is to group complete products (or component parts of products) which are related in size and shape and which go through similar production stages.

Even if there are only batch quantities required for each product (or part), when *added together* the total family or group requirement could be similar to the large batch sizes coped with on product layouts.

When sorting is complete, the sequence of operations is worked out to accommodate all products in a family group. A consequence is that not every related part will go through all the equipment assembled in a cell: not every machine in a cell will be in use at any one time. (See examples in cells 1 and 2 in Figure 9.3.)

Machine setting times are reduced: with related products only minor adjustments are necessary. Work in progress is low. Only the tools required for the specific jobs envisaged are purchased or made. Inspection is relatively simple. There may be, however, more than a rearrangement of existing machines to fill cells: new equipment may have to be purchased to provide each cell with a self-sufficient set of facilities. A recent example[3] of an interesting cell-type group layout is to be found at Rolls-Royce, Derby. A special 'creep-feed' grinding line has been established for carrying out various operations on engine turbine root areas. As with other group technology layouts, more than one type of blade can be accommodated in the six cells (a seventh is available as a back-up). Each cell contains two grinders, a robot for loading and unloading, and normal clean/inspect facilities. Parts are automatically conveyed from cell to cell.

---

[2] The term 'cell' is properly used to describe a group of machines in one area, disposed along a conveyor: work supplied at one end is sent out complete at the other.
[3] As reported in 'Machinery and Production Engineering', 5–1–83.

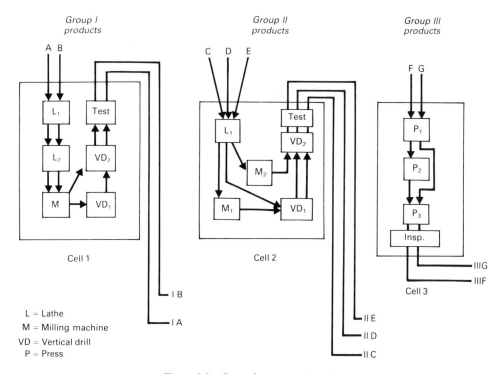

Figure 9.3 *Group layouts: engineering.*

9.8 Buying out

To complete the possible production layouts or methods, mention should be made of buying out. This is a versatile method for any quantity (provided suppliers can be identified), with wide product ranges, little materials handling, low work in progress and normally requiring only one inspection. It is a very useful alternative where a firm is temporarily over-committed, or if an order received is not suitable for existing layouts.

9.9 Evaluation of layouts

Table 9.1 is a *Which* Report, in tabular form, on the production facilities layouts considered, including the buying out alternative. Many questions concerning the

Table 9.1 Types of basic layout facilities compared.

Factors	Fixed position	Process (functional)	Product (line)	Flow	Group	Bought out
Quantities handled	Unit, small batch.	Medium/medium large batches.	Large/very large batches.	Virtually continuous.	Medium batch.	Any.
Product ranges accommodated	Wide in size, shape and type.	Wide range possible: frequent changeovers possible but tool-setting expenses high.	Limited range of products. Changeovers difficult and expensive.	Very limited. Changeovers very difficult.	Wide in size, shape and type.	Very wide.
Labour required	Mostly highly skilled and versatile, some semi and unskilled.	Mixture but modern machinery permits de-skilling.	Mainly skilled.	As product.	As process.	Nil.
Materials movement and handling	All materials to place of work — storage areas required.	Considerable intermittent movement between operations. Large storage areas required.	Less movement between stages. Low handling and storage costs.	Very small but flow rate needs careful control.	Little movement between facilities.	Little.
Work in progress	Often low in volume, high in value.	High, dependent on firm's size and product ranges and PM balances in production.	Low, but line balancing necessary.	Usually very low.	Low.	Low, unless part-finished items are sent out.
Length of production time	For large complex items. Long delivery period.	Long manufacturing time (often queuing between operations).	Short manufacturing times.	Very short.	Reasonably short.	Nil.
Effects of breakdowns of facilities or absenteeism	Stoppage if no duplication of facilities or labour.	All production does not cease. Buffer stocks and substitute machines could help.	Serious. One failure could stop whole line.	Very serious. Total factory stoppage could result.	Basically as process. One line only would be affected.	Could delay delivery.
Inspection	Usually easy.	Frequent inspections needed — expensive.	Difficult to inspect during process. Costs of errors or re-works high.	Unless built in, inspection only possible at the end of sequence.	As process.	Required on delivery.
Maintenance of facilities	PM not difficult as not all facilities in use at same time.	PM possible in or out of normal hours.	BM affects production. PM out of normal hours.	As product.	PM possible in or out of normal hours.	Nil.
Other comments	High prime cost. Technically competent management needed. Wide range of general-purpose machinery needed.	Lower prime costs. Overheads greater proportionally. General-purpose machinery.	Very low prime costs. Total costs low if large throughput is maintained. Fairly specialised machinery.	As product.	As process but fewer changeovers needed. Capital costs of cells.	Can be useful for over-committed facilities or orders not suitable for layouts.

choice of layout can be answered by using a table such as Table 9.1, but any proper evaluation (or feasibility study) of the most appropriate facilities layout for a firm, or the most appropriate way of making a particular product, will need hard facts and not just general guidelines. The following does not claim to be exhaustive or totally appropriate for every business, but is an example of a set of searching questions which, if answered honestly and fully, will provide information for a firm decision.

1. *Costs*. What are the:
   (a) initial capital and installation costs of any new buildings, plant, equipment, etc., including standby equipment;
   (b) running costs of these assets;
   (c) unit costs of production by each method?
2. *Customer demand*. What are the:
   (a) depreciation of assets;
   (b) current, future forecasts of demand;
   (c) usual individual orders for product X;
   (d) fluctuations in demand expected;
   (e) variations/versions expected;
   (f) delivery rates/times required?
3. *Production aspects*. What are the:
   (a) processes needed to manufacture;
   (b) problems associated with manufacture;
   (c) possibilities of standardising, simplifying the product?
4. *Production space*. What are the:
   (a) physical constraints on production or siting of facilities;
   (b) distances between buildings;
   (c) total floor areas;
   (d) storage facilities?
5. *Materials handling*. What are the:
   (a) problems associated with materials and materials handling (steps, corners, distances, etc.);
   (b) new facilities needed;
   (c) costs?
6. *Maintenance*
   (a) What are the maintenance arrangements now?
   (b) What changes are needed?
   (c) Can PM be carried out easily?
   (d) What are the possible effects of breakdowns?
7. *Labour*
   (a) What are the types of labour required?
   (b) What is the present labour force?
   (c) What are the new requirements/training needed?

It should finally be noted that, in any given firm, several product layouts could be in use side by side: the fixed position for specials and the process layout for components and parts, with the assembly line using a product layout.

9.10 Layout planning: simulation aids

When planning a layout, various methods can be used. To set up a layout in the shop and try it out could be excessively expensive: if planning can be done on paper or by computer, the cost becomes minimal and the effort vastly reduced.

Pictorial representations

An artist's impression will give a general view of the layout, but not much else.

Scale plans

A scale plan of the available floor space and scale 'cut-outs' of the base outlines of each piece of equipment enable planners to gauge distances travelled, how machines would fit into space available, etc. It will be important to include all sills, pipes or other obstructions.

String diagrams

Using the scale plan, the expected flows of materials (with alternative layouts) can be plotted on the plan by sticking in pins at the spots where operations are performed, and joining the pins with string or cotton. The string may then be removed from the plan and measured to determine distances travelled. Such a diagram will also throw up back tracking.

Three-dimensional models

This is a development of the previous idea. A drawback of two-dimensional models is that they give a faulty impression of the space available: heights (beams, conveyors, etc.) could be constraints, especially during an initial move of equipment. Such models can be made in cardboard or wood (balsa is best).

Travel charts

Travel charts (sometimes called 'cross charts' or 'relationship charts') are summaries in a matrix form of the actual or possible relationships between departments, or occasionally within a department. There are:

(a) distance charts, which show flow between departments;
(b) frequency charts, which show the frequency of journeys between departments;
(c) proximity charts, which show which departments should close, and why.

Examples of string diagrams and a travel chart are shown in Figure 9.4.

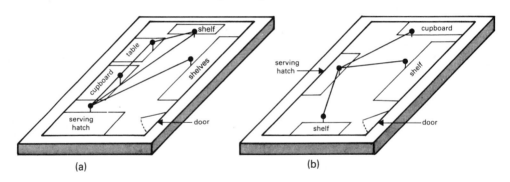

	From				
To	Main door	Table 1	Table 2	Table 3	Book-out point
Main door		× × ×	×	× ×	× × × × × × × × × × × ×
Table 1	× × × × ×		× ×	× × ×	
Table 2	× × × × × × × ×	× × × × ×		× ×	
Table 3	× × ×	×			
Book-out point		× ×	× × ×	× × × × × × × × × × × ×	

(c)

Figure 9.4 *(a) String diagram: stores assistant. (b) String diagram: repositioned stores. (c) Travel chart: goods from stores. (Illustrates movements within stores by staff collecting items required and booking out; this information can be used to determine whether changes are needed in layout, positioning of stores, etc.)*

Computer programs

Various computer programs exist which can be used for calculating costs, as well as changes in movement of materials by adopting alternative layouts.

Summary

1. A facilities layout is the way in which production plant, equipment and fixtures are set out or positioned.

2. A fixed position layout is where the product remains stationary during assembly or manufacture.
3. A process (functional) layout is where facilities of a similar type are grouped together in a recognisably separate work area or department.
4. A product (line) layout is where all facilities applicable to one product (or related group of products) are laid out in line or sequence.
5. A flow layout is an extension of the product layout in which production is virtually continuous without break from raw material to finished item.
6. A group layout is where products are made in batches but on a modified line process.
7. Buying out is where products are made in a supplier's factory.
8. The evaluation summary of the various layouts is set out in Table 9.1, and further considerations are listed in the same section.
9. Various paper methods exist to assist in layout planning. They include pictorial representations, scale plans, string diagrams, three-dimensional models and travel charts.

Questions

Review questions

9.1 Define 'facilities layout'. What are the three situations in which this term is applied?
9.2 What is a fixed position layout? Give three examples where it could be used to advantage.
9.3 Explain what is meant by a functional layout. Why is it suitable for batch production of items required in varying quantities and styles?
9.4 Describe a product layout and state two advantages it has compared with a functional layout.
9.5 Why is line balancing necessary in a product layout?
9.6 How are flow layouts related to product layouts?
9.7 Explain group layouts and the reason for developing this type of layout. Outline its advantages.
9.8 Outline ways in which the efficiency of two layouts can be compared.

Discussion topics

9.9 What are the implications (human as well as financial and technical) of adopting a completely automatic production line serviced by robots?
9.10 Discuss (in groups) the most appropriate facilities layouts for the manufacture of the following:
   (a) a new space rocket;
   (b) an order for 500 000 pairs of jeans;
   (c) a new family car;
   (d) a range of cylinder lawn mowers, some electric and some petrol-driven, of varying sizes.

Assignments

9.11 The class is to visit a local manufacturing unit (preferably *not* one to which class members belong) to view the production areas, processes and facilities. Divided into small groups (say five or six), preferably with guides, each group should ascertain and report on:
   (a)   the types of layout to be found;
   (b)   details of the facilities (with diagrams);
   (c)   an explanation why these facilities were used;
   (d)   comments on the findings.
   (If the company is large, the groups could examine separate areas of work.)
9.12 Students should examine the college's own manufacturing facilities and asertain what kind of production layout could be organised with them, with the minimum amount of disruption. (Scale plans could be used here.)

10
Ergonomics

In this chapter, after ergonomics and the worker/machine relationship are defined, the principles revealed are applied to information presentation, the layout and design of controls, and the working environment. The principles of motion economy are discussed.

10.1 Ergonomics: definitions

There are many definitions of ergonomics.[1] Here are three:

1. The scientific study of people in their working environment, including their relationships to the machines they use.
2. The study of tasks in relation both to those persons performing them, and to the environment in which such tasks are performed.
3. The science of fitting job to person. It is concerned with people, machines and the work environment, and how all three should be combined for good health, safety and efficiency.

Each definition puts a slightly different emphasis on what has become a complex area of study. Besides the basic discipline of physics, and product design techniques, a complete study of ergonomics would need to include at least the following:

(a) applied (human) anatomy and physiology (the way in which the human body reacts to the strain of a particular job);
(b) anthropometry, the study of body shapes and sizes (the design of seats, machine controls, etc.);
(c) industrial psychology (the effects on morale and motivation of work environments; fatigue, its causes and possible remedies);
(d) environmental studies (the effects on productivity of different kinds of lighting, room decor, temperature and humidity, etc.);

---

[1] Ergonomics is often called 'human engineering' in the USA.

(e)   social questions (e.g. the effects of shift work, how the ageing and disabled can be accommodated at work).

In this course, most of such work is beyond our scope, and we shall concentrate on three areas only: the presentation of information, the layout of controls, and the working environment. However, the total extent of ergonomics should be understood.

It should be noted that all three definitions above seem to assume that the study of ergonomics is solely directed to workers and machines in the industrial workplace. The same principles have been applied to the *consumers* of industry's products: the user/machine relationship is as important as the one between the producing worker and machine. Thus designs for kitchen equipment, aircraft cockpit arrangements, stereo unit controls, car seats and wheelchairs for the disabled all have an ergonomic input.

10.2 The objectives of ergonomics

The basic objectives of ergonomics as applied to the workplace are:

1.   To increase human efficiency, and thus productivity, by providing the workforce with the best possible working environment.
2.   To examine the worker/machine relationship and, by ensuring that the interaction between them is as effectual, efficient and safe as possible, to increase productivity.
3.   To design specific jobs or tasks in such a way that they are compatible with the people asked to perform them.

10.3 The worker/machine relationship

Concentration on the worker/machine relationship is a recent development. Earlier (i.e. prior to the Industrial Revolution) approaches to machine making often involved *personal experience* of the task to be carried out: thus the original machine (or equipment or tool) users tended to be its designers and makers too. When *engineers* ('people who design or construct') arrived on the scene, they began to plan on paper and worked at some distance from the ultimate machine operators and their problems. This pattern became more fixed when engineer-designed equipment was made and sold to users in firms far from the makers.

The performance limits on primitive eighteenth- and nineteenth-century machinery were largely set by the machines themselves: people did not worry about operators when just getting things to work was the prime concern of designers. However, as machines became more efficient, their performance began to outstrip the unaided abilities of operators to control them. The attention suddenly switched to the operator, but it was quickly realised that worker and machine are so interdependent that they must be considered as one: in fact as a mutually dependent system.[2]

Systems

A system is an assembly of components, arranged or connected together in an organised way. The normal method of expressing a system diagrammatically is shown in Figure 10.1 (see also Chapter 3).

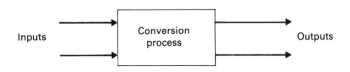

Figure 10.1 *An open system.*

A system reacting to its environment (an 'open' system) receives inputs, reacts to them, and converts them into outputs. A factory, Acme Engineering Ltd, receives raw materials (inputs), makes them up into finished goods (conversion), and sends them off to customers (outputs).

Feedback (control loops)

Acme Engineering Ltd would not want to go on buying raw materials and sending out finished goods without both getting information (on new orders, raw material prices, etc.) and sending information out (delivery notes, invoices, etc.). In other words, a proportion of both inputs and outputs will not be materials but *information*. Whenever output information is fed back into the system as an input, there is said to be a *feedback* or control loop. Diagrammatically the situation is as shown in Figure 10.2.

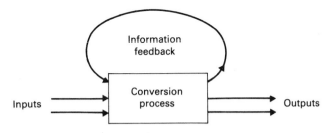

Figure 10.2 *Feedback loop.*

---

[2] For those interested, this theme is considerably developed in Shingleton, W.T. (1981) Man-machine systems, in Open Systems Group (ed.) *Systems Behaviour.* London: Harper & Row and Open University.

The feedback information can obviously affect the system's future performance. Machine-only feedback control systems are common: examples are ship-steering mechanisms, auto-pilots and Sidewinder missiles. Worker/machine control systems are everywhere. A simple example is the rider of a bicycle who (through his or her senses) receives information on distance and balance, which is used to help the cyclist steer (i.e. control) the machine along the road.

Worker/machine control loop systems

A feedback loop used to provide information for control purposes is often called a *control loop system* (Figure 10.3). A person operating a machine can be said to be part of a control loop system, receiving information from the machine, evaluating it, and taking appropriate decisions to control the way the machine works.

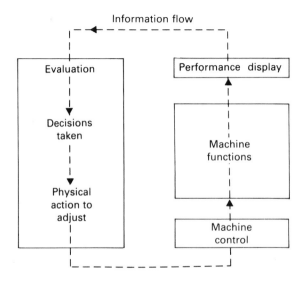

Figure 10.3   *Worker/machine control loop system.*

After the machine starts, it sends information through a *performance display* (dials, flashing lights, thermometer, etc.) to the operator, who evaluates it, decides whether or not to act, and takes appropriate physical action (turning a wheel, pressing a pedal, etc.) to adjust the machine control. The machine responds to information from the control, and the performance display alters accordingly.

10.4 Ergonomic applications

In this section three major areas of 'applied ergonomics' are considered. In order to maximise the quality and quantity of information received by an operator, and to ensure that the information is properly used to control the machine, attention should be paid in designing equipment and workplace layouts to:

(a)   the way in which information is displayed;
(b)   the way in which controls are designed/laid out;
(c)   the total working environment.

Display of information

Information can be displayed or transmitted visually (the most common), aurally (by sound) and sometimes by vibration, 'touch' or 'feel' (the last is very important for blind workers).

Visual displays.   The main categories of visual indicators include:
1.   Moving pointer (analogue). The scale remains fixed; the pointer moves (see Figure 10.4).

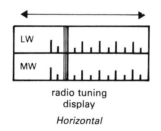

radio tuning
display

Horizontal

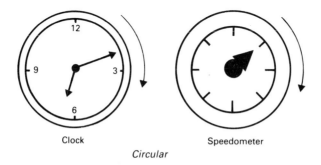

Clock   Speedometer

Circular

Figure 10.4 *Moving pointer displays.*

2. Moving scale (analogue). The scale moves; the pointer remains fixed (see Figure 10.5).
3. Digital. The display is in numbers (see Figure 10.6).
4. Lights. Lights can be plain or coloured, steady (machine or function 'on') or flashing regularly as a warning (see Figure 10.7).

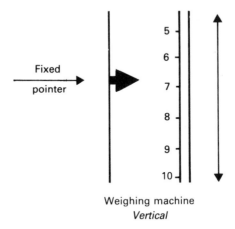

Weighing machine
Vertical

Figure 10.5 *Moving scale display.*

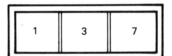

Tape counter (usually horizontal)

Figure 10.6 *Digital display.*

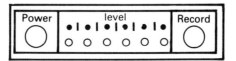

Figure 10.7 *Light display.*

Design considerations. In designing display indicators the following considerations should be borne in mind:

1. Scales should be as simple as possible, with clear calibrations.
2. Display should be clearly visible to the operator, with no glare, dirt on glass or obstructions to the line of sight.

3. Display should be at a suitable height (people see better, with less fatigue, looking straight ahead or slightly downwards).
4. Display should be properly illuminated (internally or externally) in dark areas.
5. Operators should be able to evaluate without asking for guidance on the interpretation of information presented.
6. Scales provided should be usable without conversion (e.g. letter-weighing scales should have up-to-date prices on scale).
7. When clear, precise measurements are required, digital readouts are to be preferred. (Compare the alternatives in Figure 10.8.)

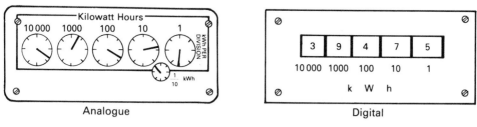

Figure 10.8 *Alternative electric meter displays with the same reading.*

Other methods.   Where speed or urgency of the message is paramount, warning bells, hooters or 'bleeps' are useful. Tactile sensations (vibrations) may indicate that something is amiss with a machine, but no great accuracy is contained in such information.

Design and layout of controls

The term 'controls' includes switches, handwheels or knobs, levers of various kinds, including 'joysticks', push buttons and pedals. The choice of control will depend upon its purpose. Examples are:

(a) handwheels and knobs for pin-point positioning (e.g. in radio tuning);
(b) levers for quick action (e.g. a break release, or railway point change), or in the case of joysticks as used on model controls capable of small adjustments in several directions;
(c) push buttons, which act quickly, but are usually restricted to electrical on/off functions (e.g. TV set channel changeover).

Typical design considerations.   Designers should not only establish the purpose of a control and what essential characteristics are required, but also consider such factors as:

1. The design should enable the controls to be handled and recognised easily (particularly in dark areas).

Figure 10.9 *Car hazard light switch.*

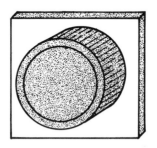
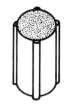

Figure 10.10 *Varieties of knobs.*

2. Where controls are marked or identified, symbols are better than words alone (equipment travels internationally). See Figure 10.9.
3. Different shapes of control may be used to indicate differences in function. See Figure 10.10.
4. Controls should not normally require much physical exertion to manipulate.

Control layout considerations. An inspection of the instrument panel on a typical car, with attendant controls for brakes, lights, steering, wipers, etc. shows how much careful ergonomic work was done at the design stage. Such an inspection should reveal at least some of the many considerations that designers have to bear in mind. The more important are:

1. All controls, dials, handles, switches, etc. must be positioned to be within easy reach of the operator, so they can be both seen and operated. Those used most frequently should be closest to the operator.
2. Account must be taken of 'typical' layouts for particular machines.
3. Controls should have movement travel compatible with the machine's behaviour (turn a steering wheel clockwise, and a vehicle's wheels should turn to the right).
4. Display elements should have movement compatible with the movement travel of controls (turn a wheel clockwise, and the dial with which it is linked should turn clockwise also).

5. Display elements should be consistent and arranged by function: all zero points in the same relative position, pointers all moving clockwise, unless, exceptionally, this is either undesirable, or a scale has a central zero.
6. Information displayed should be kept to an absolute minimum, consistent with meeting functional requirements.
7. All sound warnings should be easily distiguishable from each other, and from any background noise.

Now that the computer age has arrived, much can be done to eliminate banks of controls. For example, in the new Westland Helicopters' Lynx 3, there is not the usual (aircraft) massive instrument display. Instead, the crew can call up data needed on three separate video screens. One screen gives the pilot vital or urgent information, the second displays the craft's combat status information (including, for example, the amount of fuel in reserve), and the third has details of the journey pre-programmed— land contours, overland wind speeds, etc.

The working environment

The working environment can be considered in terms of both the immediate work area (machine, bench, etc.), and the whole work environment (conditions in the department or factory building).

Immediate work area.   Considerable study of immediate work areas has resulted in such sets of rules or guidelines as the *principles of motion economy* (discussed in section 10.5).

At this stage we can say, however, that ideally all tools and work material should be in definite and pre-positioned locations, ready for use, and preferably laid out in the sequence that the work will follow. As it is more restful to sit than to stand, seats of appropriate heights should be available wherever possible for the operator to work comfortably.

The wider environment.   In general, workshop and factory environments have improved over the years, despite well-publicised disgraceful examples (e.g. the cotton industry). Acts of Parliament (such as the Health and Safety at Work etc. Act[3] and the Factories Acts) lay down *minimum* standards of lighting, ventilation and temperature, and deal with overcrowding, fire precautions, first aid and accident reporting. Statutory duties are placed on employers to maintain safe workplaces, and to keep plant in such a condition that there are no risks to health or safety.

Wise managements would go further and try to establish an environment which is comfortable. Some guidelines are:

1. Ventilation: provide additional fresh air or recycled air to ensure air movement without causing draughts.

---

[3] A more detailed treatment of safety legislation can be found in Evans, D. (1981) *Supervisory Management*, pp. 435–450. Eastbourne: Holt, Rinehart and Winston.

2. Temperature: maintain 20°C to 22°C in winter, 21°C to 24°C in summer.
3. Humidity: maintain humidity compatible with comfort, between 20 per cent and · 50 per cent.
4. Noise: attempt to restrict to below 80–85 dB overall.

10.5 Principles of motion economy

An extension of the ideas discussed in this chapter, and those associated with value analysis, is the related area of work study (covered in Chapter 12). A set of rules or precepts or guidelines (with implications for all the three related areas of study) is the *principles of motion economy*. Originally devised by Frank Gilbreth (an associate of F.W. Taylor; see Chapter 12), these principles have been expanded and refined over the years, and appear in various forms. The essential principles are as follows.

Body movements

1. Two-handed work is more natural than one-handed: where possible, work should be arranged so that in each cycle the two hands start together, move apart in unison, symmetrically, and in arcs.
2. In carrying out a task the *least* movement necessary is to be preferred: provided a task can be done satisfactorily, a 'fingers only' movement is more economical than, say, using the whole arm and shoulder as well as the fingers.
3. Smooth, continuous and rhythmic body movements (with no sharp changes of direction) are to be preferred.
4. Whenever the job allows, natural or habitual movements should be encouraged: situations are to be avoided where careful control of movement is required. (Throwing or tossing articles is preferable to placing them carefully.)

Workplace layouts

1. Tools, equipment and materials should have their own definite, predetermined locations (which should be as near as possible to the workplace, and assembled to provide the best sequence of operations).
2. The lighting should be adequate for the work in hand, and the general surroundings clear, adequately heated and ventilated.
3. Workers should be able to work in comfort, whether standing up or sitting down (no low roofs, bad seating, etc). Seating should be designed to suit both the individual workers and the task in hand (i.e. a wide coverage of each work area).
4. The amount of noise and vibration around workers should be kept to a minimum.

Tools and equipment

1. Whenever possible, use should be made of suitably designed equipment for holding work (e.g. clamps, jigs, tool holders) rather than using hands. (These need to be free for more productive work.)
2. The use of multi-purpose tools (e.g. double-ended spanners) is desirable (since this speeds up work).
3. Machine controls (levers, switches, buttons, etc.) should be within easy reach, to allow operation with minimum body movement.

These principles seem, in the context of contemporary knowledge and practice, to be mostly common sense, but at the time they were first promulgated they were a revolution.

10.6 The need for follow-up and review

The work of ergonomics is the integration of worker and machine, in as scientific a manner as possible. However, so many new ideas, machines, systems and layouts abound that problems often arise before they can be sorted out. Ergonomists (where they exist) have to resort to a 'try it out' approach more often than not. This means that once a plan for a machine control system, instrument layout panel, or workplace layout has been put into effect, the matter does not end there.

There is a constant need for appraisal and review of every worker–machine control loop. The original telephone hand-set had no dials at all: the system was primitive, and had manual control at major stages in the communication process. An ergonomic improvement was the dial hand-set. The equipment was now multi-purpose (caller initiating contacts direct to respondents). More recently, push-button sets can additionally dial more accurately, be more easily used by the blind, and store frequently used numbers (and dial them when required).

The same principles of re-appraisal apply to the simplest and most common layout on the factory floor.

Summary

1. Ergonomics is a scientific study of the worker–machine relationship, including the wider environment in the workplace, with a view to increasing efficiency and productivity.
2. It is a multi-disciplinary study, bringing in applied anatomy and physiology, anthropometry, industrial psychology, environmental studies, social questions

and health and safety, as well as the basic discipline of physics, and engineering skills.

3.   Ergonomics is applied not only to the processes of manufacture, but also to the products made. The user's relationship to the finished product is as important as the manufacturing worker/machine relationship.

4.   The basic objectives of ergonomics are to increase efficiency and productivity, to examine the worker/machine relationship, and to design tasks in such a way that they are compatible with the people asked to perform them.

5.   After a period when design engineers were more concerned with making plant and machinery more efficient, it is now realised the *operator* is a vital part of production: worker and machine together are now accepted as one mutually dependent system.

6.   A system is an assembly of components, arranged or connected together in an organised way, with inputs, a conversion process and outputs. Some systems are designed to monitor the outputs (information about outputs is fed back into the system as inputs). Such systems are called 'control loop' systems.

7.   A worker/machine system is a control loop system, the machine sending back information to the operator, who uses the information to take appropriate decisions to control the machine's outputs.

8.   Ergonomics can be usefully applied to maximise the efficiency of the worker/machine control loop system. Three areas of importance covered are the way in which information is displayed, the way controls are laid out, and the total working environment.

9.   Visual displays include moving pointers, moving scales, digital and lights (flashing or steady).

10. Scales should be clearly visible, be at a suitable height, properly illuminated and easily understood. For precise measurements a digital display is preferable.

11. The *choice* of control will depend upon the purpose to which it is intended to put it. The *design* of a control should enable it to be recognised and used easily.

12. Identification of controls can be by symbols, words or shape.

13. Control equipment should be within easy reach of the user, having movement travel compatible with the machine's behaviour, and display elements. Display elements should be grouped to function and behave in similar ways.

14. Information displayed should be kept to a minimum, and warnings should not be so similar in sound as to be confusing.

15. The working environment includes the immediate work area and the wider (department, building) area around.

16. Attention should be given to ventilation, temperature, humidity and noise.

17. The principles of motion economy cover body movements (concentrate on the minimum effort necessary for a task), workplace layouts (concentrate on orderly positioning of tools and workers' comfort), and tools and equipment (concentrate on multi-purpose tools and positioning of controls).

18. Installed systems require monitoring to establish whether improvements need to (or can) be made.

Questions

Review questions

10.1 What is ergonomics? What other areas of study contribute to it other than physics and engineering?

10.2 What are the objectives of ergonomics?

10.3 What is a 'control loop' system? Why is the worker/machine relationship a control loop system?

10.4 What are the main categories of display information? What is the difference between an analogue display and a digital one?

10.5 Why are descriptive symbols better than words on control knobs?

10.6 What is meant by saying that:
(a) controls should have movement travel compatible with a machine's behaviour;
(b) display layouts should be consistent and arranged by function?

10.7 What four areas of the wider environment need particular attention to ensure comfort (and increased work)?

10.8 What is meant by Gilbreth's 'principles of motion economy'? List the important principles.

10.9 Why is it necessary to review layouts once they have been introduced?

Discussion topics

10.10 Discuss and compare the essential requirements of displays, indicating the following:
(a) the internal pressure of a steam boiler;
(b) the capacity of a fuel tank;
(c) the weight of material, such as sand (where precise quantities are needed).

10.11 Discuss and compare the essential requirement of controls for the following:
(a) 'cut out' switch on a petrol-driven chain saw;
(b) temperature regulation in a factory building (i.e. a thermostat);
(c) flying an aircraft.

10.12 Discuss (and compare the differences in) the ideal general working environment for;
(a) a packing department where people walk about frequently;
(b) a design office (with drawing boards);
(c) an assembly department, where people sit down for long periods.

10.13 Discuss the layout of your classroom/laboratory. Are working conditions satisfactory? If money were no object what changes would you make to information-presentation equipment?

Assignments

10.14 Assume a class member is disabled and confined to a wheelchair. Taking a piece of machinery (in, say, the college workshops) with which you are familiar, suggest the modifications required to it (and/or the workplace layout) so that the disabled person could operate it.

10.15 Consider a piece of equipment (such as a car or motor-cycle) to which you have access. Describe the actual layout of displays and controls (a diagram is essential). If you were asked to redesign the layout, what changes would you make to the type and location of the displays and controls? Justify your changes (or alternatively state why the present layout cannot be improved).

Case study

10.16 'I can't understand why production is down this week,' exclaimed Ken Foreman, the machine shop manager, last Friday afternoon. 'I know it's been a bit cold here this week, but I did offer to issue spare pullovers, overalls and gloves to those who wanted them.

'And then there's Charlotte. She's always grumbling about having to operate her lathe. She says the controls are placed so that the only person who could operate them would need to be 4½ feet tall with a 8-foot arm span! She's exaggerating, of course.

'Finally, Joe's really becoming a worry. He failed to notice the 'fault' light on one of his bank of autos. The wretched thing wasn't attended to for hours. He complains that there are so many red lights about the shop, he can't tell one from the others.'

Before turning to go home, Ken put a step ladder against the wall, climbed up, and turned off the lights. 'Another week gone,' he said in the darkness.

(a) Why do you think production was down this week?
(b) What problems seem to exist in Ken's department?
(c) What would you do to start putting things right?

11
The Functions of Production Planning and Production Control

The twin functions of production planning and production control are considered together in this chapter as they are interrelated and complementary.

After the scope, tasks and objectives of production planning are defined, the planning sequence, including the activities of scheduling and loading, is examined. Finally, the control activities are reviewed, especially those of dispatching and progressing.

11.1   Production planning

Production planning can be defined as that function of production specifically concerned with deciding what production facilities are required in a manufacturing enterprise, deciding how such facilities are to be sited and laid out, and deciding in what way these facilities are to be used in manufacturing products.

This definition implies planning at three levels in the organisation:

1. *Long-range planning.* A consequence of demand forecasting is an indication of the products that have to be made both in the immediate future and in the long term. Decisions will have to be made about the general factory layout and the location of the various departments—total factory planning. Such long-term planning is particularly important when designing a new plant or factory from scratch to ensure that processes are sequenced in the most appropriate way.
2. *Process or departmental planning.* Each process and/or department is now considered separately, and the general layout of plant and equipment is decided. Included in this activity will be the sequencing of individual operations in a process or within a department (see Chapter 6).
3. *Individual operation planning.* Finally each individual operation is considered separately, and each work element within an operation planned. The layout of individual machines is now decided.

This chapter concentrates mostly on planning at operation level.

The objectives of production planning

The major objectives of production planning are:

(a) to work to the company objectives, laying down the relative importance of customer service and cost (it is, unfortunately, normally impossible to achieve the shortest delivery times, the highest possible plant utilisation and the lowest material stocks/work in progress all at the same time);
(b) to create facilities which (bearing in mind the first objective) will provide the shortest throughput time from receipt of order to dispatch commensurate with the cost involved;
(c) to create facilities which (bearing in mind the first objective) will control stocks and work in progress to a minimum commensurate with efficient operation;
(d) to create facilities to provide accurate information for delivery dates;
(e) to ensure that a system exists for the identification of all parts, materials, assemblies and products;
(f) to institute control systems on all material movements descriptions and records;
(g) to establish the optimum length of manufacturing cycles (the shorter the cycle the tighter the control necessary; the longer the cycle, the greater the opportunity to balance the work and achieve production efficiency).

In addition, the firm must ensure that production planning and control are independent of both sales and production, and that all judgements made are unbiased.

Relationship with other departments

Like most departments in an organisation—especially those involved intimately with the basic activity, such as production—production planning and control have relationships with various departments. Figure 11.1 sets out the major relationships and information flows.

11.2 Pre-production planning

Pre-production planning is a term which covers all the activities necessary before production planning can begin. The majority of these activities involve data collection from sources outside production planning. The most important items of data include:

1. Up-to-date *information on orders* for products to be made, including existing orders, new orders and potential orders. Specific data include product types and models, quantities ordered, order completion dates, and rates of delivery (marketing/sales).
2. *Production methods* to be used in manufacture. Such data could be provided by a separate process planning section or manufacturing methods department where those exist. However, work study will also be greatly involved in this aspect whichever department initially produces the information.

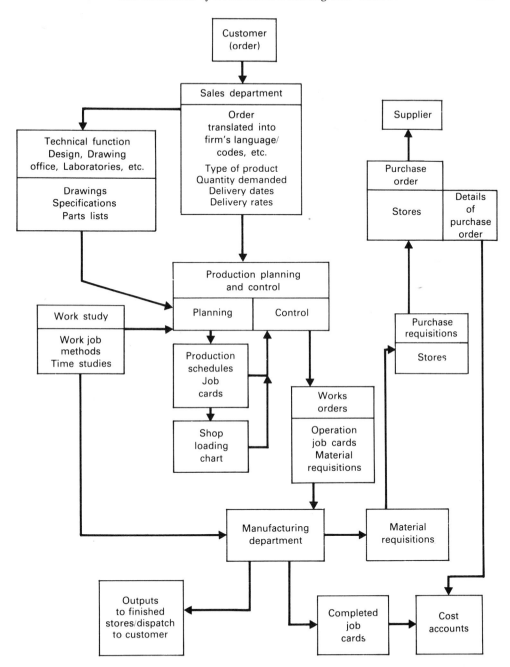

Figure 11.1 *The relationships and information flows between production planning and control and other associated functions within the enterprise.*

3. Details of estimated *standard times* for all operations possibly involved in production of items on order (process planning work study).
4. Details of *job routeing* through the factory, that is the sequence of processes through which a job passes towards completion (process planning).
5. *Part lists* and other materials embodied in the product (technical departments/ drawing office).
6. Details of *material stocks* (stores control).
7. Information on the 'three Cs'—capacity, capability and condition—of *equipment and tools* used in manufacture. Such information would also include, of course, details of repair and maintenance schedules for the equipment, as availability is a crucial factor to be taken into account (production engineers).

11.3 Scheduling

Scheduling can take place once all the available data have been obtained. It is basically that activity (coming under production planning) which aims to devise the most cost-effective ways of programming and sequencing work through a factory. However, scheduling is not confined to factory manufacturing processes: working out the future use of rooms in a conference hotel, a college timetable, the deployment of buses on standard and non-standard routes, and the servicing of cars in a garage are all scheduling activities.

Example 1

Philip Smart is supervisor of the New Life Garage, and is planning the following day's servicing arrangements for the 'Rebirth Servicing Scheme' for the older car. The Rebirth service comprises: (a) lubrication; (b) testing for mechanical defects and necessary repairs; (c) testing for electrical defects, then repair; and (d) the final road test.

The work is done in four separate areas, A, B, C and D, in the fixed order (a), (b), (c) and (d). Philip knows that only one job at a time can be done in each department. All four cars to be serviced tomorrow are already in, and from his examination of them he knows roughly how long each operation—(a), (b), (c) and (d)—will take.

Philip then prepares a schedule based on the estimated times (in minutes) shown in Table 11.1.

Company policy has always been to do jobs in the order they are received and Philip's schedule looks like the Gantt chart he drew up (see Figure 11.2).

Examining this schedule, it can be seen the work on the Triumph Herald is discontinuous (because of the lunch break), which might lead to problems, and as work after 5 p.m. is overtime, two employees will be on time and a half for about one hour each. Two cars, the Morris Minor and the Hillman Avenger, will not be ready for collection until after 5 p.m., so Philip will need to stay on to cope with (possibly) impatient customers. On the credit side, the mechanic employed on lubrication in the morning is free to road-test in the afternoon, so only three workers are required for the four operations.

Table 11.1 *Estimated servicing times (minutes).*

Operation area	Austin A40	Triumph Herald	Morris Minor	Hillman Avenger
A	60	70	40	30
B	120	175	30	60
C	40	35	90	40
D	20	20	20	20
Total	240	300	180	150

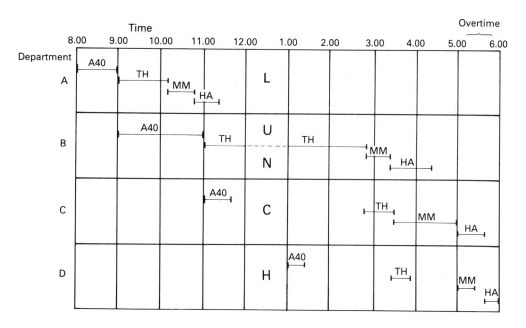

Figure 11.2 *Garage work schedule: first version (Gantt chart).*

Example 2

Philip wonders if any other sequence of work would be effective, and decides to programme the car with the shortest first operation first, and the car with the longest first operation last. (This car, incidentally, also has the longest second operation.) He draws up a second Gantt chart (see Figure 11.3).

This revised schedule cuts out all overtime and ensures that even the Triumph (the last car to be completed) is ready by 5 p.m. The others are ready even earlier. No work spans the lunch break. Finally, if Philip re-allocates the first two road tests to the early afternoon, again he could ensure that all the work was done by three workers.

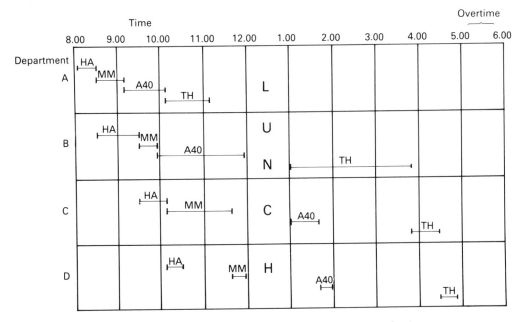

Figure 11.3 *Garage work schedule: second version (Gantt chart).*

Principles of scheduling

Scheduling always involves a balance and a compromise between a variety of competing factors: the importance of the customer, and the delivery required; the optimum use of labour and machines available, and keeping all costs to the lowest possible level. The position becomes even more complicated when operations on the same product vary in length.

Gantt charts are indeed useful ways of preparing schedules when (as with Philip Smart) operations and locations are few. Much more difficult would be to prepare a schedule of, for example, 25 cars each with ten operations, or a schedule for a typical factory with a wide range of products undergoing a large number of operations. In such cases, recourse must be made to one or more of the so-called 'principles of scheduling'. Unfortunately none of these principles has universal application: each production planner must choose that principle which most closely fits the particular circumstances. Typical principles are:

1. *FIFO* or first in, first out. (Philip has in effect followed this rule in Figure 11.2. A long first operation will hold up *all* the other parts/items made in the queue.)
2. Most urgent first. This means making the items with the earliest delivery date promises first. It is useful for any urgent order but it could jeopardise the rest of factory output. (A great problem often arises when schedules have been prepared and put into operation, and suddenly a low-priority order becomes much more important. Stopping production and rescheduling is an expensive option.)

3. Item with the most operations first. This is a useful rule, but not where operations vary in length, and where there are items with a few very long operations.
4. Item with shortest first operation first. (Philip has followed this rule in Figure 11.3. It allows least delay on the second operation location starting work.)
5. Item with longest total operational time first. If the order is fairly urgent this is a useful rule, but large quantities of other parts could be held up.

Over 100 'principles' of scheduling have been identified by researchers into these methods.[1] Conclusions from these investigations are that, while principles are usually better than a *random* arrangement of work, any chosen principle should be carefully reviewed in the light of experience and modified to get the 'best fit' for the organisation.

Scheduling by computer

Computers are ideally suited to sort data into columns and rows (under headings), and in accordance with predetermined rules to calculate optimum use of resources. Therefore increasing use is being made of computers in scheduling, especially where production levels are known reasonably well ahead, and where steady output is expected.

Even where greater variety and uncertainty exist, by placing processing times, parts details and machine capability in a computer memory, scheduling can be greatly assisted. Interactive working (that is, a dialogue with the computer), despite the somewhat greater complexity of programming a computer in this mode, greatly reduces overall software development time. Using interactive working eliminates the need to cater for exceptional cases on programs. Skilled schedulers can assess computer-produced schedules, decide whether sequencing improvements need to be made and revise the schedule accordingly.

Critical path analysis (CPA)

Critical path analysis (CPA) is a network analysis technique the main use of which is to provide efficient scheduling of a single, but large and complicated, task. Examples of the use of this technique (developed in the 1950s) are in planning the building of a ship, bridge or house, overhauling an aircraft, or the installation of a new machine. In fact CPA excels in scheduling projects where the accomplishment of the total job is more complicated than completing a short series of tasks in a straightforward sequence.

Certain phases of a project have a natural sequence (digging foundations precedes the building of walls), and the next cannot be started until the last is complete. Other phases (decoration, glazing) fit into the scheme of the project rather more flexibly. CPA provides a method of scheduling each phase of the project so that the total project is completed in the minimum possible time. When complete, the network will reveal that any delay in some phases will delay the whole project. This sequence of phases is the *critical path*.

---

[1] Students are referred, for a full account of contemporary scheduling, to Byrd, J. Jnr and Moore, L. T. (1982) *Decision Models for Management*, pp. 293–329. New York: McGraw-Hill.

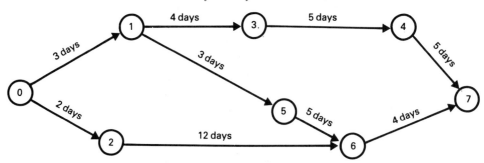

Figure 11.4 *Sample activity (CPA) network.*

Note

Path no. 1 is 0–1; 1–3; 3–4; 4–7. Time: 17 days' duration.
Path no. 2 is 0–1; 1–5; 5–6; 6–7. Time: 15 days' duration.
Path no. 3 is 0–2; 2–6; 6–7. Time: 18 days' duration.

An example of an activity (CPA) network is shown in Figure 11.4. It should be noted that once sequences are planned, they are rarely varied: in fact natural sequences often make changes impractical.

It will be noted that the third path (18 days' duration) is the longest: any delay in completing scheduled times on this path will delay the total project beyond 18 days. If actual progress is continuously monitored as the project proceeds, decisions can be made, when hold-ups seem likely, to draft in extra labour.

The technique of CPA is more fully described in such books as *Network Analysis for Planning and Scheduling Studies in Management*,[2] but from the brief treatment here, it can be seen that where it is important to keep activities on the critical path on schedule, management can concentrate scarce supervisory resources on these activities. It is often not worth exercising the same effort on keeping other (slack-path) activities to schedule. Demand for labour can be smoothed out as slack-path activities can be achieved at the most suitable times.

The initial network can be reviewed and refined, and in many cases paths can be shortened by more careful planning, or scheduling tasks simultaneously. As with other scheduling methods, CPA is now extensively computerised so that complete printouts of all the activities, with locations and possible starting and finishing times, can easily be obtained.

The objectives of scheduling

It will be noted from the points raised in this section that the scheduler is attempting to attain several objectives simultaneously. Regrettably, some are mutually conflicting, and it is hard to envisage circumstances in which *all* could be attained.

---

[2] Battersby, A. (1978) *Network Analysis for Planning and Scheduling Studies in Management.* London: Macmillan. Students are also recommended to try the programme-learning approach of the Atomic Energy Authority.

Four major objectives of scheduling are:

1. To ensure that customers' delivery requirements/producers' delivery promises are kept to. (To do this for a particular order, A, could involve orders B, C...N being delayed. All a scheduler can do in practice is to attempt to maximise the number of orders meeting delivery criteria.)
2. To ensure that goods are produced in the shortest time from start to finish. (This is especially important in such processes as pasteurisation of milk or cooking of food, where these processes *must* take place within specified times, and where the final product has a very limited shelf life, and the maximum time available is required to get it to the customer.)
3. To ensure that plant, equipment, etc. is working—as far as possible commensurate with safety, reliability and adequate servicing—continuously. (The degree of plant utilisation is, of course, often a function of the quantity, quality, reliability and capability of machinery available. The fewer machines used, the more heavily they are likely to be loaded. Included in this objective is the need to keep product changeover times or set-up times to a minimum.)
4. To ensure that employees are fully utilised. (Making sure work is continuously available for employees may entail 'standby' or surplus capacity: directly contrary to the previous objective!)

Scheduling: the basic problems

From the consideration of scheduling it can be seen that there are two major problems for schedulers. In the first place they must be clear what the 'best' schedule is—a very difficult matter to decide unless very clear policy decisions have been taken in advance. Is the best schedule one which gets the goods out in the shortest time at whatever cost, or one which completes the job at the least cost whatever the delay, or something in between?

Second, for any given order there could be different ways in which it could be scheduled, and here a combination of aids such as carefully programmed computers and the skill of the scheduler is invaluable.

11.4 Loading

Loading is a complementary activity to that of scheduling. Deciding to repair a Morris Minor at 9 a.m. tomorrow at New Life Garage may be desirable in order to meet scheduling objectives, but there is no assurance, for example, that the lubrication bay will be empty by 8.55 a.m. Loading enables the scheduler to check on the bay's availability.

Again, while scheduling attempts to establish starting and finishing times for operations, loading is concerned more with what capacity is available at any given time at various locations, or places where machinery or equipment is sited ('work centres', as they are often called). The job of a loader can be compared to that of the manager of a small bank which does not allow overdrafts on current accounts. The bank manager holds ledger cards for each customer's current account: every time a cheque is cleared, the amount of money withdrawn is noted and the balance is adjusted downwards. Money that is not there cannot be spent.

In the same way the loader manages time available at each work centre: each time resources are allocated (or loaded), the allocation is noted and the balance of time available in the period under review (one day, one week, one month, etc.) is adjusted downwards.

Capacity available

The capacity of any work centre available for loading (that is, for use in production) is not the *total possible* capacity (often called 'maximum machine capacity'). It is unlikely in most manufacturing organisations that equipment can be run productively 24 hours a day, seven days a week, indefinitely. Perhaps only one or two shifts a day are worked, or regular machine stoppages for maintenance may be required. Operator absence (for example for lunch breaks) can reduce capacity available.

After all the possible reasons and the time involved are taken into account, a more realistic net figure of capacity available is obtained; this is often called the 'standard running time' of the machine. This time is expressed in hours/minutes.

(Where individual jobs are required to be done at specific times at work centres, checks will need to be made that the facility has not already been allocated to other work, and that no ancillary activity such as cleaning or setting up has been arranged for that time. Additionally—depending on the type of production—space may be deliberately left until the last minute on loading schedules to accommodate rush orders.)

Shop and machine loading

Loading can be done on a general, less detailed basis (at shop or department level), or on a more specific basis onto groups of machines, or even onto individual machines/work centres.

Shop loading. This involves treating a complete department or shop as a work centre. As shop loading is more useful (and therefore more common) in the job/small batch firm, complete departments are not likely to be very large in any event. Shop loading in these circumstances overcomes the problem of mapping out complicated programmes for individual machines where many orders might take only a few minutes to complete on individual machines. Another typical case would be a final assembly department where a wide variety of products are put together using a high proportion of hand work. (Here both the capacity available and the loading programme are likely to be expressed in *labour hours*, rather than in terms of any machinery used.)

Machine loading.   This involves separate records being kept for machine groups (that is, machines of similar character which may be physically adjacent in the shop). In a well organised system, sheets or cards can be raised for each loading period, which could be a week or even a half week. Thus if an order is received well ahead of its required delivery date, the loading can be entered on a forward-dated sheet rather than on current production.

The loader can see at a glance (as Figure 11.5 illustrates) whether a machine or group of machines can handle any additional work. It is unlikely, for example, that the machines in Figure 11.5 will be able to take on further orders unless the number of hours is increased by the addition of overtime or cancellation of agreed maintenance, or a decision is taken by sales to give an existing order lesser priority.

			Machine Load Schedule				
	Machine type	221			Week ending		
	Machine group	16			16.2		
	Planned machine				[All times in hours]		
	running time	80 hours					

Works order	Part No.	Operation No.	Quantity	Set-up time	Machine running time	Total time	Cumulative time
A00761	33/681	13	1000	2.0	10.0	12.0	12.0
A1010	17/513	5	2000	2.5	21.0	23.5	35.5
A01035	20/001	9	2750	2.0	20.0	22.0	57.5
A01211	20/009	9	2750	0.5	20.0	20.5	78.0

Figure 11.5   *Machine load schedule, machine shop.*

In the example, set-up times are shown separately: where long runs predominate, set-up times become less significant and could be calculated as a fixed percentage of running times, based on experience.

Loading with matrices

A common-sense (and commonly used) method of assigning work when there is a choice of several machines or machine groups is to assign orders as received to the 'best' or most suitable machine. The 'best' machine is usually the one which will do the job in the least time or at the lowest cost, or both.

Example. Assume that two machines, X and Y, are both capable of performing a particular operation. X can produce 100 items per hour, after a setting-up time of five hours. Y, conversely, needs only three hours for setting up, but produces only 30 items per hour thereafter. An order for 250 items would 'best' be done on machine X, whereas one for just 15 items would be finished more quickly on machine Y.

In more complicated situations, particularly when limited capacity is available, there is always a possibility that, with better organising, jobs could be produced more quickly and efficiently. The use of a matrix can throw up alternative solutions, as Table 11.2 shows.

A comparison between a conventional and a matrix method could yield the results shown in Table 11.3.

To deal with more complex loading situations the matrix method can be supplemented by 'index number' methods, which are beyond our present scope.[3]

Table 11.2 *Matrix loading details.*

	Machines		
Orders	A	B	C
1	16	24	33
2	18	20	28
3	20	20	22
4	18	20	30
5	18	24	26
6	16	24	33
Capacity in hours	60	50	40

Table 11.3 *Conventional and matrix methods compared.*

	Order numbers			
Machine	Conventional		Matrix	
A	1, 2, 3	(54 h)	2, 4, 5	(54 h)
B	4, 5	(44 h)	1, 6	(48 h)
C	6	(33 h)	3	(22 h)
		131 h		124 h

[3] Students can find two different versions in Wild, R. (1979) *Production and Operations Management,* pp. 275–277. Eastbourne: Holt, Rinehart and Winston and Rynfeld, N.W. (1982) *Production and Inventory Control,* Virginia: Reston, pp. 234–249.

Incomplete programmes

At the end of a period orders not completed as per programme must be re-entered (with high priority) on the next period's programme.

Objectives of loading

It can be seen that the major objectives of loading are:

(a)   to attempt to ensure that the most efficient use is made of work centres in meeting current production requirements;
(b)   to ensure, as far as possible, that the work required is planned to be completed in the shortest time/at the lowest cost;
(c)   to check on availability of capacity needed to meet current production demands, and additionally to provide information in preparing delivery promises.

(Delivery promises are often required by customers when placing orders: similar requests are made when customers send out inquiries to prospective suppliers. Such promises can be assessed against capacity available at the time orders or inquiries are received.)

11.5   Production control

As noted elsewhere, all control systems involve the setting of objectives, targets, and budgets or programmes to work to, the devising of methods of measuring performance against the agreed objectives, evaluating performance (especially deviations from the planned results), and taking corrective action (where this is possible) to get back on schedule. The production control function does all these things, but besides monitoring and reporting on deviations from the programmes laid down by production planning, it is also actively engaged in putting the plans into action.
    The two basic objectives of production control are accordingly:

(a)   to ensure, as far as possible, for any given order for a product (or group of products), that the required number of items is manufactured to the required quality, at an appropriate rate, and in the most economic way;
(b)   to direct generally the activities in the production function, and specifically to ensure, as far as possible, that the right material is available at the right time in the right place to the right specification (the 'four rights').

These objectives clarify the distinction between production planning and production control: activities performed in advance of/in preparation for production are *planning* activities; those performed during/as aids to production are *control* activities.

11.6 Ordering

This stage occurs when all the items necessary for production are organised, that is, when all the planning information including production schedules and shop loading information has been prepared. Reference to Figure 11.1 reveals that production control at this stage passes on or issues a series of documents to manufacturing departments generally to instruct or help them to perform tasks.

Works orders

These are official written instructions on standard forms for the making of products, including parts and components. Taking into account the original order from the customer, a works order may need to be modified as to both the description of the items ordered and the quantity produced. Works orders would normally contain most (if not all) of the following information:

(a)   part numbers/description of products ordered;
(b)   quantity to be made;[4]
(c)   date of delivery required;
(d)   rate of delivery required;
(e)   operations required;
(f)   departments involved;
(g)   materials needed;
(h)   tools needed.

(Space may be provided to record the order's progress through departments with inspection's comments.)

Route cards/operation layouts

These contain more detail than the information on a works order. They detail the material to be used, the sequence of operations required, and details of jigs and gauges needed.

Operation/job cards

These are issued for each operation, and are filled in by operators when the operation is complete, recording the time taken.

---

[4] The quantity made may fall short or exceed that on the order from the customer. Fewer items may be required if a good proportion of the order is in stock, and more if it is felt there could be a significant scrap or reject percentage, a need for spares, or an extra quantity put by for stock.

Material requisitions

These are produced at the planning stage and are issued by the production controller either to release materials from the stores or, if special material is required, to order-out through the purchasing department.

11.7 Dispatching

Dispatching is a term which is often confusing. In its normal business context it is used to describe the organising of a firm's resources so that finished products can be delivered to the customer. In the context of production control it means a collection of activities which facilitate and monitor production.

In effect dispatching takes the job of loading a stage further, and translates general decisions into very specific ones. Loading, as already noted, sets out jobs within a department in terms of time and location, but within a broad time period, for example a week, and often to a group of machines. Dispatching determines exactly what jobs are to be done, and in what clearly defined sequence; it lays down at which precise times the work is to be undertaken, on which specific machine, by which individual operator.

The duties of the dispatcher (who is likely to be the shop/departmental supervisor in small/medium-sized firms) will vary according to the type of production (that is, small-batch, large-batch/mass or process/flow production). However, basically the following major tasks are undertaken:

1. Organising the receipt, filing, issue and disposal of all paperwork, including works orders.
2. Sequencing the jobs undertaken in the department. The dispatcher decides how the various jobs are to be allocated—to which machine, to which operator, in what order. In making allocation decisions, the dispatcher aims to meet completion dates for the operations under his or her control, to minimise machine-use time on each job, and to maximise the output of the department. (All scheduling and loading decisions not previously specified are made by the dispatcher.)
3. Organising the tooling required. Particularly in the small/medium-batch production firm, correct tooling is of vital importance. Whether or not the dispatcher arranges delivery or delegates this to setters or operators, the dispatcher will need to control all tool movements both to and from the stores and within the department.
4. Instructing the setters. When the dispatcher has decided which machines are to cope with the next jobs, the setters are advised accordingly.
5. Issuing the jobs. The dispatcher issues job cards to operators—just enough at any one time to maintain the flow of production, plus the next job for each operator.
6. Reporting back on any incomplete or unstarted orders at the period end. (Such orders can then be rescheduled for the next period: nothing should be left 'outstanding' at a period end.)

11.8 Progressing

Progressing is the central activity of production control. It can be described as that activity which obtains, records and evaluates information on what is actually produced. In particular, it identifies and highlights variances (differences) between the original programme and current production figures. Significant variances are reported to management for appropriate action. Such action could include increasing production by redeploying labour from elsewhere, introducing overtime or starting extra shifts, or decreasing production by reducing overtime or laying off some operatives, or starting sales drives on particular products.

The recording and reporting activities can be classified as follows.

Overall programme control

Here the emphasis is on the total productive output of the firm. Actual current production levels are compared with the production budget and overall programme. Reports on variances go to senior management for action. (The emphasis will be on statistical reports and supporting explanations, though some Gantt charts may be used.)

Departmental programme control

Sometimes called 'compliance reporting', at this level the work of a shop or department is assessed against schedules or loads. (Figure 11.6 illustrates one method, the Gantt chart, of highlighting loading variances in a machine shop.) Usually the shop supervisor or departmental manager is accountable for such variances.

Individual order progressing

It is important to check on the progress of works orders as they pass through production. Works orders are often synonymous with customers' original orders, and the progress of these orders is also a matter of concern for the sales/marketing department. This department will want delivery information from time to time; it could well have its own order progress staff, and may bring pressure to bear on production if it seems as though orders may become overdue. (Overdue lists or lists of orders potentially overdue are prepared. Senior management could be involved if the customer or order is important, or if significant bottlenecks arise.)

Material shortage reporting

Production control is also responsible for collecting information on actual or potential 'material shortages', that is, cases where insufficient material is available to complete any or all of current production programmes. As well as alerting management,

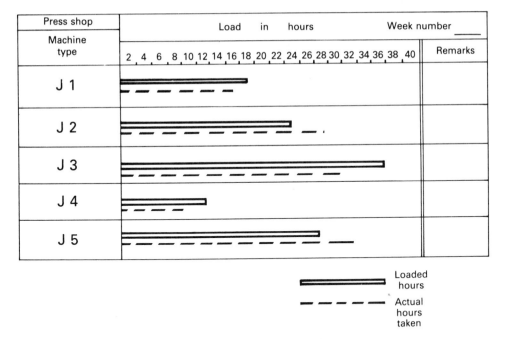

Figure 11.6 *Gantt chart showing actual machine load on various machines in department: press shop.* Note: *J1, J3, J4 — work completed ahead of schedule; J2, J5 — work completed later than schedule.*

production control will need to send 'hasteners' to the purchasing department in good time. In this way bottlenecks in production can be reduced or eliminated.

11.9   Final remarks

It is difficult to cover all the possible ways in which production planning and control can be organised over the whole spectrum of manufacture, and individual firms may have quite different methods of ensuring control over production. In any event, in any complex production situation with interrelated activities, only a relatively small proportion needs to be stringently controlled.

While Gantt charts and various types of peg boards are used to assist in control, there has recently been a much greater use of computers. Where such computers are programmed to log information and highlight variances, and are accessible through visual display units (VDUs), considerable savings in time and documentation are achieved. Even more spectacular savings are available when production information is transmitted electronically from the plant or equipment used directly to the computer data banks. Thus a VDU can give information on production progress over a range of machines as work is completed. Control is considerably enhanced.

At the other extreme, in a small organisation, both the planning and control functions can be amalgamated into one department.

Summary

1. Production planning is concerned with determining what production facilities are required, where they are to be sited, and how the facilities are best used in manufacture.
2. Planning at the overall factory level is *long range; medium-range* planning is at departmental level when deciding on plant layout; and *short-range* planning is at operational level, when individual tasks or operations are planned and allocated.
3. The aims of production planning are to work to fulfil company objectives: to create facilities so that jobs can be completed, and to keep stock levels and work in progress as low as possible consistent with efficient operation. Further, production planning aims to control material movements and records, to ensure that all parts, materials, assemblies and products are properly identified, and to create facilities for the provision of delivery date forecasts.
4. Ideally, production planning (and production control) should be independent of both sales and production.
5. Pre-production planning covers those activities to be completed before production planning can begin. They include:
    (a) obtaining current data on existing and future orders;
    (b) identifying the precise methods to be used in manufacture;
    (c) the estimation of standard times for all possible operations required;
    (d) deciding on job routeing through the factory;
    (e) obtaining details of parts lists and other materials required in production, and of current material stocks;
    (f) obtaining current information on the capacity, capability and condition of equipment and tools available.
6. Scheduling is that activity of production planning which endeavours to devise the most cost-effective ways of programming and sequencing work through a factory.
7. At all times it is essentially a compromise or balance between competing objectives: customer satisfaction, minimisation of production expenditure, and the optimum use of all resources, both human and machine.
8. Attempts have been made to lay down rules or 'principles' of scheduling to try to reconcile some of these (often) contradictory objectives. Examples include:
    (a) FIFO (first in, first out)—work is completed in the order it arrives, throughout the factory;
    (b) most urgent items first;
    (c) item with most operations first;
    (d) item with shortest first operation first;
    (e) item with longest total operational time first.
9. Such scheduling 'principles' can be encoded into computer programs. The effects of applying these rules in particular situations can then be studied. The process can be assisted by interactive working with the computer, and sequencing decisions further refined by skilled schedulers.
10. Critical path analysis (CPA) is a network analysis scheduling technique, particularly for single, but large and complex, tasks. The critical path (the related sequence of activities taking the longest time to complete) can be

identified by CPA, and scarce management resources can be used to monitor this sequence more closely than other activities.

11. Loading is an activity related to scheduling: it enables a scheduler to check on the availability of the resources to be used—what capacity is available at work centres.

12. The loader needs to assess what capacity is realistically available in any given loading period (for example one week), taking into account all times when machinery, plant, etc. is being cleaned or serviced, or when the labour force is not at work. The net figure of capacity expected to be available (the standard running time) is expressed in hours/minutes.

13. *Shop loading* means treating a department or a shop as a work centre when loading, rather than mapping out complicated programmes for individual machines in advance. *Machine loading*, by contrast, involves loading work onto specific groups of machines, or even onto individual machines.

14. Tabular loading charts or Gantt charts are popular methods of recording the loading decisions made. To assist in the decisions, use is often made of matrices, and a final allocation delayed until the latest possible moment.

15. All orders scheduled and loaded but not completed at the end of a period must be re-entered on the next programme.

16. Loading attempts to ensure that the most efficient use is made of capacity available during one production period, that the work is completed in the shortest time at the lowest cost, and that 'double booking' of capacity is avoided. Delivery promises can also be assessed against capacity available.

17. Production control puts into action the plans made by production planning and monitors the production performance, reporting on variances from the plans. It aims to see that products are manufactured of the right quality, at an appropriate rate, in the most economic way.

18. Production control also aims to ensure that the right material is available at the right time in the right place to the right specification.

19. The organising stage begins with 'ordering'. Here a series of documents is raised to facilitate production:
    (a) *Works orders* are official written instructions, in some detail, to production to put work in hand.
    (b) *Route cards*, or operation layouts, specify in more detail the operational sequence and the jigs and gauges required.
    (c) *Job cards* record the time taken for each operation.
    (d) *Material requisitions* are release instructions for materials from stores, or ordering instructions to the purchasing department.

20. *Dispatching* takes loading a stage further, and organises the sequence in whch jobs are done and the tooling required. The dispatcher instructs the setters, gives the work out to operators, and reports back to production control on all orders incomplete at the end of each scheduling period.

21. *Progressing* is the activity of checking on the progress of orders through the production system, and reporting bottlenecks or shortages as necessary.

22. The work of both production planning and production control can be enhanced by the use of computers.

Questions

Review questions

11.1   Describe and compare the aims and objectives of production planning and production control.
11.2   What is pre-production planning? Why is it necessary?
11.3   What is scheduling? What conflicting objectives does a scheduler have to take into account?
11.4   How does loading differ from scheduling? Explain why the maximum machine capacity is not always available for loading.
11.5   Describe the activity of machine loading. Explain how the use of a simple matrix assists the loader.
11.6   What are the functions of (a) works orders, (b) route cards, (c) job cards and (d) material requisitions in the context of producton planning and control?
11.7   Describe the job of the dispatcher and compare it with that of a progress clerk.
11.8   Explain the use of Gantt charts in production planning and control.

Discussion topics

11.9   Can the introduction of production planning and control techniques affect the productivity of a firm's workshops?
11.10 Which is more important: satisfying the customers 100 per cent of the time in respect of delivery demands, or making items at the least possible cost, at the most suitable time for production?

Assignments

11.11 Imagine you have a week's holiday. You wish to service your motor-cycle, dig the garden, finish off some set course work, visit a tennis match, go fishing, keep a dental appointment and play squash.
       (a) Indicate what scheduling strategies you would use (and why you chose them) to ensure that all these activities were covered.
       (b) What differences are there between this type of scheduling and sequencing work in, for example, a machine shop?
11.12 Visit a local manufacturing organisation by arrangement to look at the work of production planning and control. In a short report indicate what scheduling, loading and dispatching techniques are used, and what use is made of Gantt charts and other visual recording methods. Finally, list the three most important problems facing the production control staff.
11.13 Given the following constraints:
       (a) total throughput time to be kept to a minimum
       (b) both machines work continuously as far as possible
       (c) all jobs processed in the order X, Y
       (d) all jobs started are finished
       solve the following loading sequencing problem with two machines, X and Y, and six jobs, 1–6.

Job	Time per machine (hours)	
	X	Y
1	9	6
2	7	8
3	4	11
4	7	5
5	6	10
6	8	8

Case study

11.14 Dynamic Engineering, a small general machinists in the Midlands, has progressed well, despite the recession. As Bill Beaver, the production director says, 'Orders are coming in faster than they are being turned out. All the directors are young and dedicated to hard work; their enthusiasm has rubbed off on the workforce.'

When a customer's order is received Bill Beaver passes it to Jill, the general supervisor. Jill ensures that all drawings and other relevant information are attached to the works order raised, and these documents are passed to the operator Jill feels is best suited to the job.

Basically orders are allocated to workers as they arise, but individual operators have a free hand in deciding what to do next. 'After all,' Bill says, 'with so much to do, workers can plan their overtime ahead to suit their social lives.'

Yesterday Fred Taylor, a work study student at a local college, finished two weeks' work experience and said goodbye to Mr Beaver. 'I'm very impressed with all your modern equipment, and everyone's attitude to work,' Fred said, 'but only about 55 per cent of orders get finished on time—and those parts for Mammoth were ten weeks late! At the same time the place is full of finished components not yet required, or parts awaiting the next operation.

'Another thing—poor Jill seems to spend half her time placating customers on the phone, and the rest chasing urgent orders.'

(a) Discuss the problems at Dynamic. How have they arisen?
(b) If you were Fred, what advice would you offer Bill on how to improve matters?

12

Work Measurement and Incentive Schemes

Work measurement cannot be considered apart from other areas of work study, and it will therefore be necessary to examine method study in some detail before describing the techniques of work measurement.

The uses to which information and data derived from work measurement can be put is explained. Finally, the role and operation of various incentive schemes are reviewed.

12.1 Work study[1]

Work study is the overall term (or family name) given to a set of ideas, techniques and activities which together add up to a complete study of work (or jobs). From its earliest beginnings the whole approach of work study was influenced by the way in which scientists go about their work, and in particular by what was then understood to be 'scientific method'. In scientific method, considerable emphasis was laid on the use of *systematic observation* and *measurement*, plus a rigorous checking of results.

It is therefore not surprising to find that the current official British Standards Institution's definition of work study is 'the systematic examination of activities in order to improve the effective use of human and other material resources'.[2]

---

[1] Work study is sometimes known as time and motion study or industrial engineering, particularly in the USA.

[2] Students who wish to consult 'official' definitions of *all* specialist terms used in this chapter are recommended to see a copy of the *Glossary of Terms used in Work Study and Organisation and Methods (O & M)*, British Standard (BS) 3138:1979, prepared by the British Standards Institution, issued by the Institute of Management Services and available from either of these.

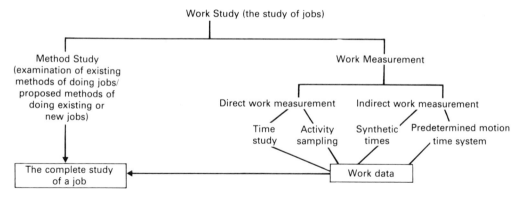

Figure 12.1 *The work study family tree.*

The work study 'family'

The work study 'family' can be best understood by examining Figure 12.1. From Figure 12.1 it will be noted that the two 'branches' of the work study family tree are not only related but complementary. The study of a job involves looking at the *way* it is done (method study) and also at the *time* it takes for the job to be completed (work measurement). Although work measurement seems to have been developed first, by the time F.W. Taylor (1856–1915), an outstanding pioneer in the development of a variety of techniques of study and measurement, wrote his book *Scientific Management*, the two subject areas were treated as if they were one. Taylor regarded time study as part of the investigation into methods.

(Not mentioned in Figure 12.1 are some other related activities. Ergonomics and value analysis have been covered already. Organisation and methods (O & M) is the general principles of work study applied to whole organisations, and in particular to office and administrative services. This chapter is confined to a review of method study and work measurement.)

12.2 Method study

Method study is basically a 'scientific' examination of the way a job or task is done. The current BS definition is 'the *systematic recording* and *critical examination* of ways of doing things, in order *to make improvements*'.

The key words in the definition are:

(a) *systematic* (that is, the way in which recording is done is ordered, logical and consistent);
(b) *critical* (the review of present methods is wide-ranging and ruthless);
(c) *improvements* (the major objective of method study is to discover better ways of doing things—method study implies method improvement).

A method study investigation

Those employed in conducting method study investigations are trained to follow a set procedure. This procedure has been analysed under different sets of headings,[3] but it will be useful to take the British Standards Institution's 'six-step' version to illustrate the way a method study investigation proceeds. This explanation is necessarily brief,[4] but adequate for our purposes. The steps are:

1. Select.
2. Record.
3. Examine.
4. Develop.
5. Install.
6. Maintain.

Step 1: Select.   The first step is to select or identify the job to be studied. Sometimes jobs are studied in rotation, or in a planned sequence, decided upon well in advance. Very often the pressure of events makes the choice of the next investigation only too obvious. Typical reasons for carrying out a study are:

(a)   a new process being introduced;
(b)   bottlenecks in production;
(c)   too much work in progress;
(d)   purchase of a new machine;
(e)   competition, and the need to reduce costs;
(f)   present working methods found to be unsafe.

The precise jobs to be studied, and the reasons for the choice, must be agreed upon at the start. The aims or objectives of the study are called its 'terms of reference'. Often included in the terms of reference are constraints (or limits) on the time available to do the study and the number of trained staff who can be used; additionally, the techniques to be used can be stated.

Step 2: Record.   The second step is to record all the known facts about the way the job is being done (if the job is one currently being done in the factory) or might be done (if the job is a new one, yet to be put in hand). A description of a current job is called the 'present method'; a description of a new job is called the 'proposed method'.

Particularly with a 'present method' investigation, the job studied, the hourly/daily/weekly output, the number of workers involved, how the job is done and where it is done must all be carefully recorded.

---

[3] Students are referred to question 12.19 at the end of the chapter, which lists several alternative presentations of the method study process.

[4] The whole subject of method study is too complex to cover in detail here. Interested students are recommended to read a suitable book, such as Currie, R.M. (1963) *Work Study.* London: Pitman.

Facts recorded arise from observation, from looking through records, from looking at drawings or specifications, from interviewing people, or even from using question-naires. Methods of recording include the use of charts, diagrams, graphs and films. The aim in recording facts is to present a volume of data in a simple fashion that is easy to understand.

Many types of charts are used as standard practice in method study. Typical is the flow process chart, which sets out the sequence of events studied in diagrammatic form, though a choice has to be made about the particular aspects of job to be studied. 'Worker charts' record what the worker does, while 'material charts' record what happens to material. Figure 12.2 illustrates the five most widely used symbols in process charting.

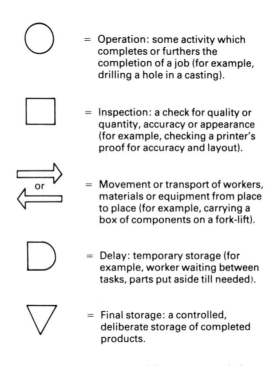

Figure 12.2   *Conventional flow process symbols.*

Another of the many types of chart used in method study is the multiple activity chart. Such charts allow for different kinds of activity—both that of workers and that of machines—to be compared, where these activities go on at the same time.

The primary objective of multiple activity charts is to highlight 'idle time' in the case of workers and 'non-productive time' as far as machines are concerned. For example, in Figure 12.3 it can be seen that the worker is idle 25 per cent of the time and the two machines are non-productive for more than 50 per cent of the time.

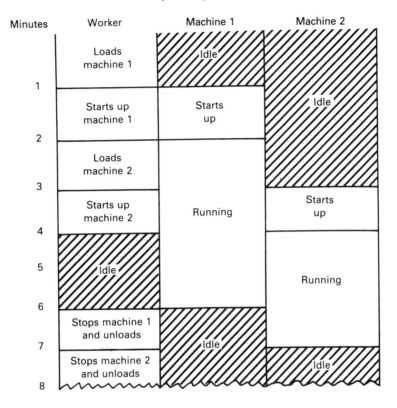

Figure 12.3 *Multiple activity chart.*

Step 3: Examine. The third step is to examine critically all the information collected in Step 2. A complete and ruthless examination of present or proposed methods of work is the basis of a successful study. The aim is eventually to develop new, improved ways of doing jobs. Possibilities to be examined at the 'examine' stage are to:

(a) eliminate the job reviewed altogether;
(b) combine the job under review with other jobs;
(c) change the sequence in which the job studied is done;
(d) simplify the job (in a similar way to value analysis).

The examination is done by posing (and then answering) a series of searching questions. *Primary* questions explore the *present* situation, or ways of doing things. *Secondary* questions pose possible *alternatives* to be considered. As this comprehensive review not only is important in method study inside the factory, but also has equally valid uses in many facets of life, an abbreviated form of these questions is given in Table 12.1. 'Number 1' questions are primary ones; 'number 2' are secondary.

Table 12.1 *Critical examination questions (for any job, task, activity, etc.).*

A	Purpose of job	1. *What* is achieved?	*Why* is it achieved?
		2. What else *could* be achieved? (Is achievement really necessary? Could it be eliminated/modified?)	What *should* be achieved? (Consider alternatives.)
B	Means of doing job	1. *How* is it done? (Consider materials, equipment, methods employed, etc.)	*Why* that way? (Consider pros and cons.)
		2. How else *could* it be done? (Formulate alternatives.)	How *should* it be done? (Pros and cons of alternatives, including costs, considered.)
C	Sequence position of job	1. *When* is it done? (How does it fit in with sequence of product operations?)	*Why* then?
		2. When else *could* it be done? (Earlier/later stage in sequence? Combined with another job?)	When *should* it be done? (Pros and cons of alternatives, including costs, considered.)
D	Place in which job is done	1. *Where* is it done? (Consider place, distances from previous and subsequent activities.)	*Why* there? (Pros and cons considered.)
		2. Where else *could* it be done? (Consider layout, distances, people involved.)	Where *should* it be done? (Pros and cons of alternatives, including costs, considered.)
E	People involved in job	1. *Who* does the job? (Consider numbers, grades, pay, etc.)	*Why* that person? (Pros and cons considered.)
		2. Who else *could* do it? (Consider alternative people, grades, types of workers.)	Who *should* do it? (Use work measurement. Is work properly balanced between operators?)

The critical examination stage is the central pivot of method study: the effectiveness of a study stands or falls by the use made of the procedure. Present methods are systematically criticised; new and imaginative ideas to improve and update methods are encouraged, then treated to the same systematic criticism.

Step 4: Develop. The fourth stage is to develop detailed and constructive proposals for improvement. These are based both on the work during the critical examination stage and on other considerations such as the principles of motion economy (and ergonomics, as discussed in Chapter 10). The advice and views of all who will be involved in the changes should be taken into account, particularly those of the shop-floor management and workers.

Ideally the chosen new method should have demonstrable improvements in layout, working procedures, use of people, equipment and materials, working conditions and environment.

Step 5: Install.   The fifth step is to install the new method. Mention has been made of consultation with the workforce in the shop. Continual co-operation is vital at the implementation stage. A programme is drawn up for the installation of the new method so that there is a minimum of interference with normal production.

Workers may need to be retrained in the use of new equipment, machinery or methods.

The new method is now standard practice until the next review.

Step 6: Maintain.   The final step is to maintain the new method. This implies follow-up checks to ensure that the new method is actually being followed (workers may 'slip back' to old, preferred methods), and that no unforeseen problems have arisen. Experience may also reveal the need to make some adjustments or further improvements to the new method.

To be maintained properly, a method must be clearly defined and set out on paper. Workplace layouts and, where appropriate, body movements must be specified exactly to avoid any risk of misinterpretation.

12.3 Work Measurement

For thousands of years people have been able to measure (reasonably accurately) materials, buildings and even people in terms of quantities such as cubits, metres, tonnes or pence per cubic metre. It was, however, not so easy to measure human effort, or 'work' since work could involve many different activities in a day, or making a few large items or many small ones. Products could hardly serve as common denominators.

The Industrial Revolution brought changes. Many workers performed the same repetitive tasks daily, and it was soon realised that *time* was the common element or factor at work. Attention became concentrated on *how long* it took to complete a task. *Time study* (a technique of work measurement) was used as a basis for payment by results incentive schemes, and as a yardstick against which the performance of individual workers could be judged. Regrettably, some people in industry still believe that work measurement and incentive schemes are interrelated activities. In fact, work measurement techniques can be applied to a variety of different activities.

Definition of work measurement

British Standard BS 3138 of 1979 defines work measurement as the 'application of techniques designed to establish the time for a *qualified* worker to carry out a task at a *defined* rate of working' (author's italics). (Note that no mention is made here of incentive schemes.) The emphases in this definition are on a *qualified* worker (one who is properly trained, with the necessary skills and knowledge to do the job effectively) and on *defined* rates of working (that is, at some standard pace or speed of working).

In summary, then, work measurement is that set of techniques which assists in defining tasks and then establishes how long *people* involved in those tasks should take to complete them satisfactorily, in given circumstances.

Stages in the work measurement process

As already noted, work measurement is a set of techniques by which information is obtained about how long jobs take to complete. It usually concludes with a description of the (effective) work done in carrying out a specific job or task in *time* units— seconds, minutes, etc. Work measurement can be both *descriptive* (describing an actual work performance) or *prescriptive* (laying down what time *ought* to be spent on a particular job).

The measurement of the work content of a job is usually done in three stages:

(a) breaking down the job into parts (easily identifiable as being distinct and suitable for separate observation and measurement) called 'elements', for example, picking up a bolt;
(b) timing each element;
(c) assessing a worker's overall performance by comparing his or her speed (or 'rate') of working against some predetermined standard.

12.4 Work measurement techniques

Work measurement techniques can be classified under two headings:

1. *Direct measurement.* In direct measurement techniques, the work is observed directly (i.e. while in progress) and measured. Examples are time study and activity sampling.
2. *Indirect measurement.* In indirect techniques, the times applicable to a complete job are built up from existing data banks of known times for job elements. Examples are synthetic times (synthetics) and predetermined motion time systems (PMTS).

Basic terms used in work measurement

Before examining the four techniques mentioned, it will be useful to understand some of the basic terms used.

Timing. This is the practice of observing and recording the time taken to finish a chosen work element by using a stop-watch or a data capture terminal — hand-held and linked to a computer.

Rating. This is the speed (or rate) at which a worker works (usually given a number value), as assessed by a trained observer. (It includes 'effort' as well as speed of movements.)

Standard rating. This is the speed (or rate) of working which is equal to that at which qualified workers will naturally work, provided they follow the method laid down to the letter and are willing workers.

To rate. To rate is to assess and compare a worker's speed (or rate) of working relative to the standard rating for the job.

Observed time. This is the time (in time units) taken to complete a work element, as observed by direct measurement.

Basic time. This is the time taken to complete a work element by a worker working at a standard rate, with no breaks.

Relaxation allowance. This is a time added to basic time to give a qualified worker time to take a rest from time to time, or to attend to personal needs.

Contingency allowance. This is a time added to basic time to allow for unavoidable interruptions in work activity.

Standard time. This is basic time and relaxation allowance plus contingency allowance.

Standard performance. Standard performance is the rate of output that qualified workers can achieve without over-exertion (represented by 100 on the BS Rating Scale) over a working day.

Time study

The basic steps in time study are as follows.

Step 1: Identify. The first step is to identify the job elements to be timed. Such elements should be clearly distinct and should last long enough to be measured. Ideally an element should last about 0.5 minute. Heavy and light work should be separate: audible actions (snapping a switch) provide natural element boundaries.

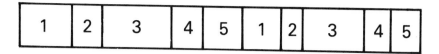

Elements 1 = Pick up plastic moulding from machine output.
        2 = Cut off 'spare'.
        3 = Check for moulding 'flush', defects and remove.
        4 = Place moulding in collection bin.
        5 = Wait for next part.

Figure 12.4 *Elements of a job.*

Step 2: Time. The second step is to time each job element. (The decimal minute, flyback stop-watch, calibrated in 0.01 minute intervals, is much used.)[5]

The time-study observer records each element many times, observing several workers (if possible) who work at the same task, over a period of time. Sometimes different observers are used on different days. All results are collated and averaged.

Step 3: Assess. The third step is to assess the rate of working, noting that effort ratings can vary from element to element. In effect this is an assessment by the time-study observer of whether the worker observed is working faster (or slower) than the average or 'standard'. Such an assessment, called 'rating', is inevitably a subjective activity: people's ideas of standard ratings can vary. Correct training and regular checks are needed to ensure that time-study observers are consistently accurate.

In rating, then, the observer compares what is observed with his or her notion of the standard rating for that element. To enable more precise comparisons to be made, observed ratings are given numerical values, which are compared with the value given to the standard rating. The BSI Standard Rating and Performance Scale is the simplest to use. The standard rating is given a value of 100 BS; see Figure 12.5.

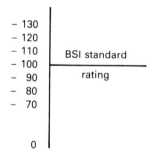

Figure 12.5 *BSI rating scale.*

---

[5] A detailed review of all the kinds of timing equipment (including electronic) is beyond our scope here.

The observer can now convert the time taken by the worker to complete an element to 'basic' time by using the formula:

$$\text{Basic time} = \frac{\text{Observed time} \times \text{Observed rating}}{\text{Standard rating (i.e. 100 BS)}}$$

Suppose the average of 25 observations of worker W completing element E is 30 seconds, and W is rated at 120 BS, then:

$$\text{Basic time} = \frac{0.5 \times 120}{100} = 0.6 \text{ minutes (36 seconds)}$$

Step 4: Estimate (allowances). The fourth step is to estimate 'allowances' or extra times to be added to basic times. No worker can work non-stop every moment of a shift or working day, so work does not proceed at the basic rate without interruption. Allowances (usually as a percentage) are added to basic times, therefore, to cover workers' personal needs or other reasons for not working.

Amounts of allowance vary, but allowances for personal needs vary from 3 to 4 per cent, allowance for heavy work is around 10–12 per cent, and allowance for noise is up to 7 per cent. 'Contingency' allowances include waiting for work, especially where waiting times are variable, adjusting machines, or seeking advice from a supervisor. Other allowances include tool allowances (for altering tools, etc.) and policy allowances.

Step 5: Calculate. The final step is to calculate the 'standard time' for the complete job (see Figure 12.6):

Job standard time = Basic times, all elements added + Allowances

Unless there are any other special circumstances the standard time becomes the 'allowance time' for the job.

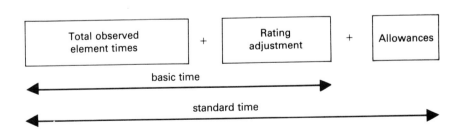

Figure 12.6 *Build-up of a job standard time.*

Activity sampling

A total contrast to time study is activity sampling, a quick, simple and cheap way of gathering facts. It is little more than its name suggests: activities are *sampled* rather than observed continuously (as with time study). For example, to find how much a particular machine is used in a workshop, observers simply take intermittent looks at it. When enough observations have been made, the results can be used to assess (with a known degree of accuracy) what percentage of total available work time the machine has been in use.

Observers need no special equipment: notebook and ball-point pen are sufficient (special forms, however, are often used). All that observers do is to 'snap' what they see (just as a 'still' camera does), that is, they record the activity/inactivity of a worker or a machine at a precise instant of observation. Observers need not be trained work-study staff; the study can be completed in a few days, and work is not interrupted while the sampling takes place.

Random times during the day are obtained from tables of random numbers, or from a computer. Alternatively, observations can be made at regular intervals.

Steps in the technique
1. *Select* an activity to be studied (e.g. use of a machine).
2. *Carry out* a pilot study (to get a rough estimate of the proportion of time taken up by the chosen activities).
3. *Decide* on accuracy required (e.g. to within ± 10, 5 or 1 per cent) and confidence level in result.
4. *Obtain* random times.
5. *Observe* the required number of times (see below).
6. *Calculate* results and check accuracy.

Number of observations required. To calculate the number of observations required the following formula has been developed:

$$N = \frac{KP\,(100 - P)}{L^2}$$

where: N = the number of observations required
   L = the percentage error to be allowed in the final result
   P = the estimated percentage activity (found from pilot study as a proportion of the whole time)
   K = the constant
The constant, K, which indicates the 'level of confidence' to be placed in the answer, is chosen from the table below:

Level of confidence	*K*
Very high indeed	9
High	4
Moderate	1

(Usually 4 is chosen.)

Example. The management of Acme Engineering Ltd decided that an activity sample should be taken of a particular surface-grinding machine. Twenty observations were made in a pilot study on Monday. It was found that the grinder was in use twelve times only. A ±5 per cent accuracy was required in the final figure, with a high degree of confidence in the result. Calculate the number of observations necessary to meet the requirements.

Answer

$$N = \frac{4 \times 60 \,(100 - 60)}{5^2} = \frac{4 \times 60 \times 40}{25} = 384$$

(Note: Widen the accuracy to ±10 per cent and only one quarter of the observations (i.e. 96) would be required.)

Synthesis

The direct methods of work measurement considered above, if introduced into a firm for the first time, will lead to a considerable amount of work. However, after a while it will become apparent that to time *every* element in every job could be wasteful, as the same elements (for example tightening a nut) can occur again and again.

When such elements re-appear it makes sense to refer back to previous studies and pick out the old data 'ready made' for new studies, thus eliminating the need for re-timing and re-rating. It makes even better sense to extract on cards information on 'commonly occurring elements', basic times, etc. and gradually to build up a complete data bank. Eventually, basic job times can be built up without having to carry out direct studies.

Synthesis is thus an *indirect* measurement technique for building up the basic time of a job by totalling element times obtained previously from time studies of similar work containing the elements concerned, or from a data bank of element times.

Predetermined motion time systems (PMTS)

Predetermined motion time systems attempt to overcome the problems of subjective assessments in time study, and of timing with stop-watches elements of very short duration. (Time study and the very visible stop-watch are not exactly welcomed by the average shop-floor worker.)

Frank Gilbreth recognised that all human activities (including work) could be analysed into basic movements, such as search, find, select, grasp, assemble, etc. He assigned the word 'therbligs' (an anagram of his name) to these movements. A full list of therbligs in current use, with appropriate symbols, can be found in BS 3138:1979.

From the work of Gilbreth, and that of Taylor and others, several PMTS systems have been developed. The earlier ones were complex and too detailed, but modern systems combine some simple motions, so there are fewer of them to consider. However, even modern systems still retain the essential PMTS characteristic that each simple motion considered is smaller than the 'work elements' of conventional time study (but still, of course, being allocated a basic time).

In using PMTS, each job is broken down into elements (as for time study), then considered to establish what simple motions a worker will need to use to complete that element. The element's basic time is now easily calculated by adding the (already known) basic times of its constituent motions. Relaxation allowances are then added to obtain standard times (see Figure 12.7).

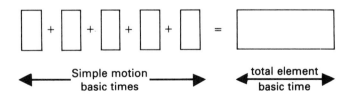

Figure 12.7 *Synthesis of an element's basic time using PMTS.*

Great care in analysing an element into its constituent simple basic motions is required: considerable use is made of *micromotion* photography. Film is made of a work cycle, exposing as many as 1000 frames per minute. Very small movements can be then spotted and recorded. Although stop-watches are not used, PMTS methods require skilled observers.

Analytical estimating

Analytical estimating (first developed in the 1940s) is used to cope with situations where conventional time-study techniques are not suitable, for example long jobs, non-repetitive work (repairs, maintenance, construction) or the production of single items.

After splitting the job into elements—which tend to be rather longer in duration than elements chosen for a time study—times are allocated. Where standard times are 'on file' for some elements, these times are used. Otherwise, standard times are established by *estimation*, which is rather more than inspired guesswork. It is rather an assessment based on the knowledge and experience of the estimator gained on similar kinds of work. A further development is *comparative estimating*, involving the comparison of the work in job A with that in a series of jobs, B, C, D, etc., the work content of which is known. The times for the job nearest in content to A are used for job A (not a very scientific method).

12.5   Applications of work measurement

The information and data gained from work measurement techniques are used to:

(a)   assist in the better planning of all operations and processes in the production areas;

(b)   establish the optimum ratios of operators to machines or machines to operators;
(c)   compare the times taken by different methods of doing a job;
(d)   enable direct labour costs to be calculated;
(e)   provide a sound basis for incentive payment schemes—comparisons can be made between jobs, and between individual workers doing similar jobs.

Operator and machine performance reports

In practice, reports are commonly compiled on the output and performance of both operators and machinery, such reports having a wide circulation, including production control and the cost department. Based on the *standard* minutes desirable in a given period, the reports show also the *actual* minutes worked as a comparison. Reasons for shortfalls are analysed numerically and some kind of performance rating is calculated.

Figure 12.8 illustrates a day's work done by a group of operators, a report which is self-explanatory once it is realised that SM = standard minutes. Figure 12.9, however, covers a range of machinery over a period of a week. It contains at the foot explanations of how the figures in columns 9, 14, 15 and 16 are calculated. It is essential that the variances thrown up are investigated and appropriate remedial action taken, such as changes in methods or staffing, more preventive maintenance, etc.

12.6   Incentive payments schemes

The term 'incentive schemes' is rather vague. BS 3138:1979 merely defines an incentive scheme as 'a method of encouraging appropriate response from worker(s)'. Such a definition could apply equally well to pats on the back, threats or awarding medals!

Examination of incentive schemes associated with work study reveals that they are:

(a)   *financial* (rewards are paid in money);
(b)   *payment by results* schemes (earnings are related to output or work done);
(c)   *direct* (money earned is related to workers' own efforts);
(d)   related to *manual* workers.

The kind of schemes examined below have in the main all four characteristics in common.

Simple (or 'straight') piecework

Piecework has a long history. Under this system workers are paid a fixed amount for each item produced in an industrial or manufacturing situation, regardless of the time taken to do the work. For many years miners were paid so much per ton for coal at the pit head, 'navvies' so much per ton for earth moved, weavers in accordance with the length of cloth woven, and so on. Piecework prices were fixed by bargain between

Daily Return
Location: Horizontal Milling

Day: Thursday
7 December 1982

1	2	3	4	5	6	7	8	9	10	11	12
No.	Name	Possible SM	Waiting for work	Waiting for inspection	Machine break-down	Miscellaneous	SM Lost $(4+5+6+7)$	Available SM $(3-8)$	Actual output SM	Operator perf. $\frac{10}{9} \times 100\%$	Comments
018	Bloggs J.	450	21	8	—	9	38	412	350	85	
121	Smith S.	450	16	12	—	20	48	402	366	91	
131	Jones T.	510	42	14	—	7	63	447	465	104	1 hour OT
211	Kent R.	570	38	10	65	12	125	445	396	89	2 hours OT
219	Allen B.	450	16	—	10	4	30	420	407	97	
332	Singh J.	450	12	5	14	31	57	393		102	
	Totals	4320	215	79	95	106	495	3825	3592	94	

Figure 12.8 *Labour cost control data: operator performance records. Reproduced with the permission of Mr B. Hitchings.*

Weekly Report

Week No. 15
Week ending – 9 December 1982

Resource Centre
Machine Shop

1	2	3	4	5	6	7	8	9	10	11	12	13	14	15	(16)
Machine group	Available SM	Actual output SM	SM lost waiting for work		SM lost waiting for insp.		SM lost machine breakdown		SM lost miscellaneous		SM lost total		Section index	Average of index	Overall perf.
			Act.	%	Act.	%	Act.	%	Act.	%	Act.	%	%	%	%
Milling 1	15400	12900	1230	6.9	160	0.90	310	1.75	745	4.20	2445	13.7	86.3	84	72.5
Milling 2	22300	20980	1110	4.6	206	0.80	219	0.90	445	1.80	1980	8.2	91.8	94	86.3
Milling 3	12600	12100	1260	8.5	260	1.75	497	3.35	252	1.70	2269	15.3	84.7	96	81.3
Drilling	9200	8200	180	1.83	45	0.50	120	1.22	270	2.75	615	6.27	93.7	89	83.4
Turning	28700	29800	3450	10.0	300	0.85	570	1.65	1720	4.95	6040	17.4	82.6	103	85.1
Grinding	16800	16050	3200	15.3	72	0.35	333	1.60	509	2.45	4134	19.7	80.3	95	76.3
Totals	143700	137400	15370	9.15	1580	0.94	1980	1.18	5490	3.26	24420	14.6	85.4	96	82.0

$$(14) = \frac{(2) \times 100}{(2) + (12)}$$

$$(15) = \frac{(3)}{(2)} \times 100$$

$$(9) = \frac{(8) \times 100}{(2) + (12)}$$

$$(16) = (14) \times (15)$$

Figure 12.9 *Labour cost control data: machine group performance records. Reproduced with the permission of Mr B. Hitchings.*

workers and employers. When the job went well and workers worked hard they earned good money: when work was scarce or difficult, earnings suffered.

The one great advantage was that the system was easily understood and payments were easily computed. Employers could estimate labour costs in advance. However, simple piecework is little used today, and is confined mostly to work of a casual nature (Figure 12.10).

Payment varies directly with effort. No work done means a zero payment, but there is no ceiling on the total wage which could be earned.

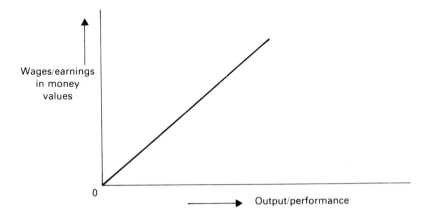

Figure 12.10 *Simple piecework.*

Standard time systems

As time went on, the influence of Taylor's scientific management school meant that management began to look for 'more efficient' methods of working, and offered to pay not what had been agreed upon as the price for the job, but what was a 'fair' price based on some technique such as work study or time measurement. Bargaining did not disappear from the scene, but rather was relegated to the querying of rates fixed as the result of time study, or attempting to modify upwards the figures put forward.

The introduction of such methods as work study and time measurement had other implications: first and foremost we can now fix not only a rate per piece, but also an acceptable rate of production. This 'acceptable rate' is called the 'standard time' and attracts a 'base rate' payment. Workers who produce more (or take less time than the 'standard time' to produce a given output) earn more than the base rate payment.

Differential piecework

Basically, differential piecework systems are those which normally have various *steps* of piecework prices for different levels of production. The straight proportional

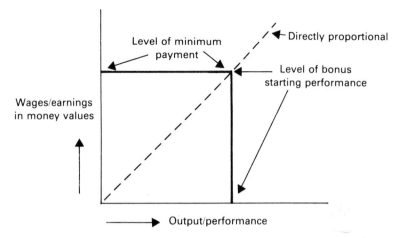

Figure 12.11   *Straight proportional system.*

system is one where earnings are *directly proportional* to the results achieved (subject to meeting a bonus starting performance as in Figure 12.11). Thus this straight proportional system is the same as simple piecework when based on output only.

This scheme can be based, however, on the standard time system, and any increase in worker performance over an agreed *base* performance results in workers receiving an increased payment *directly proportional* to production output, up to an agreed ceiling, say 130 performance.

We can compare this type of system to 'progressive' or 'regressive' differential systems, in which the payments made are not proportional to production (i.e. the price per unit of output is *variable*). Figure 12.12 illustrates this situation.

Once a minimum level of performance is reached, the steps may be progressive (to encourage more production) or regressive (to discourage production over a certain level). The regressive schemes are obviously favoured by management as they can recoup some money if the time rates fixed were inaccurate (in the workers' favour) when calculated or if production rises through some other unexpected factor. Clearly, there is a disincentive for workers to strive even harder in these circumstances.

Finally, we can consider two further, related schemes: *geared schemes* (or 'premium bonus' schemes) and *multi-factor bonus schemes*. In the geared schemes worker performance and bonus payment will not be directly related. For example, bonus payment may commence below base 75 performance to give some encouragement to lower-output workers, or we could have higher bonus payments in the lower range 60–90 performance, but bonus payments over 90 would be reduced. This gearing could also be applied vice versa, to give a *reduced* payment for performances in the lower range, with a (considerable) increase for performances in the higher ranges, say 90–130 performance.

Multi-factor schemes are those schemes where rewards are related to a number of (agreed) factors, typical examples of factors being output, material utilisation, quality of the product, or yield from the process. Each factor can be weighted (i.e. given a greater or lesser degree of emphasis, according to its importance), and should be

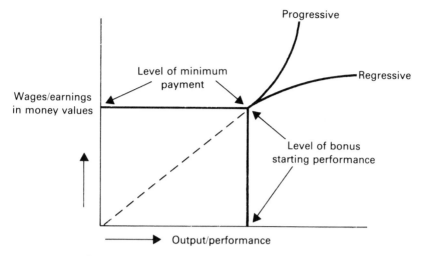

Figure 12.12 *Progressive/regressive differential system.*

within the control of the worker and measurable. Normally the number of factors is limited, and not more than three.

Implications of piecework systems. The use of strict methods of observation, i.e. checking, before and after a scheme is introduced, plus a strict inspection of work to monitor quality, now becomes a necessity. Some workers may not only skimp on quality to earn more, but also disregard safety regulations. Absenteeism may increase if workers feel they are 'earning enough' in four days' attendance, or output may be restricted for fear of lack of work in the future.

It should also be noted that calculation of standard times would take into account both the performance rating of the worker and additional allowances which would include personal needs and relaxation allowances to cover increasing fatigue (depending on the nature of the job). The standard time could also include a contingency allowance to meet legitimate delays which might occur during the work cycle and which may be inconvenient or uneconomical to measure because they happen infrequently (e.g. adjusting a cutting tool).

Certain *waiting time* which may be incurred (e.g. waiting for fresh material supply, machine breakdown, waiting for further instructions) and which is beyond the control of the worker would *not* be included in the standard time, but would be calculated independently and paid for at some agreed rate (e.g. basic hourly rate or a figure based on a percentage *above* this).

Group piecework/bonus schemes

To overcome the problems of individual workers who are put together in a team or gang where the flow of the work is such that D depends upon the work of C, C of B, B of A, and so on, group piecework systems have been evolved. It is said that such schemes encourage team spirit and co-operation, but experience has shown that the success of group schemes depends partly on the size of the group. Sub-groups tend to form with groups of more than 15, for example, and some feel that a group of eight people is as large a group as you can get without fragmentation.

It is necessary with this type of scheme to consider also the compatibility of the working group in terms of skill, experience, age, physical ability and background.

Indirect labour bonuses

The argument is advanced that as indirect labour (labour not totally involved in producing, such as supervisors, tool setters, labourers) can make or break incentive schemes, they too should be offered incentives to work harder. Schemes exist where a total department's production performance can be measured, and whatever bonus is due is divided between the productive and non-productive workers — typically 75 per cent to production staff and 25 per cent to indirect labour.

Schemes of this kind are not always popular: it is argued that some indirect labour cannot become more productive and does not have to work harder even when production workers do (cleaners, for example), and there is a reluctance to share the bonus payment.

Total factory bonuses

In total factory bonus schemes typically most workers are on a basic wage or piecework system, but increased production (on a factory basis) over a certain predetermined level is converted into a percentage figure, which is added to the basic figure to arrive at the gross wage for the period concerned. All employees can benefit, from managing director downwards, but a major criticism is that the higher-paid workers get more in actual cash than the lower-paid ones.

Measured day work

Payments by results schemes can become complicated to design and administer. The work involved in the recording of standards, the logging and checking of results, and the sophisticated calculations to work out exactly what an individual worker would receive is non-productive, and some firms have felt that there is something to be said for getting rid of it, provided an incentive element could be retained. Such considerations led to the introduction of measured day work, which offers a fixed rate of pay for a defined and agreed standard of daily performance.

The high time rate is usually set so that earnings are at least as high as under any previous system, and work measurement is used to establish the time standards for each job and to define a given level of performance expected. Provided that the worker meets the targets set, he or she is guaranteed a regular weekly wage; if the required standard is consistently not reached, the worker is transferred to a less demanding job at a lower rate of pay.

Unfortunately (unless we add other incentive elements, thus defeating the objective of making the scheme simpler), there is no incentive to exceed the predetermined level of output. Thus workers on measured day work can either 'spin the work out' as the day wears on, or cease work altogether when they have done their quota for the day. Such (legitimate) behaviour can be frustrating to a hard-pressed supervisor.

One way out is to introduce a 'banded' or *stepped* measured day work scheme (Figure 12.13). Although such a scheme is similar to the one described above, it has (agreed) bands or steps of payment related to various predetermined output performance standards. Thus a worker may move into a *lower* payment band if he or she consistently returns a lower output than the preferred norm, or into a *higher* band if the output is higher than the preferred norm. Certain time limits would have to be agreed for reviewing payment band changes.

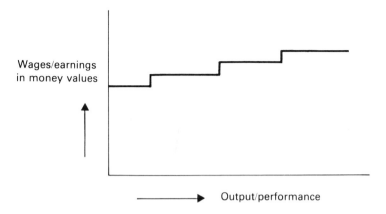

Figure 12.13 *A 'stepped' measured daywork scheme.*

Summary

1. Work study is the name given to that set of ideas, techniques and activities which together add up to a study of work (or jobs).
2. Work study is normally divided into two major areas:
   (a) method study (an examination of either *existing* methods or *proposed* methods of doing jobs);
   (b) work measurement (a set of activities and techniques which first defines tasks, then establishes how long people involved in those tasks *actually* take, and finally calculates how long they *ought* to take, in given circumstances).
3. Method study is built round a critical appraisal of the existing (or present) methods, or alternatively the proposed methods, of doing a job. Such an appraisal is *systematic* in investigation and recording, *critical* in its wide-ranging review, and suggests *improvements*.

4. A method-study investigation can be said to proceed in a series of six steps:
    1. *Select* the job to be studied.
    2. *Record* all the known facts about the job.
    3. *Examine* critically the known facts.
    4. *Develop* detailed and constructive proposals for improvements.
    5. *Install* the new method.
    6. *Maintain* and monitor the new method.
5. In particular, during the *examine* stage, questions are asked about the *purpose* of the job, the *way* it is done, the *sequence* of operations, the job environment, and the workers/people involved in the job.
6. In contrast, work measurement consists of preparation (the initial examination of a job) and observation. First, the job is broken down into parts (elements). A time is allocated to each element. Finally, the performance of individual workers on the job is assessed against a predetermined standard.
7. *Direct* work measurement techniques (e.g. time study and activity sampling) rely totally on direct observation of the job under review by a trained observer. The results are then recorded.
8. *Indirect* work measurement techniques (e.g. synthesis and PMTS) rely on the records built up from direct techniques.
9. A time study can be said to proceed in a series of five steps:
    1. *Identify* the job elements to be timed.
    2. *Time* each job element.
    3. *Assess* the rate of working (rating).
    4. *Estimate* allowances to be added to times.
    5. *Calculate* the standard time.
10. The time taken by the worker, when timed and rated, can be converted to a 'basic' time by the formula:

$$\text{Basic time} = \frac{\text{Observed time} \times \text{Observed rating}}{\text{Standard rating (i.e. 100 BS)}}$$

11. The 'standard time' for the job is calculated by the formula:

$$\text{Job standard time} = \text{Basic times, all elements added} + \text{Allowances}$$

    (Usually the standard time becomes the allowed time for the job.)
12. Activity sampling entails sampling (at random, or sometimes regular, frequent intervals) activities during a working day, or succession of days. The six steps in the technique are:
    1. *Select* an activity to be studied.
    2. *Carry out* a pilot study.
    3. *Decide* on the accuracy required.
    4. *Obtain* random times.
    5. *Observe* the required number of sample times.
    6. *Calculate* results.
13. The number of observations required is calculated by the formula:

$$N = \frac{KP\,(100 - P)}{L^2}$$

where: N = number of observations needed

L = the percentage error acceptable

P = an estimate of the percentage of the chosen activity to the whole time

K = confidence constant (usually 4)

14. Synthesis is an indirect measurement technique for building up the basic time of a job by totalling element times established from records of previous direct time studies.

15. The determined time systems are a basis from which to build standard times of elements, known times for the various basic movements (e.g. grasp, put, assemble). 'Action replay' photography can be used to follow very quick movements.

16. Analytical estimating is used for special jobs, for long, non-repetitive work, repairs, etc. The job is split into elements. Where times are known (from synthesis) these are used; the remaining times are *estimated*.

17. Work measurement techniques are used to:

(a) assist in improving operation/process planning;

(b) establish optimum machine/operator ratios;

(c) compare times of alternative methods;

(d) enable direct labour costs to be calculated;

(e) provide a basis for incentive payment schemes.

18. Incentive schemes associated with work measurement are: financial; related to output and effort; and applicable to manual workers.

1. Simple piecework: payments are directly related to the amount produced by the worker.

2. Standard time systems: payments are related not only to the amount of work done, but to the *speed* at which it is done.

3. Differential piecework: piecework systems which normally have various *steps* or piecework prices for different levels of production.

4. Group piecework/bonus schemes: payments schemes where the members of a work gang participate in a shared scheme.

5. Indirect labour bonuses: payments schemes where the non-productive workers (i.e. those not directly involved in the production process) participate in bonus schemes, though often receiving a lower level of bonus than production workers.

6. Total factory bonuses: payments schemes where all workers participate in a bonus usually based on total output/sales.

7. Measured day work: payments schemes which offer a fixed rate of pay for a defined and agreed standard of daily performance.

Questions

Review questions

12.1 What is meant by the term 'work study'? Describe briefly the two major branches of work study.

12.2 Distinguish between present and proposed methods of doing a job.

12.3 Explain why method study is often described as 'systematic' and 'critical'.
12.4 What are the six steps in a method-study investigation?
12.5 In the 'examine' step, what are the differences between primary and secondary questions?
12.6 Define 'work measurement'.
12.7 What is meant by saying that work measurement can be either descriptive or prescriptive?
12.8 Distinguish between direct and indirect work measurement techniques.
12.9 What is meant by the following terms:
    (a) timing;
    (b) rating;
    (c) standard rating;
    (d) observed time;
    (e) basic time;
    (f) relaxation allowance?
12.10 What are the five steps in a method-study investigation?
12.11 What are the formulae for establishing:
    (a) the basic time (of a job);
    (b) the standard time?
12.12 What are the six steps in activity sampling? How is the number of observations required calculated, given that a high level of confidence ($K = 4$) is to be placed in the answer?
12.13 Describe briefly the indirect techniques of synthesis and predetermined motion time systems.
12.14 What are the possible applications of work measurement?
12.15 Distinguish between simple piecework and standard time systems.
12.16 Define a progressive differential bonus system.
12.17 What is measured day work? In what way does a banded or stepped scheme differ from a simple measured day work scheme?

Discussion topics

12.18 At the beginning of the chapter it was stated that ergonomics and value analysis are activities related to work study. Discuss, from what you now know about these three activities, their similarities and differences.
12.19 Method study is said to consist of six steps: select, record, examine, develop, install, and maintain. Other summaries of the steps are:

Select	Initiate	Prepare
Identify	Consult (supervisors,	Collect
Record	workers)	Collate
Examine	Collect (data)	Appraise
Develop	Examine	Implement
Submit (for approval)	Develop	
Install	Present (for approval)	
Maintain	Install	
	Maintain	

Discuss which list seems to be the best summary.
12.20 Which work measurement technique do you think is most suitable for applying to each of the following jobs:
    (a) finding out how long a particular machine is idle;
    (b) servicing and repair of a fork-lift truck;

(c)   a combination of jobs which has never occurred before, but where each job has individually been time-studied in the past?

12.21 'Piecework is an evil system; it encourages greed and selfishness, makes workers slaves to their machines, and discourages safety; favours the strong at the expense of the weak.' Discuss this view.

Assignments

12.22 In small groups observe someone attaching a standard length of three-strand flex to a new three-pin plug.
       (a)   Subject the work to method study. Record (in any suitable way but preferably on a flow process chart) the way the job is done (present method).
       (b)   Subject the activity to the critical examination questions and record the group's comments.
       (c)   Suggest improvements to the recorded present method.

12.23 In small groups break down the information obtained from Assignment 12.22 and identify individual job elements. Watch the job again several times (it would be useful to have a video-tape of the job being done). One group is to time the job elements using a clock; a second using a stop-watch; and a third using a digital watch. Compare results and discuss any difficulties encountered in carrying out the assignment.

12.24 In groups, visit the college refectory during the lunch hour. Under the guidance of the class lecturer, carry out an activity sample of the cashier and analyse the percentage of times the cashier was *assessing* prices, *operating* the till, *giving* change or *waiting* for the next customer.

(*Notes*. A pilot study will be required, so it will be necessary to observe on more than one day or session. It will be necessary to calculate the number of observations required: take the 'waiting for the next customer' percentage as the one to use in the formula. The use of random times probably means that few observations can be made in a session. It is suggested for this exercise that one observation is made each minute or half minute. Each group will need to devise a simple form in order to carry out the study.)

13
Elements of Costing

Costing was first introduced in Chapter 4 and some basic concepts were described. This chapter revises and develops the earlier material, starting with the cost accounting function.

After revising the basic elements of cost, various costing approaches and methods are described and evaluated. Finally, the technique of break-even analysis is explained.

13.1 The cost accounting function

Many manufacturing organisations now have a cost accounts department (sometimes called the cost office). Cost accounting as a separate activity and function is, however, a comparatively recent development. When organisations became large and more complex around the beginning of this century, the simple costing procedures which had served industry before became inadequate and unreliable. Cost control is as important as the control of production or quality, and needs to be done equally thoroughly, carefully and accurately.

Headed by a *cost accountant*, usually a person with professional qualifications, the department is normally engaged in examining all expenditure (money spent) incurred by the various departments in the firm. Such expenditure details are collected, recorded, classified, collated, allocated and apportioned (to cost centres). The purpose of such work is not only to identify and control expenditure, but also to ascertain the costs of products (and services), upon which data pricing and other marketing decisions can be taken. Costing also provides information for budget preparation.

Thus, as well as examining *actual* expenditure and *current* costs, costing techniques can be used to forecast *future* expenditure and costs. Such techniques can also be applied to the determining of the costs of proposed, new or modified products, even while these products are still in the design or value-analysis stages.

212

Because of the need to look into every aspect of the firm's activities, the cost accounting function (despite being a separate department) has to be totally co-ordinated with the (financial) accounts department, with stores and payroll procedures, with production and work measurement activities, and with the budgetary control operation.

The objectives of the cost accounting function

From the considerations above it can be seen that the objectives of costing are:

(a) to ensure the systematic measurement and recording of the money spent in any sub-system (department) of the firm on the use of its resources—workers, money,[1] machines or materials;

(b) to relate this expenditure to agreed standards, expenditure targets or budgets;

(c) to note and report to management any significant variations from these standards, targets or budgets, for appropriate action (in other words, the control function appears again in a financial setting).

The tasks of the cost accounting function

In achieving these objectives, the department will undertake the following tasks:

(a) establishing cost centres, which are precisely defined areas in the firm whose expenditure will be recorded separately (examples are the toolroom, canteen, sales department, paint shop—see Chapter 14)—essentially any part of the organisation where the operations performed are similar;

(b) working out the targets or standards to be set for costing and budgetary control;

(c) calculating (from information received from various sources, including cost centres) the costs of jobs, processes, products, individual orders, materials used, labour employed, etc.;

(d) following on the previous task, providing information to management/sales on the unit costs of existing products, or estimating the unit costs of potential or modified products, so that selling prices can be fixed in each case;

(e) analysing the expenditure incurred in all departments and comparing it with the targets, standards or budgets, and reporting significant variations to management;

(f) being associated with stocktaking (either at precisely defined intervals, e.g. six months, or on a continuous basis) of both work in progress and finished goods, and establishing a money value of these stocks;

(g) providing management with information as required on present or projected future levels of expenditure.

---

[1] The use of money (especially if borrowed) costs money.

13.2 The advantages and disadvantages of costing

In addition to the objectives and tasks outlined above, the following benefits and drawbacks of costing to management can be noted.

Advantages

1. The establishment of cost centres involves a very careful look at the whole firm's organisation. Those individuals responsible for expenditure can be identified clearly.
2. Standard costing and budgetary control methods help production to see what the ideal (or optimum) levels of output are, even if these targets are not reached.
3. Regular (better still, continuous) stocktaking leads to a stricter control over stock levels and 'wastage'.
4. Inefficiencies in production — idle time, scrap, expensive material used, etc. — are highlighted.
5. Costs of different times can be compared and decisions made on future production.
6. Costs of different methods of manufacture of the same product can be compared and choices made. The need for method study on particular expensive operations can be revealed.
7. 'Make or buy' decisions can be made where costs of each method are known.
8. Profit margins can be clearly identified.
9. The need for cost-reduction programmes can be revealed.
10. Incentive schemes can be monitored.

Disadvantages

1. If not carefully controlled, the operation can get very 'paper heavy'. (This is a central problem in all control systems — whether the cost of running them exceeds the cost of savings made.)
2. Management may demand information that is very difficult and costly to obtain and then not use it.
3. There may be resentment on the part of supervisors or managers of cost centres at being monitored constantly.

Undoubtedly the advantages far outweigh the disadvantages, particularly if the costing system is so well organised as to minimise the latter.

13.3 Basic elements of cost

It will be recalled from Chapter 4 that the basic elements of cost are:

(a) *Prime costs*: the total of *direct* costs of manufacture — materials, labour and expenses;
(b) *Factory overheads*: the total of the *indirect* costs of manufacture — materials, labour and expenses;
(c) *Non-manufacturing overheads*: the total of expenses not directly or indirectly related to production — costs of administration, selling and distribution, research and development.

Note: Factory costs = Prime costs + Factory overheads
  Total costs = Factory costs + Non-manufacturing overheads

Other cost classifications

Other cost classifications are as follows.

Classification under function.   Here costs are classified as belonging to particular functions in the organisation, such as the transport department, paint shop or sales representatives. Such functions are called *cost centres*. Cost centres can be *producing* cost centres, that is (normally) producing departments or *service* cost centres, departments such as maintenance or quality control which in some way contribute to the effective and efficient working of producing cost centres.

Classification under cost units.   Items of cost can also be collected under *cost units*, which in the case of manufacturing organisations will normally be units of finished products, such as a specific model of electric motor, a particular kind of garment or an edition of a textbook.

Classification under direct/indirect.   In this classification *prime costs* are direct: all other production costs are indirect. It is a comparatively simple operation to allocate direct costs either to cost centres or to cost units. More difficult is the dividing up or apportionment of indirect costs to cost centres or cost units. (This chapter explains ways in which indirect costs and other overheads can be apportioned.)

Classification under fixed variable.   Fixed costs are those costs which are not affected by output, and bear no relation to changes in the volume of output. Some factory overheads and all non-manufacturing overheads come under this heading. Obvious examples are rates, directors' fees and office heating costs. (Such costs can change, however, if, for example, the rates are increased, fees go up, or fuel charges rise.) Variable costs are those which can be seen to vary with output volume, though not necessarily proportionally.

13.4 Costing individual products

In Chapter 4 attention was given to the *contribution* to overheads and profits that individual products make. The contribution costing approach is relatively easy to use: the *prime costs* of a product can be identified, and there is no attempt to apportion other costs.

There are occasions when it would be useful to have an idea of a product's total cost. Where profit margins need to be calculated, selling prices need to be fixed, or when in stocktaking the costs of individual items held need to be established (to get a total stock value), a total cost is essential.

Two basic approaches to costing individual products are considered here. First to be examined is blanket (or full) costing; and second, adsorption costing. Both approaches (and their variants) are to a greater or lesser extent arbitrary. It is indeed possible to get different total cost values for the same product by applying the different formulae involved. (Such costing involves calculating the prime costs for each product and apportioning a proportion of overheads to arrive at the total cost.)

13.5 Blanket (full) costing

In this approach the factory and non-manufacturing overheads are combined and apportioned to individual products in a blanket fashion, that is, across the board. It is easy to apply, quick to calculate, and is a popular method in the smaller firm. In its crudest form it could involve (as in the experience of one of the authors) the direct costs of foundry castings being calculated and overheads added on the basis of £5 per pound weight of metal.

Even such a crude, rule-of-thumb method illustrates clearly the basic approach to blanket costing: choose a definite basis for allocation and stick to it. At the year's end, all overheads *should* end up by being spread out over all the products sold.

Figure 13.1 illustrates the steps to be taken in blanket costing for each product manufactured.

Step 1: Identify and calculate the prime costs.   Accurate information is required on:

1. Material costs, that is, money paid to suppliers per kilogram (or other basic unit) of material, or prices paid for bought-out components. (It is usual to add an arbitrary figure, say 10 per cent, to cover materials handling.)
2. Labour costs, that is, money paid in wages, extracted from appropriate direct labour records such as clock cards, time sheets, job cards, overtime claims or bonus payment sheets.
3. Expenses. Examples would be costs of special tools made, drawings prepared, or visits made to suppliers.

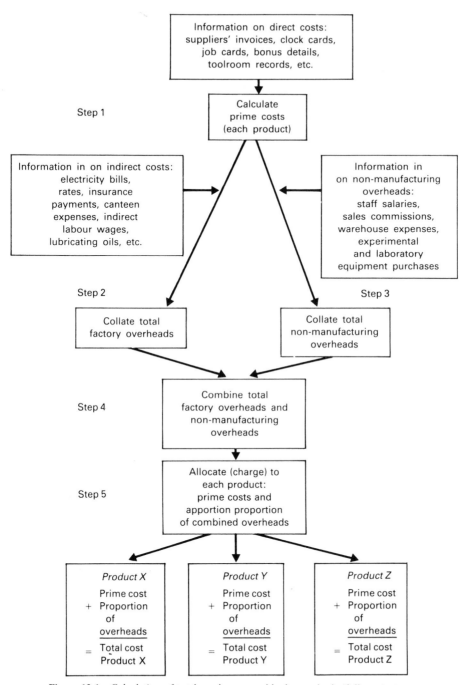

Figure 13.1 *Calculation of total product costs: blanket methods (full costing).*

Step 2: Collate total factory overheads.   All indirect costs are recorded and collated. Sources will be indirect wages records, power bills, stores operating costs, etc.

Step 3: Collate total non-manufacturing overheads.   Similarly, payments falling under this heading are recorded and collated.

Step 4: Combine all overheads.   The total amounts of factory and non-manufacturing overheads are combined into one overall figure.

Step 5: Apportion the overheads and total all costs.   This final step gives the total cost. Methods of apportionment of overheads are discussed below.

Overhead apportionment

The most common methods of apportioning overheads in blanket costing are as follows.

Direct materials cost percentage.   It is convenient to use this method only when the direct materials cost forms the major part of the prime cost. A jeweller using gold, silver or other very expensive material might consider this method, but frequent changes in material prices could cause problems. Formula:

$$\frac{\text{Direct materials}}{\text{percentage rate}} = \frac{\text{Total overheads}}{\text{Direct materials cost}} \times 100$$

Direct wages cost percentage.   This is easy to use, and all the records are available as a matter of course. However, this method is suitable only where the direct wages cost forms the major part of the prime cost, or where wage rates, machine usage and work content are similar for all the products manufactured. Formula:

$$\frac{\text{Direct wages}}{\text{percentage rate}} = \frac{\text{Total overheads}}{\text{Direct wages}} \times 100$$

Prime cost percentage.   This method is easy to operate, as information to calculate the figures is readily available. The most appropriate situation for using it is where wages increase proportionally with time (i.e. workers paid by the hour) and the ratio of materials to wages costs is reasonably constant across all products. Formula:

$$\frac{\text{Prime cost}}{\text{percentage rate}} = \frac{\text{Total overheads}}{\text{Prime costs}} \times 100$$

Labour hour rate. This method is most appropriate where jobs taking varying times, with different material costs, predominate. It divides the total overheads by the direct labour hours forecast over the period under review. These direct hours exclude 'idle time' and maintenance or servicing work. A typical application would be in clothing factories with widely different work in different styles. Formula:

$$\frac{\text{Direct labour}}{\text{hour rate}} = \frac{\text{Total overheads}}{\text{Direct labour hours}}$$

Machine hour rate. This method is becoming increasingly important as manufacture becomes more automated or roboticised. It becomes more and more accurate as the operating hours of machines become a dominant feature of production. Formula:

$$\frac{\text{Machine}}{\text{hour rate}} = \frac{\text{Total overheads}}{\text{Machine hours (operated)}}$$

Rate per unit produced. This final method in our review divides the total overheads by the number of units the firm is expected to produce in the period under review. This gives a rate per unit rather than a percentage addition. This method only becomes accurate if and when what is produced has a uniform work content. It would be ideal in a firm producing large quantities of a single product. Formula:

$$\text{Rate per unit} = \frac{\text{Total overheads}}{\text{Units produced}}$$

Example 1. Acme Engineering Ltd has produced the following figures for next year's estimates for its products X, Y and Z.

	£
Total direct materials cost	200 000
Total direct wages cost	90 000
Total direct expenses	10 000
Total prime cost	300 000
Total overheads	600 000

Number of articles forecast to be sold:

Product X   10 000
Product Y   20 000
Product Z   30 000

                                        60 000
Direct labour hours   36 000
Machine hours   30 000

Calculate (using the six methods listed above) overhead recovery rates.

Answer

1. Direct material percentage rate: $\dfrac{£600\,000}{£200\,000} \times 100 = 300$ per cent of direct cost

2. Direct wages cost percentage: $\dfrac{£600\,000}{£90\,000} \times 100 = 666\frac{2}{3}$ per cent of direct wages

3. Prime cost percentage: $\dfrac{£600\,000}{£300\,000} \times 100 = 200$ per cent of prime cost

4. Labour hour rate: $\dfrac{£600\,000}{36\,000} = £16.66$ per direct labour hour

5. Machine hour rate: $\dfrac{£600\,000}{30\,000} = £20$ per machine hour

6. Rate per unit produced: $\dfrac{£600\,000}{60\,000} = £10$ per unit produced

Example 2.   Acme Engineering Ltd receive a small order for a new product, A, during the year. The details for producing 100 units are as follows:

	£
Total direct materials cost (100)	1000
Total direct wages cost	170 (includes overtime)
Direct expenses	30
Prime cost	1200
Direct labour hours	60
Machine hours	50

Calculate the overheads which could be applied, assuming that all the information obtained in Example 1 is used here.

Answer

1. Direct material percentage:	300% × £1000	= £3000
2. Direct wages percentage:	666% × £170	= £1132
3. Prime cost percentage:	200% × £1200	= £2400
4. Labour hour rate:	60 × £16⅔	= £1000
5. Machine hour rate:	50 × £20	= £1000
6. Rate per unit:	100 × £10	= £1000

(Students should consider these different answers. Why do methods 1 and 3 give such different results from the rest?)

13.6 Absorption costing

In this approach, rather than combine overheads and allocate them on an arbitrary basis, an alternative is to look at costing somewhat more 'scientifically', and to apportion overheads (indeed all costs) to cost centres, and then to cost units. Figure 13.2 shows this in detail.

After obtaining details of prime costs and factory overheads, all are allocated or apportioned as necessary to cost centres. The direct wages of a paint sprayer and the indirect wages of paint-shop inspection and supervision are all initially charged to the paint shop, for example. By this method the total costs applicable to each centre can be built up. (This information is not wasted: it forms the basis of budgetary control.)

When the total costs of service cost centres are known, these are re-apportioned to producing cost centres. The result is that *all* prime costs and factory overheads are eventually allocated to producing cost centres. Every product passing through each cost centre can now be charged with a percentage of factory overheads (as well as with all its prime costs). The parcelling out of the factory overheads is carried out using one of the six methods considered in the previous section, or some other appropriate method.

Next, non-manufacturing overheads are apportioned. Some firms would do this on a 'blanket' basis: others would adopt a more detailed analysis, for example treating selling and distribution costs separately and apportioning them using a predetermined rate such as:

$$\frac{\text{Selling and distribution overheads}}{\text{Total factory costs}} \times 100$$

(The percentage resulting from the calculation is added to each product cost.) The other non-manufacturing overheads are similarly treated.

Finally, each product can be costed. From the producing cost centres come details of *prime costs* and *factory overhead* apportionments. The administrative and other non-manufacturing overheads can now be added to achieve a total cost. (In the case of Acme Engineering Ltd, perhaps the choice for dealing with the non-manufacturing overheads would be to divide them in the proportions of 1:2:3.)

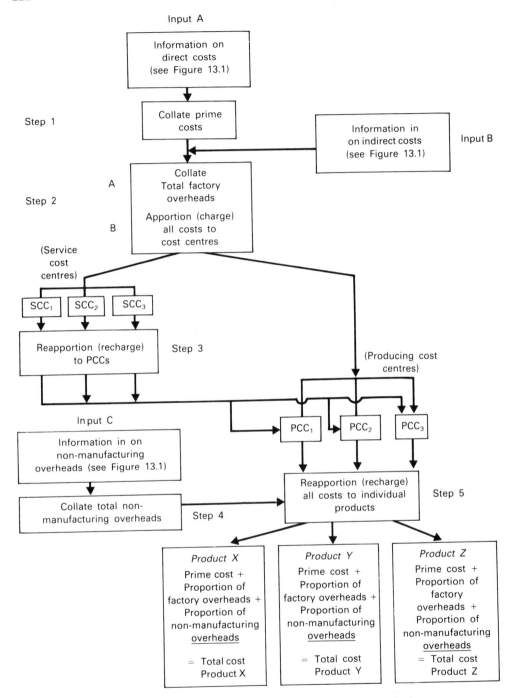

Figure 13.2 *Calculation of total product costs: absorption methods.*

13.7 Historical and standard costing

Historical costing is the process of identifying and recording costs *after* the event. To employ only historical costing is not advisable: past performance is not necessarily a reliable guide to the present, or indeed to the future. Merely to record costs does not in itself raise questions such as whether the best use was made of materials (how much scrap?), or of labour (was excessive overtime worked?), or whether production facilities were properly used.

Standard costing, however, is a method of costing which aims to provide information on such matters. Standard costs (like standard times) are worked out in advance of the event; they are predictions (or budgets). Thus if we predict that the cost of product Z is £10.59, and it actually costs £11.05 to make, we can investigate the discrepancy. Standard costing is one more weapon in the control armoury, when it is used in conjunction with historical costing.

Setting standard costs

Standards are set for every element of cost. For example, in setting standard material costs it will be necessary to set standards for *quality* (agreed specifications), *quantity* (in terms of how much material is to be used for each unit produced) and *price* per metre, kilo, etc. (The price figure is difficult to assess in times of inflation. Real skill is needed to fix a price which can be used over a period without revision.)

Similar considerations will apply to wages costs and every overhead cost, even down to such matters as the grade of labour used on a particular job, or the possible outcome of the next set of wage negotiations, is examined.

Over-recovery or under-recovery of overheads

Provided the estimated production and sales take place during the budget period, and all costs remain as predicted, overheads will be recovered exactly. If more sales occur than envisaged, overheads will be *over-recovered*, that is, the 'overhead element' in all units of production made after the recovery is complete can be considered to be extra profit.

Conversely, lower output or fewer sales than forecast can lead to *under-recovery*. If the trend appears serious, either higher recovery rates will be needed, or overheads will have to be looked at carefully and pruned. A third possibility is to increase prices.

Thus changes in material costs, wage rates or overhead costs could affect the position either way.

13.8 Job costing and process costing

These two approaches to costing must be clearly distinguished. *Job costing* is appropriate for special orders to customers' requirements (in 'singles' or small quantities). A bridge, a ship or hand-made spares for a veteran car are examples. Job costing thus goes with job production.

Prime costs are relatively easy to record and calculate: overheads are added in a 'blanket' fashion (see section 13.5).

Conversely, *process costing* is appropriate for a company engaged in process production, that is, production where fairly standard products pass through a sequence of operations. Chemical manufacture, food processing, blanket making and paper making all employ process costing. All costs are allocated or apportioned to cost centres, and then to the individual product *ranges*. Unit costs are obtained by dividing the cost of the complete process sequence by the number of units of that range produced. Process costing lends itself readily to standard costing.

13.9 Marginal costing

Marginal costing is the name given to that process of establishing the *contribution* that individual products make to overheads and profits, as explained in detail in Chapter 4.

13.10 The ABC of product costs

Mention is made in Chapter 15 (section 15.6) of the ABC or Pareto analysis of the costs of holding stocks of the various lines in a firm's total stock. This section should be read first, and the example referred to in Table 15.1 understood. (It would also be useful to consider the case study at the end of Chapter 15.) The usual result of carrying out such an analysis is to demonstrate that a relatively smaller percentage (say 20 per cent) of a firm's total stock lines accounts for the greater proportion of the firm's stock-holding costs (say 80 per cent). This relationship is often called, therefore, an '80–20' relationship.

A similar relationship can be found when analysing the costs of individual products. Roughly 80 per cent of the total cost of a product can be found to be incurred by 20 per cent of its components, that is, there are a few costly components and a larger number of comparatively cheaper ones.

To construct (in a graphical form) a Pareto distribution for a product's components' costs, it will be necessary:

(a) to ascertain the total number of individual components;
(b) to ascertain the cost of each individual component;
(c) to rank the individual components in descending order of cost (i.e. the most expensive first).

The information in (c) is then plotted on a graph with the *x* axis showing the percentage of total cost (from zero to 100) and the *y* axis similarly showing the percentage of components arranged in descending order of cost. The resultant curve will be similar to that obtained on completing the case study in Chapter 15.

13.11 Break-even analysis

Any company interested in controlling the financial aspects of its operations will be especially interested in the relationship of its costs, sales and profits (or losses).

In fact all three variables can be shown on one diagram: the *break-even chart*. As its names implies, it shows the break-even point (BEP), which is that amount of sales which produces neither a profit nor a loss. However, in addition, it shows the amounts of costs which are *fixed* (costs which do not alter with production, such as factory rent or rates), and those which are *variable* (costs which vary with production, such as all direct costs). Some charts portray the contribution made by a product.

Constructing a break-even chart

The use of graph paper is recommended in constructing break-even charts. The following steps are followed.

Step 1: Construct the axes. The axes are divided into suitable class intervals. The *vertical* axis shows *money values*, i.e. costs, and sales (sometimes called 'sales revenue' or just 'revenue'). The *horizontal* axis is reserved for *sales in units* (or sometimes the capacity of a plant, expressed in percentages from 0 per cent to 100 per cent). Both axes begin at zero.

Step 2: Insert the total fixed costs. As already indicated, the fixed costs (overheads) do not depend in any way on levels of output. They usually remain constant. Thus they are shown (after totalling) as a horizontal line parallel to the horizontal axis. The diagram is now at the stage shown in Figure 13.3.

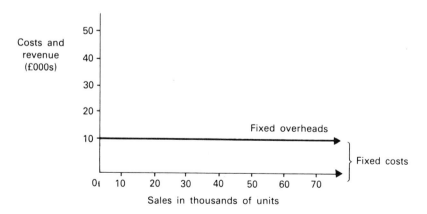

Figure 13.3 *Break-even chart, product 2, stage I.*

Step 3: Add the total variable costs. Next the variable costs are added. As these costs (normally) vary proportionally with output, they will appear as a *straight, sloping line*, rising from left to right. As variable costs are added to fixed costs to obtain the total costs, in this example the 'start point' is at £10 000 (the total of fixed overheads). The resultant plotted line is therefore the *line of total costs*. The diagram is now at the stage shown in Figure 13.4.

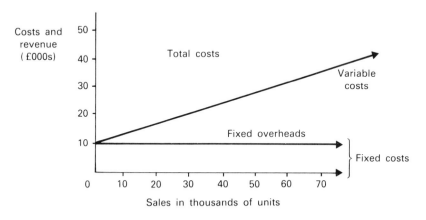

Figure 13.4 *Break-even chart, product 2, stage II.*

Step 4: Plot the sales revenue line. The final step is to plot the sales revenue line (the expected/actual sales income applicable to the period under review). This line starts at zero and moves upwards to the right in a straight line,[2] to the value of sales to date.

Where the total costs line and the sales revenue line cross is sometimes called the equilibrium point, or more usually the break-even point. To the left of this point losses are incurred: to the right, profits are made.

By adding a dotted line *vertically downwards* from the BEP, the number of units which needs to be sold to reach the BEP can easily be identified. By plotting a dotted line *vertically upwards* from any given quantity of sales the expected profit or loss at that particular quantity of sales can be read off. The profit or loss (expected or actual) is indicated by the distance between the sales revenue line and the total costs line.

Now the chart is complete (Figure 13.5), the BEP can be read off (at sales of 35 000 units in this example). When the BEP appears at the *far right* of a break-even chart, little overall profit can be expected; there is also little margin for any cost increases. However, when, as in the case of Figure 13.5, the BEP is to the *left* of the chart,

---

[2] In reality, if some customers are given discounts, the line could be curved, not straight. Similarly, costs could increase (through inflation) during manufacture in an uneven way. To keep the explanation simple, however, only straight lines are used.

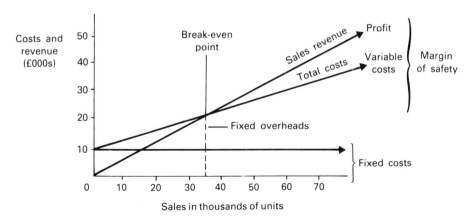

Figure 13.5 *Break-even chart, product 2, stage III (final stage).*

substantial profits can be expected and increases in cost can be absorbed. The revenue in excess of the BEP expressed in £s is known as the *margin of safety* value.

Calculating the BEP mathematically

The BEP can be calculated mathematically. Several versions of the formula exist, the simplest of which is as follows:

$$BEP = \frac{TFC}{TFC + NP} \times S$$

where: BEP = Break-even point
TFC = Total fixed costs
NP = Net profit
S   = Sales revenue

Example. In a period of twelve months, product P of Acme Engineering Ltd (launched in January) shows the following performance: sales 10 000 units; sales revenue £20 000; variable costs £12 000; fixed costs £3000. Compute the BEP.

Answer. Using formula above:

$$BEP = \frac{£3000}{£3000 + £5000} \times £20\,000 = \frac{£60\,000}{£8000}$$

$$= £7500 \text{ (or 3750 units)}$$

Thus, after £7500 sales, all costs (including fixed costs) are covered.
    An *alternative* formula is:

$$\text{BEP} = \frac{\text{TFC}}{1 - \dfrac{\text{VC}}{\text{S}}}$$

where VC = Variable costs. The same answer is achieved.

13.12 Contribution break-even chart

In a similar way a break-even chart can be constructed to show the *contribution* as well
as profit. It will be recalled that the contribution is the difference between total sales
revenue and prime costs. Figure 13.6 illustrates this alternative form of chart.
    The sole difference in drawing up a contribution chart is that the variable (direct)
costs are plotted first. Provided sales revenue is in excess of the variable costs, the
chart will show the contribution to the overheads at different sales levels, as well as
any profits.
    Thus Figure 13.6 shows that if product 2 sells only 40 000 units in a year, it
contributes substantially to the fixed overheads.

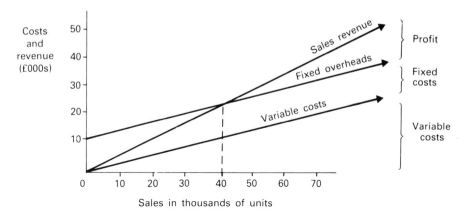

Figure 13.6 *Contribution break-even chart, product 2.*

Summary

1. Many manufacturing organisations now have a cost accounts department (or cost
    office), though cost accounting was developed as a separate activity only in this
    century.

2. Headed by a *cost acountant*, the department examines every item of the firm's expenditure. Such expenditure details are collected, recorded, classified, collated and allocated to cost centres.
3. Costing enables expenditure to be monitored, the cost of producing individual products to be calculated, and budgetary information to be prepared.
4. Thus the objectives of costing are:
   (a) to ensure the systematic measurement and recording of expenditure on workers, money, machines and materials;
   (b) to relate such expenditure to agreed targets or standards;
   (c) to report any significant variances from expected performance to management.
5. In achieving these objectives the department will:
   (a) establish cost centres;
   (b) work out targets or standards to be set;
   (c) calculate costs of jobs, processes, products, orders;
   (d) provide costing information to management;
   (e) analyse all expenditure incurred within the firm;
   (f) participate in stocktaking;
   (g) provide management with details of current or future anticipated expenditure.
6. Costing has the following advantages:
   (a) scrutinises organisation's total operation;
   (b) identifies those responsible for expenditure;
   (c) aids production to monitor performance;
   (d) helps to control stock levels;
   (e) highlights inefficiencies;
   (f) compares costs of different products;
   (g) compares costs of different methods/processes.
7. The disadvantages of costing are:
   (a) can be bureaucratic;
   (b) can be costly;
   (c) managers/supervisors may resist the control element.
8. The basic elements of cost are:
   (a) *prime costs* (direct costs of manufacture);
   (b) *factory overheads* (indirect costs of manufacture).
9. Non-manufacturing overheads: Costs of administration; selling and distribution; research and development.
   Factory costs = Prime costs + Factory overheads
   Total costs = Factory costs + Non-manufacturing overheads
10. Other classifications of cost are:
    (a) classification under function—costs are classified under cost centres;
    (b) classification under cost units—costs are collected and classified under cost units (products);
    (c) classification under direct/indirect;
    (d) classification under fixed/variable.
11. The costs of *individual* products are often required to be ascertained to help fix selling prices, to establish profit margins, to help with stock valuations.
12. Such costing involves for each product:
    (a) calculating the *prime costs*;

(b) apportioning proportions of both *factory overheads* and *non-manufacturing overheads;*

(c) adding the *prime costs* to the *overhead* element.

13. The apportioning of overheads can be done *either* by blanket (full) costing *or* by adsorption costing.

14. Blanket costing entails combining all overheads and allocating them in a 'blanket' fashion across all products. The various methods of doing this include:

(a) direct materials cost percentage $= \dfrac{\text{Total overheads}}{\text{Direct materials cost}} \times 100$

(b) direct wages cost percentage $= \dfrac{\text{Total overheads}}{\text{Direct wages}} \times 100$

(c) prime cost percentage $= \dfrac{\text{Total overheads}}{\text{Prime costs}} \times 100$

(d) labour hour rate $= \dfrac{\text{Total overheads}}{\text{Direct labour hours}}$

(e) machine hour rate $= \dfrac{\text{Total overheads}}{\text{Machine hours (operated)}}$

(f) rate per unit produced $= \dfrac{\text{Total overheads}}{\text{Units produced}}$

15. Absorption costing is a principle by which fixed as well as variable costs are allocated or apportioned to cost units (via cost centres). Factory overheads are usually apportioned on a suitable basis and the non-manufacturing overheads recovered in a blanket fashion (possibly against the total factory costs).

16. *Historical costing* is a factual recording of costs after the event. Used in conjunction with *standard costing* (in which method of costing and costs are predetermined), variances can be noted and investigated.

17. The setting of standard costs involves standards for every element of cost.

18. It is unlikely, whatever method of overhead recovery is applied, that overheads will be recovered *exactly*. Some under-recovery or over-recovery is virtually certain. Significant under-recovery could entail corrective action being taken.

19. *Job costing* (used by firms engaged in job production) involves ascertaining a job's prime costs and applying a 'blanket'-type overhead element.

   Process costing (used by firms engaged in process production) uses absorption methods for overhead recovery; in fact all costs are apportioned to the *processes*, and thence to the product batches going through the processes. Unit costs are obtained by dividing batch costs by the number produced. Product costs can be analysed on an ABC or Pareto basis, to reveal that a few components are responsible for the greater proportion of the total cost ('80–20' relationship).

20. Break-even analysis is a technique for showing on one diagram costs, sales and profits (or losses), and the relationship between them.

21. A break-even chart is constructed as shown in Figures 13.3 to 13.5. The point where the sales revenue line first crosses the total cost line is the break-even point (BEP). The BEP can be calculated mathematically using the formula:

$$\text{BEP} = \dfrac{\text{TFC}}{\text{TFC} + \text{NP}} \times \text{S}$$

where: BEP = Break-even point
           TFC = Total fixed costs
           NP = Net profit
           S   = Sales

22. A similar chart can be drawn to show a product's *contribution* as well as profit (see Figure 13.6).

Questions

Review questions

13.1 What is meant by the 'cost accounting' function? Explain the objectives and tasks of the cost accounts department.
13.2 What are the advantages of costing? Are there any disadvantages?
13.3 What are the basic elements of cost? What is meant by classifying costs under *function*; or under *cost units*?
13.4 Distinguish between fixed and variable costs.
13.5 Define what is meant by blanket (or full) costing, listing the steps involved.
13.6 What six methods of apportioning overheads are discussed in this chapter? Indicate in each case the appropriate formula.
13.7 Define what is meant by absorption costing. Describe this method of building up a product's total cost.
13.8 Distinguish between historical and standard costing, and explain how together they can form part of the control function.
13.9 Describe the effects of both under-recovery and over-recovery of overheads.
13.10 Distinguish between job and process costing and state to which type of production each is appropriate.
13.11 Explain (using a diagram) the process of constructing a break-even chart. What information is gained from studying a complete chart?
13.12 Differentiate between a conventional break-even chart and one showing a product's contribution.

Discussion topics

13.13 Discuss the view that, provided a firm makes a steady profit each year, having a specialist costing department is a time-consuming, expensive and unnecessary extra, serving only to add to overheads.
13.14 Either in groups or as a class, consider the most appropriate way of completing the following tasks:
      (a) finding the total cost of a simple, but handmade, silver bracelet;
      (b) establishing the point at which making a particular product, A, becomes profitable;
      (c) calculating the profit made on each unit made and sold of product A;
      (d) calculating the total cost of a very small item (e.g. one pin) made in large quantities.

Assignments

13.15   You are given the following information about Leviathan Ltd for April:

Materials used in production	£12 000
Direct labour	£20 000
Machine hours	16 000
Direct labour hours	8 000
Overheads	£32 000
Units made	16 000

Assuming all the units relate to *one* product, either in groups or individually:
   (a)   Calculate the six overhead recovery rates relating to the product, based on these figures.
   (b)   Using the information obtained above, calculate the total cost (using all six methods) of Job no. 789, which is a special variant of the product.

	Job no. 789
Direct material cost	£28
Direct labour cost	£40
Units made	2

13.16   Easifitt Jeans Ltd makes and sells in a given period 5000 jackets at £40 each and 2500 pairs of jeans at £20 each. Other information is as follows:

Unit costs	*Jackets*	*Jeans*
Direct labour	£9	£2.00
Direct materials	£20	£7.50
Overheads (total)	£70 000	

(Overhead recovery basis is a percentage of direct wages.)

Calculate:
   (a)   net profit for the period;
   (b)   the total unit costs of both a jacket and a pair of jeans.

13.17   Omega Ltd produced last year 400 000 units of a product, omicron, which sells at £3 each. The direct material costs are 85p per unit and the direct wages and expenses totalled 95p per unit. The total fixed costs applicable to omicron last year were £200 000.
   (a)   Determine the BEP in terms of sales revenue taken and quantity sold by graphical methods.
   (b)   Calculate by using a formula the same BEP and compare the results. Which method is the more accurate? Which method is the more useful?
   (c)   This year, sales are expected to be the same, and all other figures to remain constant *except* direct materials, which are expected to rise by 20p per unit. By any method calculate the expected BEP this year.

14

Budgetary Control: The Purpose, Preparation and Use of Budgets

Starting with a reference back to the notion of control by budgeting introduced in Chapter 1, this chapter also mentions the earlier discussions on budget preparation in Chapter 7, and relevant material in Chapter 13. The purpose and role of organisational budgetary control are then examined.

Budget preparation is next considered, with an emphasis on sales and production budgets (and their interrelationship). The ways in which budgets can be used to assist the control of the organisation's activities and resources are then discussed. Finally, both the benefits and drawbacks of the adoption by an organisation of budgetary control are reviewed.

14.1 Control by budgeting

In Chapter 1 it was seen that controlling is an essential aspect of managing an enterprise. To control we must first have targets, standards or objectives to go by, and then measure performance against these targets, standards or objectives. (Although in this chapter the prime concern is the control of *money*, similar considerations apply to the control of production, design, quality control, etc.)

Thus to control (by budgeting) we need:

(a) to set objectives (in terms, for example, of income or expenditure);
(b) to devise methods of measuring of income and expenditure;
(c) to measure actual income and expenditure and compare them with the target income and expenditure;
(d) to identify differences (variances) or deviations from the predetermined standards, and seek reasons for the variances;
(e) to take appropriate corrective action where variances are significant.

This chapter covers each of these steps in budgetary control.

14.2 Definitions

It will be useful at this stage to consider definitions of both budgets and budgetary control.

Budget

A budget is part of an organisation's overall plan for the future. As such it is a statement (approved in advance), set out in financial or quantitative terms, of what is planned or expected to happen during a forthcoming precisely identified period of time. A *financial budget*, more specifically, is a set of forecasts of costs and revenues, based in part on data taken from historical and standard costs.

(From this definition we note that a budget is *not* the total plan, but just part of it. 'Approved in advance' entails top management involvement and acceptance of the finished budget. Budgets are always for a 'precisely identified period of time', often one year, sometimes one quarter, sometimes one month.)

Budgetary control

Budgetary control is the process of striving to ensure that the responsibilities and tasks carried out by individual managers relate to the plans, policies or objectives laid down by an organisation. This process is essentially one of continuous monitoring, comparison and appraisal of actual results against those originally budgeted. The intended outcome is either the fulfilment of the plans, policies or objectives, or the provision of a basis for their revision.

(The first part of this definition is interesting, as it points to the control of the work of management as well as to, say, the control of expenditure. The second sentence describes the control function, particularly the identification of variances. The final part indicates that budgets need not be totally inflexible: the *standards* could change if experience shows that they are unrealistic.)

14.3 The purpose and objectives of budgetary control

The purpose and objectives of budgetary control follow quite naturally on what has been considered so far. They are:

1. To provide detailed and systematic plans of action (i.e. budgets) for all parts of an organisation, covering a definite period of time.
2. To co-ordinate and integrate the activities of each part of an organisation so that they all work together towards common objectives.
3. To provide a proper system of control. The preparation of a budget is the drawing up of a blueprint for control. By using a budget as a set of standards against which

to compare results, departures from the standards (variances) can be detected. Explanations for these variances can then be sought, and those responsible identified.

4. To provide information on the basis of which management can take corrective action: to eliminate the variances, for example.

14.4 Budget preparation

The preparatory stage has two main aspects: the administrative arrangements and the procedures involved.

Budget administration

It is no use introducing budgetary control if it is not administered properly. In the medium/large company budget preparation is supervised by a *budget committee*. Figure 14.1 shows how a budget committee might be organised in a company similar to that considered in Chapter 1. (This committee is often called a steering committee.)

The smaller company will probably nominate an executive (accountant or company secretary) as a budget officer, reporting to the managing director.

The chief executive is in charge of the whole budgetary control process in the example, though routine meetings are normally held by the budget controller. Each committee member is, in Figure 14.1, responsible for preparing forecasts for the departments for which he or she is responsible. The committee then review, as a body, the forecasts submitted.

Preparing and running a budget

The budget controller would usually proceed as follows:

1. Divide up the work of preparing the budgets for individual departments, sections or cost centres among budget committee members.
2. Prepare a budget calendar with target dates for completion of forecasts and a final date for the completion of all the work.
3. Advise all involved in budget production, and ensure that all the budgets submitted are co-ordinated (see below).
4. Prepare the master budget in conjunction with the accountant (if the accountant is not also the controller), for the committee's final approval before being reviewed by the board of directors.
5. Hold regular review meetings thoughout the budget period.

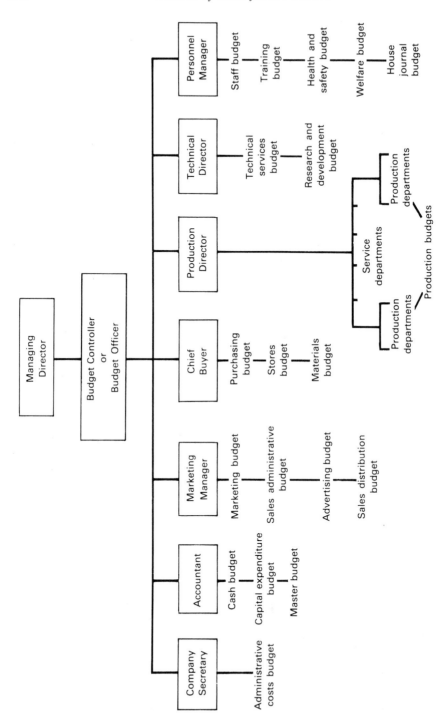

Figure 14.1 *Example of budget steering committee, and members' budget responsibilities.*

The individual budgets

Budgets are prepared for the major *functions* of the firm (production, sales/ marketing, personnel, etc.), for *departments* of functions as required (cost centres such as the press shop or the assembly department), or, in a few cases, for *assets* (the capital expenditure budget, for example — spending on new plant, etc.).

Thus a company could end up with a sales budget, a production budget, and budgets for factory overheads, administration overheads, distribution costs, research and development, purchasing, personnel etc, rather as indicated in Figure 14.1. Every organisation will choose its own particular list, but all will include a cash and capital expenditure budget and a final, overall master budget.

Attention in this chapter is concentrated specifically on sales and production budgets as being more relevant to the control of manufacture than, for example, administration budgets, but it must be stressed that the same amount of care and attention to detail should be applied to all budgets.

(Before proceeding further, students are recommended to re-read Chapter 7.)

The sales budget

This budget is usually prepared by the marketing manager or, in his or her absence, the sales manager.

It will be recalled that the sales budget is calculated from information from a wide variety of sources. The more important are:

(a) records of past sales;
(b) existing orders, still incomplete at the start of the budget period;
(c) marketing and market research;
(d) advertising plans;
(e) forecasts from sales representatives, sales staff and agents;
(f) economic predictions (for both the national economy and the particular industry);
(g) forecast technological changes, likely changes in demand through changes in taste or fashion;
(h) effect of competition;
(i) government intentions (known or predicted), particularly in respect of legislation.

All the factual or historical data will need careful evaluation: even more attention will need to be given to the more speculative forecasts or predictions. Particular care will be needed on sales forecasts for new products: not only could sales not come up to expectations, but unforeseen production difficulties or product failures in the field could limit sales.

Analysis by product type.   All the forecasts and firm information will eventually have to be converted to estimated sales figures, broken down by product type. An audio-cassette manufacturer making four qualities of cassette, for example, will need estimated sales figures for *each quality*; it will also be necessary to break the information down further into *recording times* for each quality (C60, C90, C120, etc.). (Not only does breaking down the figures in this way help pricing, but such detail also enables the production budget to be prepared more easily.)

As a further refinement, *monthly* demand can also be analysed to show fluctuations in sales expected at different times of the year.

Pricing the forecasts.   Selling prices can now be calculated or fixed for each product and its variants. Special care is needed where prices are not constant in all areas, or where special quantity discount prices are given. From this information, a total figure of predicted revenue (or income) can be arrived at.

It is clear that in order to make a profit, budgeted expenditure should be less than the total revenue expected.

The production budget

This budget is normally prepared from information provided by managers and supervisors controlling cost centres. The basis of the production budget is, of course, the expected sales volumes of the various products, plus the following further considerations.

(a)   the levels of stocks of the different finished goods agreed as reasonable at the end of the budget period;

(b)   the phasing (from month to month) of production to utilise plant and equipment at optimum capacity;

(c)   maintenance programmes for machinery or processes;

(d)   holidays;

(e)   availability of labour of appropriate grades;

(f)   overtime working policy;

(g)   forecasted factory overhead figures for budget period;

(h)   pending wage awards for production workers;

(i)   raw material price fluctuations expected.

The production budget in its final form will run in parallel with the sales budget, as it will be analysed into product types with unit production figures based on the sales forecasts. Often the production budget shows for each product the direct material and labour costs, plus that amount of factory overheads apportioned to the product.

Production sub-budgets.   After the basic production budget has been agreed, sub-budgets for individual departments, processes or cost centres are prepared in consultation with the managers or supervisors of those departments, processes or cost centres. Managers will thus receive targets to be reached either in cost terms or in terms of output (sometimes both). A whole network of interrelated budgets can be produced: control can be exercised over virtually all activities in the firm.

Example.   Bill Tappit is number 1 machine shop supervisor in the 21st Century Manufacturing Co. Ltd, who are at present preparing budgets for the forthcoming year. Bill has been involved generally in budget and target setting for the factory, and particularly in all aspects of his department's work targets.

Marketing staff advise that forecasts of sales for products coming through Bill's shop are 10 per cent down on current figures. From this information and from data from method study and work measurement, staffing levels can be established (somewhat down on current levels). Production advise on machine utilisation. Current wage negotiations are almost complete: direct labour costs can now be calculated. Material costs have been carefully extracted and forward orders placed at agreed prices. Use is made of standard costing where possible.

Account is taken of seasonal demands. Marketing levels, for example, are calculated to cover minimum demand periods plus an 'absenteeism factor'. Overtime working will take care of 'surges' expected in April, May and June.

Monthly budgets are prepared for Bill's department for production rates in units, for appropriate staffing levels, direct labour hours and costs, and for direct materials. Overheads are apportioned from service cost centres. Bill now has a set of targets to meet for the whole year.

14.5 The master budget

The budget controller (sometimes the accountant) collates all the information contained in subsidiary budgets. This collated information is now set out in the *master budget*, which will set out in summary form the overall budget picture. More specifically the master budget sets out clearly the profit (or loss) expected during the budget period.

The master budget is normally approved at board level.

Example

The case of Iota Manufacturing Ltd illustrates the budget-making process in a small firm, and the resultant master budget. Iota decide in late summer to start preparing a budget for the following calendar year, starting 1 January next. The firm bases the budget partly on the known figures for the twelve months up to June, and partly on various marketing, economic and related estimates and forecasts. Iota has three products, A, B and C. The figures to June are:

Item	A	B	C	Totals
Sales (units)	20 000	20 000	50 000	90 000
Revenue (£)	60 000	40 000	200 000	300 000
Costs (£)				
Direct labour	25 000	20 000	80 000	125 000
Direct materials	15 000	8 000	20 000	43 000
Factory overhead at 25 per cent of PC	10 000	7 000	25 000	42 000
	50 000	35 000	125 000	210 000

Gross profit (£)	10 000	5 000	75 000	90 000
Less non-manufacturing overheads				40 000
			Net profit	£50 000

The budget committee conclude that: sales of product A will decline by 10 per cent, even if the price remains unchanged; sales of B will remain steady; and those of product C, after an advertising campaign, will increase by 20 per cent. No price increase is recommended for product A, but the selling prices of products B and C are to be increased from 1 January by 5 per cent.

During the budget year, inflation is estimated to be steady at the rate of 4 per cent per annum. A wage agreement guarantees workers the expected inflation rate +1 per cent, the figure being reviewed each January. Material prices are expected to rise by only 2.5 per cent. Factory overheads are calculated at £48 016 and the non-manufacturing overheads are forecasted to increase by 12.5 per cent from the latest figure. (This is due mostly to a planned increase in research and development on a new product to replace product A in the future.) Prepare next year's budget.

Answer

Note 1. Sales volume forecast:

$$A - 10\% \quad = 18\ 000$$
$$B \text{ same} \quad = 20\ 000$$
$$C + 20\% \quad = 60\ 000$$

Note 2. Revenue forecast:

$$A = 18\ 000 \times £3 \quad = £54\ 000$$
$$B = 20\ 000 \times £2 + 5\% = £42\ 000$$
$$C = 60\ 000 \times £4 + 5\% = £252\ 000$$

Note 3. Costs forecasts:

Direct labour:

$$A = 18\ 000 \times £1.25 + 5\% = £23\ 625$$
$$B = 20\ 000 \times £1.00 + 5\% = £21\ 000$$
$$C = 60\ 000 \times £1.60 + 5\% = £100\ 800$$

Direct material:

$$A = 18\ 000 \times £0.75 + 2\tfrac{1}{2}\% = £13\ 838$$
$$B = 20\ 000 \times £0.40 + 2\tfrac{1}{2}\% = £8\ 200$$
$$C = 60\ 000 \times £0.40 + 2\tfrac{1}{2}\% = £24\ 600$$

Factory overheads:

At £48 016 these appear to be based on 25 per cent of prime costs. Thus these can be allocated to A at £9 366, to B at £7 300 and to C at £31 350.

(These calculations represent the financial implications of the information given. The figures are now used to prepare the new budget.)

Iota Manufacturing Co. Ltd
Budget for Year Ending 31 Dec. 19--

Item	A	B	C	Totals
Sales (units)	18 000	20 000	60 000	98 000
Revenue (£)	54 000	42 000	252 000	348 000
Costs (£)				
Direct labour	23 625	21 000	100 800	145 425
Direct materials	13 838	8 200	24 600	46 638
Factory overhead at 25 per cent of PC	9 366	7 300	31 350	48 016
	46 829	36 500	156 750	240 079
Gross profit (£)	7 171	5 500	95 250	107 921
Less non-manufacturing overheads				45 000
Net profit				£62 921

14.6 The principal limiting factors

Now the basic principles of budget-making have been established, at this stage it is necessary to point out that certain *constraints* (limiting factors) can affect the preparation of an enterprise's budgets. Such constraints are variously called:

(a) the principal limiting factor(s);
(b) the principal budget factor(s);
(c) key factor(s);
(d) governing factor(s).

Whatever term a firm chooses to use, essentially what is being identified is that factor or those factors which can limit the activities of an enterprise.
 The limiting factor(s) could be one (or more) of the following:

1. A limited demand for the firm's products. (Causes, for example, could range from adverse economic conditions or competition to a poor sales effort.)
2. A shortage of production facilities or machine capacity. This could be either a long-term or short-term problem.)
3. A shortage of appropriate labour. (Even in times of economic depression it can be difficult to recruit certain categories of skilled labour.)
4. A shortage of working capital. (Adverse trading conditions could result in less money being available to buy new equipment or adequate material stocks, or to take on more labour.)

There may be ways round these limiting factors: a sales drive for new markets, overtime or shift work, the subcontracting of work, or 'buying out' components. It can be clearly seen, however, in the realities of the business world, that certain desirable objectives a company would like to achieve may in fact be unattainable.

14.7 Controlling through budgets

The considerable work (and expense) invested in budget preparation will bring little return if the budgets so produced are ignored or not properly made use of. Thus some control system is required to ensure that all those responsible for activities incurring expense work to the budgets prepared.

A typical method of budgetary control starts with the analysis of the year's figures into budget periods, which could be calendar months or an often used variant, the 'four-weekly cycle' entailing a thirteen-month year; or a weekly budget period could be chosen. As each budget period passes the performance of each department/cost centre or budget area is measured. The performance data so obtained are listed against the budgeted figures. Such a report is a budget review statement.

Table 1.4, the Winnit Assembly Department, is an example of a cost-centre budget review statement. What is clear in this set of figures is that performance has been different from that expected. There are variances.

Variance analysis

Every variance of significance (adverse *or* favourable) should be investigated and its cause traced. As far as production budgets are concerned, the causes of adverse variances usually boil down to:

(a)   inefficiency of some kind;
(b)   operation of a principal limiting factor;
(c)   fall in demand;
(d)   unplanned and unforeseen events — a strike, a power failure, etc.

Material variances can stem from poor purchasing policies, the purchase of material of a higher quality than required or excessive scrap in production. *Direct wages* variances can be caused by unbudgeted overtime, re-working or taking on extra labour. *Factory overhead* variances can result from excessive materials handling, machine breakdowns and repair charges.

Action by management

The comparison of actual performance against that budgeted indicates variances: variances indicate areas for management action. Excess overtime working, for example, could turn out after investigation to be due to inefficient job methods or poorly maintained plant or equipment. Management will need to attend to these shortcomings, and ensure that such variances are eliminated as far as possible.

14.8 Fixed and flexible budgets

Budgets can be classified further into two distinct categories; fixed and flexible.

Fixed budgets

A fixed budget is the kind of budget so far considered in this book: a single target or plan to be followed. It is designed to remain unchanged whatever the level of sales or output turns out to be. No difficulties are experienced in using a fixed budget if sales (and corresponding outputs) are, in the event, on target. Cost variances can easily be spotted and investigated.

However, a moment's thought reveals that a considerable problem could arise if production increases during a budget period — say by 20 per cent — to meet an unexpected demand. Virtually every figure on the budget will go 'over budget': material costs, wages, even some overheads. It is no good telling the buyer to cease purchasing materials because he or she is over budget. In fact, it will be difficult (from the information available) to make any real comment on how well or how badly each cost centre has performed. The remedy for such a situation is to adopt flexible budgeting.

Flexible budgets

In essence flexible budgeting entails a series of budgets being prepared to cater for different levels of activity. Whilst Company A might set a sales target of £1 million turnover for next year, it will not merely work out a budget on this assumption. A flexible-budget approach would mean that complete budgets are calculated for, say, £600 000, £800 000, £1 million, £1.2 million, £1.4 million of sales.

Actual results can always be compared with the nearest calculated budget. Alternatively the budget can be updated (or re-calculated) each month to the (exact) level of activity achieved.

A useful extra tool of flexible budgeting is, of course, the break-even chart, in which levels of cost, revenue and profit/loss can be quickly read off for different outputs or sales.

Example. The following is an extract from Mammoth Engineering's customer after-sales service department flexible budget for June last (21 working days).

Repair hours	1400	1500	1600	1700	1800
Costs	£	£	£	£	£
Direct wages	2800	3000	3200	3400	3600
Indirect wages	336	336	336	336	336
Supervision	700	700	700	700	700
Spares supplied	280	300	320	340	360
Power	80	100	120	140	160
Heat and light	100	100	100	100	100
	4296	4536	4776	5016	5256

(Note which costs are fixed and which vary with output in some way.)
The recorded activity and expenditure for June were:

Repair Hours	1600
Costs	£
Direct wages	3300
Indirect wages	340
Supervision	700
Spares supplied	400
Power	105
Heat and light	97

The actual figures can be compared with the central budget. Direct wages are up (overtime ?); spares seem to have cost more (has price increased recently?); power is down (cost-saving drive results ?). Figures such as heat and light 3 per cent adrift are not significant and could normally be ignored.

Management by exception

The cost of employing managers and supervisors is high: their time is therefore valuable. Any control such as budgetary control which can throw up those *significant* areas where management attention is necessary is of considerable importance. The use of scarce management time can be concentrated on areas of significant variances. This desirable state of affairs is called 'management by exception'.

14.9 Budgetary control: final considerations

In conclusion, some of the benefits and drawbacks of budgetary control can be noted.

Benefits of budgetary control

Among the many benefits of budgetary control, the following are important:

1. *Involvement.* Managers and supervisors in all departments are brought into forward planning. They are of necessity brought to work more closely with each other, and learn to appreciate others' problems.
2. *Clarification.* The preparation of budgets involves the clarification of the role and responsibilities of each manager and supervisor, and the departments they control.
3. *Commitment.* Following on the above, because staff are involved in target and budget setting, they become more committed to achieving those targets. Motivation increases.
4. *Delegation.* Budgetary control involves controlled delegation. Delegation, as seen in Chapter 2, helps to improve decision-making skills.
5. *Cost consciousness.* As the operation of budgetary control becomes better known to the workforce, and guidelines on expenditure become understood at all levels, the level of cost consciousness increases.
6. *Early warning.* The regular review meetings of the budget committee provide all budget operators with early warning of variances. Problems highlighted can be dealt with promptly.

Drawbacks found in budgetary control

Not all control systems are perfect, nor do they work as originally planned. Examples of failings that can occur are:

1. *Invalid assumptions.* All budgets are based on assumptions or acts of faith about the future. The best forecast can be in error: the future remarkably different from the predictions made of it. Actual results may be well wide of the mark. Inflation can make even flexible budgets difficult to operate.
2. *Overcautious target setting.* Managers and supervisors will tend to play safe and argue for minimum targets for production, efficiency, etc. so that these targets can be achieved without any special effort.
3. *Spending to the limit.* Setting ceilings for expenditure — particularly in non-productive departments — may actually encourage budget-holders to 'spend what is left' at the end of the budget period.
4. *Neglect of favourable variances.* Favourable variances are, at review meetings, all too often 'passed on the nod' without much comment. It is just as important to establish *reasons* for such variances as it is to establish reasons for unfavourable variances. On the one hand, favourable variances can reveal savings and/or improved methods useful elsewhere; on the other, seemingly favourable variances could be symptoms of shortcomings in other departments.
5. *Excessive paperwork.* The whole budgetary control operation can, if its administration is not also tightly controlled, become a vast and costly paper exercise. Managers often complain that too large a percentage of their work time is spent in collecting and collating information, preparing it and passing it on, and attending endless meetings to discuss reams of figures.

Summary

1. Controlling is an essential aspect of managing an enterprise. To control by budgetary methods there is a need:
   (a) to set objectives in financial terms;
   (b) to devise methods of measuring performance;
   (c) to measure that performance;
   (d) to identify variances;
   (e) to take corrective action where variances are significant.
2. A budget is part of an organisation's overall plan for the future: a set of forecasts and revenues.
3. Budgetary control is that process of striving to ensure that what is done by individual managers relates to the plans, policies and objectives of the organisation. This process is one of monitoring, comparison and appraisal of actual results against the plan.
4. The objectives of budgetary control are:
   (a) to provide budgets for all parts of an organisation, covering a definite period of time;
   (b) to co-ordinate and integrate the activities of an organisation's sub-systems;
   (c) to provide a proper system of control, including the identification of variances;
   (d) to provide sufficient information to management, on which information decisions can be taken.
5. Budgetary control requires a proper administrative framework. In the larger firm a budget (steering) committee is formed, serviced by a *budget controller.*
6. The smaller firm usually appoints an executive as budget officer, reporting to the managing director.
7. The budget committee (or budget officer) reviews the forecasts submitted.
8. In preparing budgets, the budget controller parcels out the work of departmental or cost-centre budgets to the appropriate managers. He or she prepares a budget calendar, co-ordinates the information submitted and (in conjunction with the accountant) prepares the master budget.
9. Individual budgets are prepared for the major functions in the firm: for departments and cost centres, and for assets such as plant and equipment.
10. The sales budget (prepared by the marketing or sales manager) is a projection of the expected sales during the budget period. It is based on factual information (orders on the books, etc.) and informed forecasts (market and marketing research, economic predictions, etc.).
11. Analysis of the figures into product types, qualities, colours, etc. will be necessary. (Not only may prices be different for the separate types, but production will require this information for preparing their budgets.)
12. Further analysis into separate monthly figures caters for seasonal fluctuations in demand.
13. The forecasts are priced, allowing for differential pricing. A total sales revenue figure is then calculated. Every effort is needed to keep total expenditure below this figure.

14. The production budget is based on the sales volume forecasts plus consideration of expected end-of-year stock levels, best use of plant and equipment, maintenance programmes, availability of labour, holidays, etc.

15. Each cost centre or department will have its own budgets: those connected with production will in effect be production sub-budgets. The result is a network of interrelated budgets though which control can be exercised.

16. The information from all budgets is collated into the master budget (approved at board level).

17. There are *constraints* in budget-making — variously called the principal limiting (budget) factors or key/governing factors. Examples are limited consumer demand and shortages of production facilities, labour or capital.

18. Budgetary control, properly administered, involves:
    (a) splitting the budget year into monthly/weekly budgets;
    (b) identifying the variances;
    (c) investigating the reasons for/causes of variances;
    (d) management taking appropriate action to eliminate (as far as possible) such variances.

19. *Fixed budgets* are those containing a single set of target figures which remain unchanged during the year. In contrast, *flexible budgets* are either constructed to have a series of pre-calculated budgets for varying levels of sales/production or constructed so they can be revised in line with actual production.

20. Management time is valuable. If it can be concentrated on problems of real significance (for example large variances from budget), it is being used more effectively than if managers' time is spent checking situations which are generally satisfactory.

    The process of examining only significant variances is called 'management by exception'.

21. Budgetary control brings the benefits of staff involvement, clarification of people's roles and responsibilities and a greater degree of commitment on the part of managers; it also aids delegation. Increased cost consciousness is promoted. Early warning is given of adverse trends.

22. On the other hand, all budgets are at best informed guesses, based on assumptions. Forecasters can be over-cautious in target setting; budget-holders can spend what is allocated, whether or not it is totally desirable that they should; unfavourable variances receive all the attention when favourable ones should be investigated equally. In common with all control systems, a bureaucracy of paperwork can surround budgetary control.

Questions

Review questions

14.1   What are the basic elements of a control system? How similar is *budgetary control* to control systems in general?

14.2   Describe the objectives of budgetary control.

14.3   How might the budgetary control process be managed and administered in the larger firm?

14.4   What are the role and duties of the budget controller?

14.5   How is the sales budget prepared? Why is this budget so important in preparing the company's overall budgetary plans?

14.6   What is meant by saying that there are *constraints* in budget-making? Give examples of limiting factors.

14.7   Distinguish between fixed and flexible budgets.

14.8   What is meant by management by exception? How does this method of managing apply to budgetary control?

14.9   Explain the advantages and disadvantages of budgetary control.

Discussion topics

14.10   How useful is budgeting and budgetary control in everyday life? Discuss what could happen to those people who do not bother:
    (a)   to forecast their future income and expenditure;
    (b)   to check their current wages and what they spend their money on.

14.11   'To introduce a system of budgetary control to a company will do nothing for it, except to increase the paperwork, employ more clerks filling in the forms, and provide plenty of meetings to keep managers occupied.' Is this true?

14.12   Assume you are the budget committee of a local printers, considering the possibility of issuing a pocket guide of your locality, plus street map of the town centre. Discuss:
    (a)   how you would go about estimating the possible total annual sales (you understand the council will buy 500), the selling price being 50p each;
    (b)   what would happen to potential sales if (due to sudden increases in cost) the selling price became £1 each;
    (c)   what effect there would be on the company's plans if your committee learned that there were only sufficient suitable supplies of paper in stock to print 1200 guides, and delivery of more supplies would be at least six months.

Assignments

14.13   Day release or apprenticed students should research the budgetary control systems used by their organisations. (It is recommended that the training department be approached first.) Then each student should (for his or her organisation):
    (a)   list the various budgets that are prepared;
    (b)   choose any one budget (preferably related to production), interview the budget-holder, and discuss the problems faced in preparing and keeping to budgets;
    (c)   write a short report on his or her findings.

14.14   Full-time students or those unable to make use of their organisations should carry out similar research within the college, by arrangement with the registrar.

14.15   In groups, students are to assume that they are sub-committee members of the students' union, looking into the feasibility of making much-needed money for student funds. The proposal is to make and sell to local householders varnished wooden house name or number plaques. (The numbers and letters are to be branded on with hot tools, the work carried out in college workshops, each worker to receive a nominal 5p per job done.)
    Discuss how the job might be organised, and then consider the *budgets* needed. Particularly consider:

(a) the information needed to prepare the sales revenue budget;
(b) how details and costs of appropriate materials and tools could be obtained;
(c) what overheads — both production and administrative — there would be, assuming a contribution was made to college expenses for light and heat used, proper invoices and receipts were sent to customers, and proper records kept throughout.

Each sub-committee member should report back to the class.

Case study

14.16 Just before the year's trading commenced, Supervac Ltd produced the following budget:

Item	Icekooler	Vacstein	Totals
Unit sales	20 000	10 000	30 000
	£	£	£
Unit selling price	7.00	4.90	
Sales revenue	140 000.00	49 000.00	189 000
Prime costs	60 000.00	24 000.00	84 000
Factory overheads			28 000
Total gross profit			77 000
Deduct administrative overheads			20 000
Estimated net profit			57 000

After the year's trading has ended, the directors of Supervac decided to ascertain what the actual figures were in order to compare them with the budget. (They had rather a surprise!) The accountant produced the following:

Item	Icekooler	Vacstein	Totals
Unit sales	15 000	20 000	35 000
	£	£	£
Sales revenue	105 000	98 000	203 000
Prime costs	52 500	56 000	108 500
Factory overheads			40 000
Total gross profit			54 500
Deduct administrative overheads			25 000
Actual net profit			29 500

(a) What difference do you note between the budget and the actual results?
(b) How do you account, particularly, for the drop in net profit?
(c) Why do you think the directors were surprised? Could Supervac's budgeting system be improved?

15
Material and Stock Control

Material and stock control is a large and complex subject and this is reflected in the scope and length of the chapter. It begins with an examination of the total material control system (which comprises much more than stock control) and its role in the organisation. Attention is then given to the relationships between purchasing, stores and production, followed by an examination of the purchasing department, and the documentation of the order and receipt of materials.

Next the work of stores, and stock control is considered in detail. Ordering systems and re-ordering procedures (including ordering in *economic* quantities, contrasted with materials requirements planning) are then covered. The costs and financial implications of material and stock control are reviewed. Finally, stocktaking and stock valuation methods are described.

15.1 Material control

Reference was made in Chapter 4 to the elements of cost. Included in these elements are the *direct* costs of materials, as well as *indirect* costs of materials, particularly those consumed in production. In every manufacturing organisation the costs of these two types of materials are considerable: in some this is the greatest single item of expense.

The management of materials is thus one of the most important tasks in an organisation, though regrettably too few organisations devote sufficient attention to it, except in emergencies such as a significant upturn or downturn of sales, or adverse economic conditions.

The desire to hold stocks of goods and materials is based on a deep-rooted, primitive fear of shortage, of 'being without'. However, too often the methods used to determine and maintain stock levels are based on instinct rather than reason. Even in prosperous times, and when firms are doing well, there is a strong case for proper and strict control to be kept on both the supply and the storage of materials. When economic conditions are hard, without proper controls orders can be lost, production held up and vital finance tied up in stocks and therefore not available for investment — perhaps resulting in the failure of the business.

250

The materials control system

The materials control system is centred on the functions of stores and stock control, as illustrated in Figure 15.1.
  Materials control consists basically of the following functions:

(a) stock control/storage;
(b) scheduling of requirements;
(c) purchasing;
(d) receipt and issue of goods;
(e) recording all material movements.

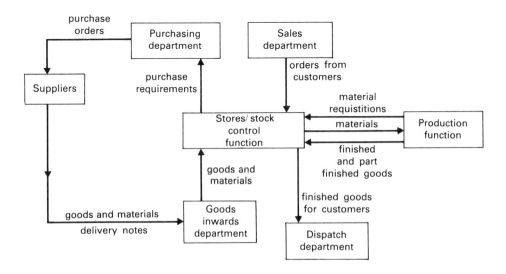

Figure 15.1 *Materials control system.*

For such a control system to work effectively the following conditions need to be present in an organisation:

(a) the co-ordination of all the separate departments involved (inter-departmental rivalries lead to a breakdown in control);
(b) all purchasing carried out by the organisation to be under the total control of the chief purchasing officer;
(c) the existence of clearly established directions on the purchase of materials, in accordance with a properly calculated materials budget, and based on demand;
(d) the introduction and use of a clear, logical and easily understood system of classification (or coding) of materials, stock and goods held in the organisation;
(e) the introduction and use of a simple and standard system of paperwork, for both internal requisitions and external purchase orders;

(f)   the provision of appropriate areas and facilities for the storage and handling of
       all the kinds of materials and goods stored; particular emphasis should be given
       to safety aspects, the avoidance of stock deterioration, and security against theft
       or damage;
(g)   the introduction and maintenance of a proper internal checking/auditing system
       for all stocks, for all movements of stocks, and for the purchasing and stock
       records;
(h)   the preparation and submission to senior management of regular and accurate
       reports on slow-moving, obsolete or deteriorating stock (decisions can then be
       taken about sale or other disposal).

Classification of materials

The term 'materials' is a very general one, covering a wide variety of goods or supplies
found in stores, storerooms, stockyards, warehouses or even within factory production areas. Most of these materials are intended for use in production but, as can be
seen in Figure 15.2, some are used in service departments and some are in fact finished
goods awaiting dispatch to customers, or scrap pending collection.
   The major classifications are as follows.

Raw materials.   These are the primary inputs to the production system, the basic
materials which are converted in the course of manufacture into the finished goods
sold by the organisation. Metals such as gold, copper, tin, lead, iron and steel, and
products such as rubber, cotton, wool, coal, wheat, PVC and leather, can all be
classed as raw materials.
   It is a mistake to assume, however, that the materials concerned must be in a
relatively simple form before use to be called raw materials. An engineering firm may
purchase as raw material supplies of a specialist grade of steel which has undergone a
series of tempering processes, and a busy furniture manufacturer could purchase
seasoned planking already cut to suitable lengths. Thus someone's finished goods
become someone else's raw materials.

Free issue material.   This term covers materials (often raw materials) or components
sent to manufacturers without charge by their customers; these materials are to be
incorporated within the finished product. At all times these materials remain the
property of the customers, who will of course not expect to be billed for such materials
when they are eventually charged for the work carried out.
   It goes without saying that particular care needs to be taken to keep the use of free
issue materials under the strictest control.

Bought-out items.   These are completely or partly finished parts, components,
assemblies or sub-assemblies purchased from outside suppliers. Such items are later
incorporated into the manufacturer's finished products, though a certain percentage
will be retained in the stores (particularly if such items are complete) as spares.

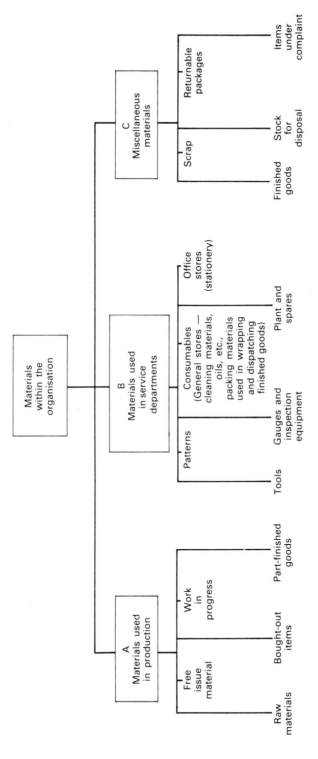

Figure 15.2 *Classification of materials. Note: Materials under A are direct materials. Materials under B are indirect materials.*

Bought-out items are usually of a specialist nature, or are used where demand is uneven or low, or the items are made by a supplier selling in bulk to a large number of customers at a price so competitive that the manufacturers cannot match it. Other reasons for outside purchase may be lack of expertise, suitable trained labour or plant to make the items concerned. (Reference has already been made to the 'make or buy' question in value analysis.)

Work in progress.   As the term implies, work in progress covers items in the course of being manufactured, but not yet finally completed. Parts awaiting machining or painting, items awaiting assembly, and even finished goods awaiting final inspection are all work in progress.

Work in progress is not normally to be found in stock or storerooms, but on or around benches on the shop floor, or piled up in corners, or temporarily accommodated in boxes, pallets or skips. Process production, as we have seen, entails a high degree of work in progress, with buffer stocks (see below) of various components or assemblies at strategic points against emergencies. Such stock is of course costly to hold: it has the disadvantage of having had the cost of labour (both direct and indirect) added to its original cost, but is not yet in a readily saleable condition.

Part-finished goods.   These are a special category of work in progress. The term 'part-finished' applies particularly to goods held in stock pending some further work. Such goods are in the basic form awaiting a final operation or series of operations which can differ between batches or even between individual items. These variations or versions of a product can be, for example, in the size, number and position of fixing holes to be drilled, the final colour or finish (red or blue, highly polished or dull finish), or perhaps the wording to be stamped or engraved on the product.

Keeping items in the pre-finished form allows flexibility in production and cuts down on the need to hold a stock of every finished version. Such items are often held in specially designated stores or storage areas. In practice they are often (incorrectly) regarded more as 'stock' than as work in progress.

Tools.   This is a wide classification encompassing, for example, large portable electric drills, tools used on machinery (such as collets, reamers and dies) and hammers, pliers, crowbars and the like. Many standard tools are purchased from outside suppliers (for example spanners or wrenches), though special tooling is often made in the factory toolroom.

Security of tools is often a problem. Many tools are light and portable, with uses outside a factory. Thus a tool control system will be required. Many organisations set up 'tool stores' in different areas of the factory, in which tools not in current use are stored. Issues and receipts are carefully recorded.

Patterns.   These are models, designs or plans from which items are made or figures from which moulds can be prepared. These need to be stored carefully.

Gauges and inspection equipment. Used mainly by inspection staff, such equipment is for the measurement of critical dimensions of materials, components and other parts, Micrometers, verniers, height gauges and thread gauges, as well as other first-principle measuring equipment, are examples. In production areas, gauges are normally the fixed, go/not go type.

Precise recording of the location of each item is important, not only from the security angle, but because regular checks on the accuracy of each piece of equipment are necessary.

Consumables (general stores). This term covers a multitude of items which are used either in the general running of the factory — cleaning rags, mops, detergents and so on — and those items 'used up' in the manufacturing process, but which are often difficult to allocate to the production of any particular product — oils and greases (used on machinery), coolants, nuts and bolts, small screws, glass paper and washers.

Plant and spares. The plant, machinery and equipment used in production are part of the total material stock, even if kept in fixed locations within the factory or used outside, as in the case of delivery vehicles. Spares for such plant are usually kept in a separate part of the stores area.

Office stores. This term covers office stationery — letters, envelopes, forms etc. — as well as office equipment.

Finished goods. These are the end products of production, items which have gone through all the stages of manufacture and are in a state where they can be dispatched to a customer.

Scrap. By 'scrap' is meant a wide variety of 'leftovers' from the production processes — swarf, broken parts or components, contaminated materials, woodshavings, obsolete machinery for disposal. As raw material prices rise, scrap metal does have value and is often worth selling on to dealers. Some used oils can be recycled.

Stock for disposal. This is a similar category to scrap, but this term applies to stocks of finished goods or plant/equipment spares which are surplus to requirements due to model changes or modifications and which it is hoped to dispose of, perhaps in a sale or auction.

Returnable packages. Although many goods are supplied in one-trip, non-returnable packing, some specialist goods can be supplied in purpose-made packages, chests or other containers. As refunds are made when such packages are returned, it makes sense to record this category of goods separately. Butane gas cylinders are a typical example.

Items under complaint/repair.   Customers may return items for repair at the factory, or complain about their appearance or performance. It is usual to segregate these items in a special part of the stores area, awaiting their inspection by works staff.

Note. This list does not claim to be exhaustive. Some companies may have stores for packing materials, or separate areas for paints or corrosive, flammable or radioactive materials.

Other definitions

A wide variety of terms are used in material control, some of which overlap. The more important are the following.

Stock (or stocks, or stock in trade).   Stock *can* be used as a synonym for materials, but in manufacturing industries is normally associated with raw materials, part-finished components and assemblies, work in progress and finished goods.

It is also used to mean the actual quantity of goods in store at a particular time: a common question is 'What is the stock of Product X?', meaning 'How many are there on the shelf?'.

Free stock (or stocks).   This is stock which is earmarked to meet normal customer demands.

Buffer stock (or safety stock or stocks).   This is stock which is held over and above normal expected demand, and which is there to meet emergencies or sudden surges in demand, or failures to obtain replacement stocks.

Stores.   This word has two distinct meanings which should not be confused. First, it can mean *the building(s)* or area(s) in which materials are kept, commonly called 'the stores', or possibly just *sub-areas* such as the 'raw materials stores' or 'finished goods stores'. Second, the term 'stores' is sometimes used to refer to the *goods stored*, and is almost equivalent to 'stock'.

Inventory.   Commonly used in the USA to mean all the materials owned by an organisation, in the UK it is more often restricted to a *part* of the total material stock, or a particular list of stock. Thus we can speak of the 'motor vehicle inventory' or of 'taking an inventory of the toolroom', that is, checking all the stock in the toolroom.

Managers or executives who are made responsible for parts of the organisation's material stocks are often called inventory holders.

15.2 The objectives of material control

The objectives of a material control system are:

(a)   to control the amounts of money spent on the purchase and maintenance of stock; to keep stock levels at the lowest possible level and yet meet the other objectives;
(b)   to keep an adequate supply of stock to the required standard available for production at all times,
(c)   to keep all stages of the manufacturing process fully operational (for example, with buffer stocks) and (if necessary) working at a steady rate;
(d)   to allow the maximum amount of flexibility in production and to permit manufacture to proceed when deemed convenient to do so;
(e)   to safeguard stock against loss, theft and avoidable deterioration;
(f)   to provide a quick service to customers, especially when finished goods are required at short notice;
(g)   to account for the movement of all materials;
(h)   to be in a position to price all material in stock.

Problems can arise if one or more objectives are pursued while others are neglected.

15.3 The purchasing function

As will be gathered from the objectives above, the purchasing function will play its part in fulfilling them by obtaining all the materials necessary for production in the right quality and quantity, at the most appropriate times, at the lowest possible costs. In Chapter 2 is found a brief introduction to the organisation and duties of the purchasing function. The ideas introduced there are now examined in more detail.

The chief buyer and the buying staff

The position of the head of the purchasing function — variously titled chief buyer, head buyer, purchasing officer or chief purchasing officer — is an important one in any organisation. His or her responsibilities include correctly identifying material needs, identifying suitable sources of supply, negotiating a price reasonable in the circumstances, and ensuring that the required materials arrive on time.

The chief buyer's terms of reference can vary, depending upon whether, for example, stores and stock control come under his or her jurisdiction, but there are two major attributes that this executive should possess:

(a)   the ability to co-ordinate the whole department;
(b)   expert knowledge of the materials purchased, particularly of the *raw materials*, and personal contact with suppliers.

To make the best use of the chief buyer's expertise, and that of the staff, purchasing can be divided between the various senior members of the department. In a department in which different buyers purchase raw materials, miscellaneous items and the subcontract work, each buyer needs to be aware of alternative sources of supply, current prices and discounts, delivery times and conditions of sale.

Further, each buyer, for each different type of material, will have to decide whether:

(a) to buy *on contract*, that is, to place a bulk or 'blanket' order with one supplier, at a constant price, to be delivered to a carefully arranged schedule over a fairly long period of time — six months, a year, or even longer; the benefits are stable prices, a constant supply assured, and administrative costs as well as stock-holdings kept to a minimum;

(b) to buy *as needed*, that is, to place separate orders to meet existing or known needs as opposed to forecast ones, with no long-term commitment given to any particular supplier; such a policy is most suitable for coping with requirements for special items or occasional small orders; the benefit is small (or even nil) stock-holdings, but small orders are relatively costly to administer, and cost per unit purchased is also higher than for larger quantities;

(c) to buy *'on spec.'* or make an opportunist purchase, that is, to take a calculated risk and purchase materials or items for which there is no immediate use in mind, or for which the requirement is well ahead in the future — a useful policy if the purchase is a 'bargain' (goods sold below normal price, or a line known to be in short supply, or where price rises are imminent); examples of this type of buying would be of metals such as gold, silver, copper or tin, the prices of which can rise rapidly overnight, or basic food processing materials such as coffee beans.

Unless specific policy directives exist, considerable freedom is given to each buyer as to the choice of supplier.

Purchasing documentation

Only in the case of speculative purchases will a buyer initiate the purchase process. Usually a buyer acts as an agent, that is, purchases materials *on behalf* of others in the organisation. Thus the buyer is both link and funnel, through which all purchase requests will flow, as seen in Figure 15.3.

Purchase requisitions (see Figure 15.4) are raised in service departments (e.g. maintenance, inspection), in the stores, and in production departments. In some cases (where, for example, stores normally hold stocks of such requirements) the requisitions go to the stores in the first instance, but in the majority of cases the purchase requisition will become the formal request to the buyer to purchase, and therefore the originator must clearly describe the goods, the quality and quantity required, and possibly the supplier. After confirming the authenticity of the requisition (that is, checking that it has been signed or approved by a senior person in the originating department), the buyer will place the order. (Service department heads should be limited as to the sterling value of an order — say £200 without approval from a higher level.)

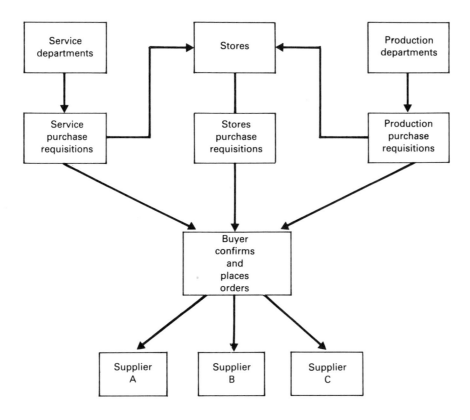

Figure 15.3 *Materials purchase: information flow.*

The buyer then places an *official order* or *purchase order* (see Figure 15.5) with a supplier. The choice could be based on price, but quality, delivery or general supplier reliability could be important considerations. Again, it is useful to have more than one supplier for particular materials. In case of strikes, shut-downs or delivery problems at one supplier's works, another can quickly be substituted, even if a slightly higher price has to be paid. Naturally, appropriate records of all orders sent will be kept, and often copies are forwarded to originators.

Receipt of materials

Goods and other materials are normally delivered to the *goods inwards department*, a department ideally sited close both to adequate yard space for turning delivery vehicles and to the stores area. Again ideally, all incoming materials should be checked against their purchase orders for quality and quantity, and of course for damage.

Stores Purchase Requisition		No.: 12345 Date:	
Please supply to stores:			
Item code	Quantity	Description	Charge
Special Instructions			
Delivery required by: Deliver to:			
Signed: .... Approved:		Purchase Order .... Date ...... Supplier .... Requested delivery date	

Figure 15.4 *Stores requisition.*

Makegood Ltd
High Street
Notown

Order No: 67890

Date: ....

To: ....

Your Ref: ....

Our Ref: ....

....

Please supply the following in accordance with Conditions set out overleaf:

Quantity	Description	Code No.	Price

Delivery required: ....

Deliver to: ....

....

....

NOTE: No orders will be recognised by the Company except those made out on our official Purchase Order forms and properly signed.

p.p. Makegood Ltd
Buyer

Figure 15.5 *Purchase order.*

Makegood Ltd
Goods Received Note

GRN 005342
Details:
Date Rec'd ....

Supplier ....

Purchase Order ....

How delivered: BR
Their transport
Our transport
Carrier

Supplies Advice
Note No. ....

Details:

Quantity	Description	Code No.	Remarks

Goods checked by ....

Goods received by ....

Good accepted into
stores by ....

Tick here if goods accepted

Uninspected ☐

Figure 15.6 *Goods received note.*

Figure 15.6 illustrates the goods received note, a document completed once goods have been checked and/or accepted. Copies are sent to the purchasing department, the originators and accounts; the actual note goes with the goods (usually to stores).

15.4 The control of stock

Stock control (or inventory control as it is known in the USA) has two major objectives:

(a) to use the money set aside for stock purchase in the most efficient way possible;
(b) to control and safeguard existing stocks.

The first objective is attained only by avoiding both over-stocking and under-stocking. *Over-stocking* uses more capital than is strictly necessary and causes problems in finding space for storage. However, stock shortages and interruptions of production will be rare. Conversely, *under-stocking* can lead to much more frequent stock-outs (that is, being out of stock). Stock-outs cause delays while fresh stocks are obtained, and these delays could entail idle plant, workers being laid off, or sales lost. However, the capital tied up in stock would be very much reduced.

It is obvious that a balance between the two extremes must be struck to establish ideal stock levels: in practice this is very difficult to achieve. No system of stock control is perfect.

15.5 Stock control systems

Irrespective of the stock control system adopted and the statistical or other methods used to establish ideal stock-holdings and re-ordering times, four significant factors must be taken into consideration:

1. *Immediate needs of production.* Production will want priority given to the availability at all times of materials in constant use during the production process: these will vary from raw materials to consumable items such as lubricating oils and coolants. Liquid and solid fuel used to provide energy to drive machinery or for heating purposes would also have this priority.
2. *Lead times.* This term is commonly used in industry to mean that time taken by suppliers to deliver materials or goods, after receipt of official purchase orders. (Sometimes lead times are called delivery times or procurement times.) While many items arrive quite quickly after being ordered, others (such as materials of unusual specification, those in short supply, or those which are difficult or inconvenient to make) can take weeks or even months to obtain. Care has to be taken to take lead times (and possible sudden changes in them) into account when working out a suitable stock control system.
3. *Capital availability.* Money spent on materials and stock has to come out of the organisation's total budget for expenditure. Normally there would be a cash limit on what can be spent on stock.
4. *Costs of stock-holding.* This point is considered in detail later. Suffice to mention here that the annual costs of stock-holding could exceed 20 per cent of its actual value.

There are three basic systems of stock control:

(a) the *two-bin* system;
(b) the *periodic review and order* system;
(c) various combinations of the first two.

The two-bin system

A tried and tested method of stock control is the two-bin or double-container system for holding stock. Figure 15.7 shows two bins, A and B, which hold the same item, say hexagonal nuts of a particular thread.

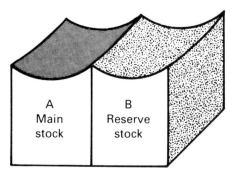

Figure 15.7 *The two-bin system.*

The first bin (A) is used to hold the majority of the stock of the items in question: all issues are made from it until bin A becomes empty. A new order for nuts is now placed, and until the fresh stocks arrive further requirements are issued from bin B. This second bin thus acts as a reserve supply or buffer stock.

When replenishment stock arrives, bin B is refilled to its previous level, the balance of stock being placed in bin A. The level of stock in bin B is calculated from past experience of demand expected in the period during which fresh stocks are awaited, plus an extra 'cushion' element against a sudden demand increase or unexpected delay in the arrival of new stock.

Such a system, when originally introduced, could easily be operated by unskilled labour, but it will be seen that no detailed records of usage would be available. Without physical counting, stock levels would be unknown. However, as the influence of F.W. Taylor's scientific management[1] approach increased, more sophistication emerged. Stock could be kept in just one bin, the reserve stock being segregated in some way. The hexagonal nuts, for example, could be held in a separate bag to which a re-order label was attached, and the label could be forwarded to the purchasing department (as a stores requisition) as soon as the bag was opened.

Bin cards. A further development to improve the system was the introduction of bin cards or stock control cards. In their simplest form, bin cards carry relevant information about the material stocked — the part numbers, descriptions, etc. — and a statement of material movements, that is, receipts and issues. Stock balances are also recorded. Such cards are kept either in the bin itself or close at hand.

More detailed cards are also kept in a central stores (while duplicating the bin card record, much more useful information is available). Figure 15.8 illustrates such a document: a stock record card (sometimes called a perpetual inventory record). It shows voucher/ticket references for issues and receipts, the amounts of stock on order, and whether some stock is already set aside, 'spoken for' or allocated to a particular job. Cost details are also included.

---

[1] For an introduction to Taylor's ideas see Evans D. (1981) *Supervisory Management*, pp. 73–78. Eastbourne: Holt, Rinehart and Winston.

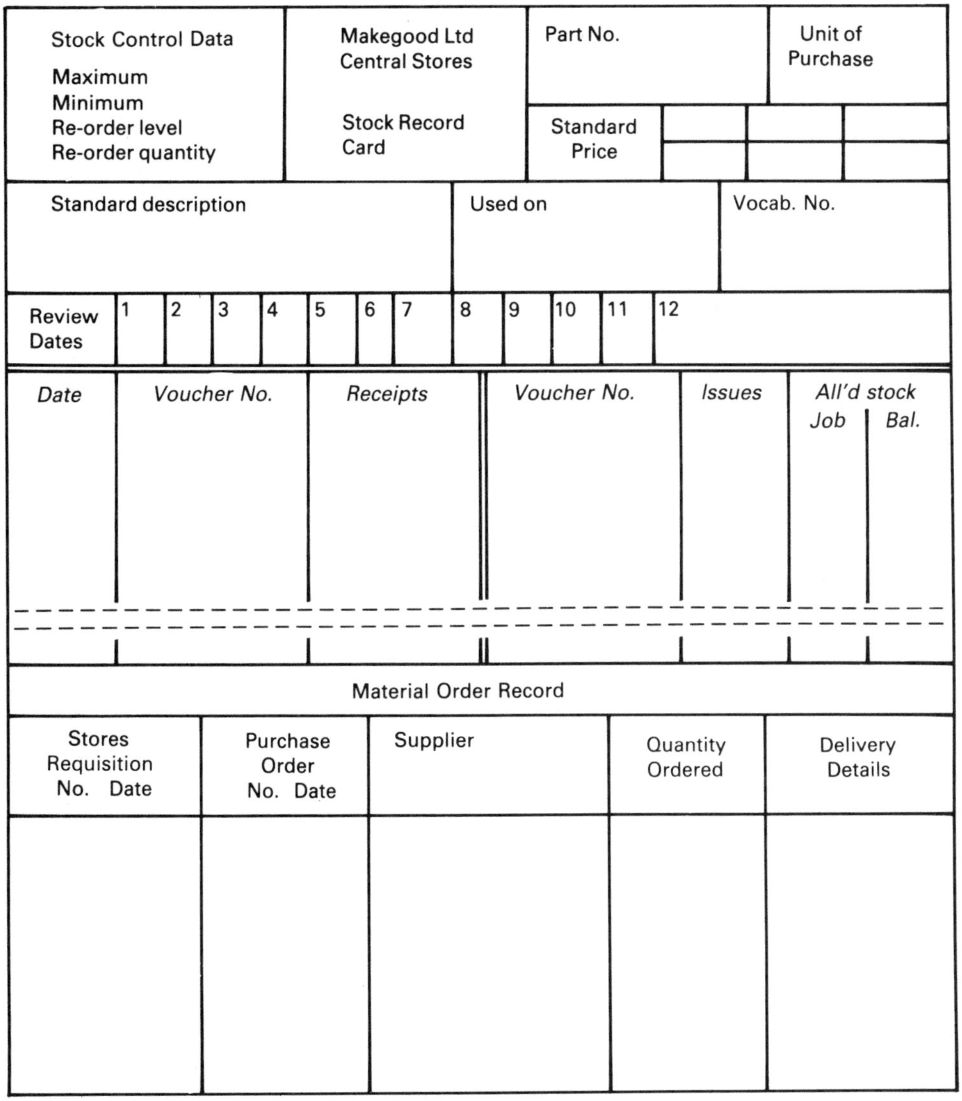

Stock Control Data Maximum Minimum Re-order level Re-order quantity	Makegood Ltd Central Stores Stock Record Card	Part No. Standard Price		Unit of Purchase		

Standard description	Used on	Vocab. No.

Review Dates	1	2	3	4	5	6	7	8	9	10	11	12	

Date	Voucher No.	Receipts	Voucher No.	Issues	All'd stock
					Job | Bal.

Material Order Record				
Stores Requisition No. Date	Purchase Order No. Date	Supplier	Quantity Ordered	Delivery Details

Figure 15.8 *Stock control card.*

Multiple stores. A variation of the two-bin system is also found where an organisation has a series of stores in different locations, each holding a similar range of items. For any given stores, X, in the system, the stock there of any given item, Y, will be in effect bin A. The reserve stock, or bin B, will be the stock of item Y in other locations. Thus if stores X becomes out of stock of item Y, while awaiting fresh stock from the supplier, stores X can call upon the most conveniently located stores in the system to provide stores X with an emergency stock. Where the firm runs a regular inter-stores delivery service for normal deliveries of materials and components, the stock for a particular stores can be brought from another location in the system at little extra cost.

Ideally this multiple-store, two-bin system should operate in conjunction with a central data bank of computerised records easily accessible by all stores locations. Real savings can be made, however, in the cost of stock-holdings; reserve stocks are not required at any location, except perhaps at the main (or central) stores.

The periodic review and order system

Another widely used system is the review and order method of stock control. As its name implies, the first principle underlying the method is a firm policy decision from management that *all* stock levels should be reviewed at regular intervals — daily, weekly, monthly, quarterly, etc. — as appropriate.

The review is accompanied by a re-order of stock, and this second principle is very similar to the well-known imprest system in accounting. In cases where an executive travels widely for the firm he or she can be given a float of, say, £200 towards incidental expenses. Periodically the executive produces evidence of how the money has been spent and receives a further sum to bring the float back to £200. In the periodic review and order system the control card for each line is scrutinised and the amount of stock used since the previous review is calculated. A requisition is then forwarded to the purchasing department to bring the stock level back to its previous predetermined level (which will be the maximum stock). Obviously, the more stock used in a given period, the greater the replenishment order.

This system ensures that replenishment orders are *automatically* placed, as the review takes place at a particular time, say the first working day in each calendar month. (There is quite a contrast here with the two-bin system, where replenishment-of-stock orders may arrive at any time on any day, and a conscious effort must be made to order.)

In practice, rather than talk in terms of ordering up to a *specific quantity* level, efforts are made to estimate *the daily or weekly usage*. Orders are then placed on the basis of thirty days' usage (in the case of monthly reviews). This enables the order amounts (and the maximum stock level) to be increased or decreased if the daily amount used changes.

Maximum stocks will then be thirty days' usage, plus a reserve to cover abnormal demands and delays in the arrival of fresh stocks. However, it must be said that this system can result in a frenzy of orders at each review period, putting a strain on the purchasing department, and increasing overheads — each order could cost £10 to administer. A possible way of overcoming this problem is to review some lines more often than others: those used less often are reviewed at longer intervals, and those in high demand are reviewed more frequently. Even so, under a periodic review system, order quantities are likely to be relatively small and, as will be seen later, uneconomic.

Comparison of the two systems

Figure 15.9 illustrates the effect on stock levels of a product of varying usage of using the two-bin system. At zero time, stock is at *W* (or maximum level). As soon as stock

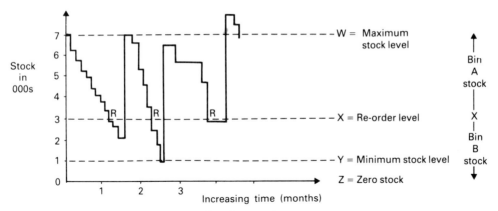

Figure 15.9 *Two-bin re-ordering system in use.*

falls to X (re-order level), or 3000 units, a new order is placed for 4000 (for replenishment of bin A), plus 1000 (an estimate of replenishment required for bin B.)

The estimate is on target and two weeks later stock returns to level W. In the following cycle, however, heavy demand eats deeply into reserve stock and the 5000 order does not bring stock levels back to W. In the third cycle, demand slackens off during the re-order period and the maximum stock level is in fact exceeded.

Figure 15.10 illustrates the effect on stock levels of a similar product to the one mentioned above, of using the period review and ordering system. The major differences are that stock levels tend to remain higher, re-ordering is more frequent, and the quantities ordered are smaller and not constant.

Combinations of two-bin and periodic review systems

Various combinations of the two systems exist. One version is periodic reviews but re-ordering only if stock falls below a specified level. This could involve a particular

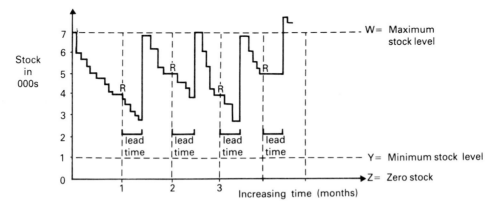

Figure 15.10 *Periodic review re-ordering system in use.*

product being checked fortnightly, but ordered on average only once every two months.

Another variation is basically a periodic review system, but a double standard operates in that while each week, month etc. a review and re-order is made, if in the interval between reviews stock level falls below the re-order level, a further order is placed immediately.

15.6 The ABC of material and stock control

A very curious phenomenon found in life generally, and in industry in particular, is what is often called an '80–20' relationship.[2] Typical examples of this relationship could be in the area of sales: 80 per cent of a sales staff's time is taken up with dealing with only 20 per cent of the orders received, or 20 per cent of a firm's products could account for 80 per cent of its total sales. Designers who use models to help them create new products or evaluate possibilities speak of 80 per cent of the value of such a model being derived from 20 per cent of its characteristics. Cost accountants often report that, for their organisation, the bulk of manufacturing cost is incurred by a relatively few products.

So it is with material and stock control. While the numerical values do not fall into a strictly 80–20 basis, they are close enough to say that a relatively small proportion of the total lines in a firm's stock accounts for the greater portion of the stock-holding costs.

Example[3]

Worried by problems besetting its stores, Acme Engineering Ltd called in a firm of consultants, Genius and Co., who first analysed the stock-holdings and obtained the results shown in Table 15.1.

Table 15.1 *Division of stock-holdings, Acme Engineering Ltd.*

Class	Items	Percentage of items	Stock value £	Percentage of stock value
A	103	10.3	802 000	80.2
B	309	30.9	141 000	14.1
C	588	58.8	57 000	5.7
	1000	100.0	1 000 000	100.0

[2] Those students who would like to examine this phenomenon more deeply are recommended to read any standard book on statistics under the heading of 'pareto analysis'.

[3] Often this exercise is carried out on annual *sales* rather than *average stocks*, but in the interests of simplicity this exercise is not carried out here.

Genius and Co. recommended that the three categories identified should be dealt with as follows.

A items. Keep a careful control on these items: order in the most economic quantities, bearing in mind that frequent small orders will keep stocks low.

B items. Re-order on the two-bin system.

C items. Re-order on the periodic review system but, because of the relatively low cost of these items, both maximum and buffer stocks can be relatively high, thus saving the costs of repeated orders.

This breakdown into three categories — A, B and C — is a conventional one. In some firms it would be more useful to have just two categories, A and C; and in others (where the company is large and stocks vast), four.

15.7 The costs of material and stock control

It costs money to hold stock. Many factors contribute to these costs, but the following are the most important:

1. *Purchasing costs.* These are the price paid for stock.
2. *Cost of capital.* The money used in stock purchase could have been used in other ways, possibly lent out at interest. If the stock is bought with *borrowed* money, then there will be loan charges payable.
3. *Warehouse and storage costs.* These are the costs of rent, rates, heat, light, mechanical handling equipment, wages and salaries, losses due to theft, deterioration or obsolescence of stock.
4. *Insurances.* Such charges are based on the value of stock, and basically cover losses due to fire and theft.
5. *Administrative ordering costs.* These are the costs incurred in paperwork, clerks' time in the purchasing department, etc. They could be £10 or more per order.
6. *Price fluctuations.* A fall in the price of raw materials could lead to a dramatic fall in stock values, loss of capital, and uncompetitive production costs.
7. *Stock-outs.* These are very difficult to calculate in money, but lead to production problems at best, and at worst could involve a complete factory standstill.

All these considerations, plus those previously considered in this chapter, lead to the inevitable conclusion that purchasing and stock controlling is as much an art as a science.

Economic order quantities

Attempts have been made, however, to find a scientific approach to material and stock ordering: searches have been made for a 'magic' formula which would reveal for any product the optimum order quantity, and which would balance all the factors. One way in which the most economic order quantity (EOQ) — sometimes called the economic lot size (ELS) — can be calculated is by means of a graph such as that shown in Figure 15.11.

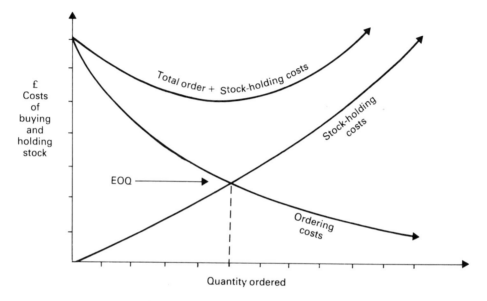

Figure 15.11 *Stock ordering and holding costs.*

The point at which the ordering costs and the holding costs intersect is the point of overall minimum cost. It also indicates the economic ordering quantity. Even using computers it would be a difficult job to keep updating information on each line, so various formulae have been developed to apply to different products in appropriate circumstances.

A typical version of these formulae[4] is:

$$\text{EOQ} = \sqrt{\frac{2C_1 Ur}{C_2}}$$

---

[4] Each version assumes different situations and this basic formula assumes that cost of purchase/ manufacture is constant, demand is known and steady, etc. Students interested in looking into this subject more deeply are referred to Wild, R. (1984) *Production and Operations Management* pp. 518–29. Eastbourne: Holt, Rinehart and Winston; and Reinfeld, N.W. (1982) *Production and Inventory Control*, pp. 159–73. Virginia: Reston Publishers.

where EOQ = economic order quantity
C_1 = ordering/set-up costs
Ur = usage rate per period (usually one year)
C_2 = holding cost per item per period

Example. Given that the usage rate of product X in a period of one year is 10 000 items, the ordering cost per batch ordered is £20, and it is estimated that it costs 10p per year to store each item, calculate the economic order quantity.

Answer

$$\text{EOQ} = \sqrt{\frac{2 \times 20 \times 10\,000}{0.10}} = \sqrt{4\,000\,000}$$

$$= 2000$$

As 10 000 are required during the year, this calls for five orders at about ten-week intervals throughout the year.

Great care is needed when using EOQ formulae to recognise the assumptions made in them, and to apply the chosen formula with common sense, considering other factors. Examples of such other factors are:

1. *Minimum order quantities.* Particularly with some small items, suppliers (or the factory) may wish to supply only in specified minimum lots, for example 1000 lots for washers.
2. *Quantity discounts.* The formula above assumes constant prices. However, many suppliers offer quantity discounts: the greater the quantity ordered, the lower the price. Such price reductions usually come in 'steps'. Consider the example of a product offered at various prices as follows: 0 – 499, £1.00 each; 500 – 999, £0.97 each; 1000 – 4999, £0.90 each; 5000 – 9999, £0.85 each. It can quickly be seen it will be cheaper to order 5000 than 4800 (assuming the EOQ formula gives a re-order quantity of 4800).
3. *Possible outdating of product.* It would be unwise to order large quantities of materials or components (as laid down by EOQ formulae) for lines it is proposed to phase out.

15.8 Stock classification and coding systems

In the nineteenth century, components, assemblies and finished products were often identified by simple descriptions: terms such as 'outside sandwich frames', 'driving axle bearings', 'Belpaire boilers' and 'gauge glass' would have been familiar to Victorian railway workers. Such simple descriptions were not enough for stores purposes: much longer descriptions became necessary — 'chairs, principal officers, for the use of'. However, even this tells us nothing about the dimensions or quality of the article.

Even for railways the need to classify more specifically became apparent when it came to engines and rolling stock. Similar locomotives were classed numerically or with a class name (Sir David class, 517 class) and each locomotive was given an individual number. Wheel classifications soon appeared: 0-6-0, 2-2-2, etc. While such classifications were not always logical, they were a more useful and precise classification system than names alone.

The enormous proliferation of products, components and assemblies in a wide variety of materials, and the overriding need to account precisely in both volume and financial terms for stocks and work in progress, resulted in more scientific stock coding systems. The arrival of the computer (stock-control records were one of the first uses to which computers were put) made accurate and ordered coding systems essential.

Stock codes

Most stock codes are based on combinations of letters and figures, though some can be figures alone. For example, a water seal on a pump could carry a code (or stores vocabulary) number such as 91/16/1303, where 91 represents the product of the firm's Midland factory, 16 reflects the fact that the water seal is the sixteenth sub-assembly listed for the pump in question, and 1303 is the number allocated to that particular verision of the pump. (The latter number is not to be confused with the individual serial number of the pump, which will be found on the pump's casing.) Where letters are used with numbers, the letters are found first (e.g. BF/16/1303, where BF = Birmingham factory). Students interested in coding systems are recommended to visit a local firm's stores to see the particular method used, and the reasons for it.

The advantages of stock classification/coding systems

However devised, stock classification systems avoid non-specific descriptions such as 'driving axle bearings'; apply to *all* parts, components and sub-assemblies, as well as complete products; greatly assist in keeping stock records; provide an easy reference for purchasing (if bought out), and could be used (by adding appropriate letters/ numbers in a prefix) to indicate the exact location of the items in the stores.

There is one more major advantage: assisting in standardisation. By grouping together all the varieties of, for example, pump parts manufactured by the firm under a major classification code, the range can be considered as a whole. Variety reduction/greater standardisation can be achieved by perhaps reducing the range, or retaining only those parts for which demand is significant.

Where parts of components are obtained from outside suppliers, it is possible, before a strict coding system is applied, for virtually the same article to be stocked under different descriptions in different parts of the same stores. A properly devised coding system would throw up anomalies of this kind.

15.9 Materials requirements planning

Materials requirements planning (MRP) systems originated in the 1960s. Such systems attempt to marry together all the aspects of organisational planning — purchasing, material/store control and production — and are related to CPM (control path method).

Basically[5] such systems recognise EOQ systems are inappropriate where production is *exactly* tied to demand. If a customer places an order for a special item (say in a quantity of 2500), which involves several special sub-assemblies, X, Y and Z, it does not make sense to order a sub-assembly or component either from the factory or from an outside supplier in any quantity other than 2500 or slightly above.

As far as the demand for parts X, Y and Z are concerned, such demand is described as *derived demand*, that is, the demand for the sub-assembly is derived from the production/customer demand. Items with a derived demand are called dependent items. EOQ formulae are not suitable for dependent items.

The MRP system needs a correct and precise parts list for each product, an accurate forward production planning forecast for at least two to four months, and a highly accurate and up-to-date stock control record system. (A computerised system is really essential here.) A master schedule is produced for the total product week by week, and component schedules are prepared for the derived-demand items.

15.10 Stocktaking

Each year limited companies are obliged (by law) to produce an annual balance sheet and accounts. (Public companies are also required to give half-year results, and directors may need monthly figures.) Stock represents cash, and as such forms part of the balance sheet. To achieve an accurate stock value in cash terms, a system of stocktaking must be arranged.

Any stocktaking system must be able to:

(a)   verify the accuracy of the stock record cards;
(b)   provide all the information necessary for an accurate money value of stocks;
(c)   reveal discrepancies due to fraud, theft, loss or poor record keeping.

Periodic stocktaking

This method involves checking *the whole* of the stock at the end of a given period, especially at the year end. A great deal of preparation is necessary. As work in progress is checked too, a complete freeze on all activity in the firm may be ordered.

---

[5] Students wishing to research these techniques in more detail are referred to Orlicky, J. (1975) *Materials Requirements Planning*. New York: McGraw-Hill.

One day's (or even two days') production lost while the staff are engaged in counting and recording can be very expensive, as well as disruptive. This method is therefore not to be recommended.

Continuous stocktaking

This method (sometimes called the perpetual inventory system), in complete contrast, involves keeping stock record and bin cards up to date at all times. A small staff of 'audit clerks' check the records of each material and stock line at regular intervals against the actual physical stock. Ideally each line is checked at least twice a year. High-value items and items vulnerable to deterioration or theft can be checked as often as required. (Assuming 10 000 lines in stock, a twice-yearly check, and 250 working days in a year, 80 lines per day will need to be checked.)

The advantages of this second method are clear: no frantic twice-yearly rush, just a steady, methodical analysis; the work of the organisation can proceed without interruption; and defects in methods or unexplained losses are brought to light more quickly.

The Inland Revenue, by arrangement, allow the figures on the stock cards to be taken on the year-end date as accurate. If the figures are on a computer, a complete print-out can be obtained very quickly.

Slow-moving and obsolete stocks

Decisions are taken on stocks revealed at the check which are slow-moving or now unusable or obsolete. Often such items are sold off as scrap.

15.11 Stock valuation

Stock valuation is in itself a complex and somewhat contentious subject. On the face of it a stock value is obtained for each line by multiplying the number (or tonnes, etc.) of items in stock by the unit price. However, the problem is to agree on a basis for calculating the unit price, which will be needed:

(a)   for valuation of the complete stock at stocktaking times;
(b)   for valuation of individual issues of material and stock to production, for costing purposes.

The main methods are used as follows.

Lot pricing

Stock is valued at the price originally paid for it. This method is useful where specific items of material or stock can be identified both when purchased and subsequently when in stock. It is complicated to work, but suitable for one-off, small-batch production.

First in, first out (FIFO)

Stock is valued on the assumption that material *first* put into stock will be the first to be issued, whether or not this is so in practice. A record is kept of the price paid for each delivery, or costs of each batch taken into stores. Issues to production are calculated on material in stock: total stock valuation involves different prices being allocated to parts of the same stock.

Last in, first out (LIFO)

Stock is valued on the assumption that material *last* put into stock will be the first to be issued. Thus issues to production will be priced at prices near to current values: in times of inflation this is useful, as costs can be updated regularly. Total stock valuation involves, as with FIFO, using several prices to value the stock of a particular line.

Replacement value

Stock issues are valued at the price which would have to be paid if a new order had been received on the date of issue, that is, the current market price. This method is useful in times of high inflation for pricing issues to production, but it is difficult to check every current price for every line when carrying out a total stock valuation.

Weighted average prices

For issues of stock to production, this method involves calculating the average price of the stock each time new stock is received. The average price is 'weighted' in that both the quantity purchased and the prices paid are considered: a small quantity at a high price and a large quantity at a low price will end up close to the low price. The calculation of the total stock value is simple, once the average is known. The major disadvantage is a price recalculation for each receipt of material.

Standard prices

As part of a standard costing system a predetermined price per unit of stock is agreed for a complete period (e.g. one year). Such a unit price is an estimate of future trends, as well as past performance, and will take inflation into account. Both issues pricing and total stock valuation are comparatively simple to operate on a standard basis.

Note. If stock becomes obsolete, or prices fall, market value (i.e. resale value of stock) could override any of the above methods.

15.12 Final comments

Students will have noted that material and stock control is a complex operation, not all of it governed by hard and fast rules. The optimum material and stock control system is a mixture of skill and statistical methods, with room for flair and intuition in the purchase of raw materials, the use of EOQ systems for independent and standard components, and an MRP-type system for products with a number of differing, dependent and non-standard components.

Summary

1. The costs of materials held and other stocks represent a large expense to all manufacturing organisations. Thus material and stock control is a vital task, and one to be carried out as efficiently as possible.
2. Materials control covers stock control/storage, the scheduling of requirements, purchasing, receipt and issue of goods, and the recording of all material movements.
3. For materials control to work effectively these separate activities need to be co-ordinated, with well organised directives and paperwork routines, the provision of appropriate storage facilities, and the presence of a proper checking and audit system.
4. Materials can be classified into:
    (a) *raw materials* — the primary inputs to the organisation, the basic materials to be used in the production process;
    (b) *free issue material* — raw materials or components supplied by customers free of charge to be used in making up their orders;
    (c) *bought-out items* — items partly or wholly manufactured outside the organisation, and purchased to be incorporated in the completed product, or held as spares;
    (d) *work in progress* — items in the course of being manufactured;
    (e) *part-finished goods* — partly manufactured items held in stock pending being finished off to customers' instructions;
    (f) *tools* — tools used both in the production process and in service departments;
    (g) *patterns*;
    (h) *gauges and inspection equipment:*
    (i) *consumables* — items used in the general running of the production areas, or used up or consumed in the production process;
    (j) *plant and spares* — the plant and machinery used in production;
    (k) *office stores*;
    (l) *finished goods* — the end products of production;
    (m) *scrap* — items, material for disposal;
    (n) *returnable packages*;
    (o) *items under complaint or repair.*

5. Terms used in materials control overlap. 'Stock' (or stocks) can be used for 'materials', but is normally restricted to raw materials, part-finished components and assemblies, work in progress and finished goods. It can also indicate the quantity of goods held.

6. Buffer stocks are stocks of a line held over and above the known and expected demand to meet emergencies.

7. Stores can mean the building(s) where materials are kept or the goods stored, i.e. another word for stock.

8. The term 'inventory' in the USA is equivalent to materials; in the UK it is more often restricted to a part of the total stock.

9. The objectives of a material control system include:
   (a) control over the amount of money spent on stock;
   (b) retention of adequate stocks for production;
   (c) keeping the production process in operation;
   (d) allowing production maximum flexibility;
   (e) safeguarding stocks against loss or deterioration;
   (f) provision of a quick service to customers;
   (g) accounting for material movements;
   (h) being able to price all material in stock.

10. The purchasing function is headed by a chief buyer or chief purchasing officer, who will need to be able correctly to identify material needs and suitable sources of supply, and ensure that the required materials arrive on time.

11. Decisions will need to be made about whether to buy on contract, to buy as needed, or to buy speculatively.

12. Purchasing documents (see Figures 15.3, 15.4, 15.5 and 15.6) include: *purchase requisitions* sent by individual departments to stores and onward to the buyer; *official orders (purchase orders)* sent by the manufacturing organisation to its suppliers asking for materials to be supplied; and *goods received notes*, completed in the goods inwards department for each delivery of materials to the organisation.

13. Any stock control system in use must take into account the immediate needs of production, the time taken for suppliers to deliver (lead time), the money available, and the costs of stock-holding.

14. The three basic methods of stock control are:
   (a) *The two-bin system*, where stock is either physically held in two containers (one main stock, one reserve stock), or the reserve stock is held in a special bag within the main stock area. As soon as the main stock is exhausted an order for replenishment stock is placed. This method can be used with multi-storage location systems.
   (b) *The periodic review and order system*, where all stock levels are reviewed at regular intervals, and orders are placed to bring stock levels up to a predetermined maximum level.
   (c) *Combinations of the two systems,* an example being where orders are placed at review times, but if demand exceeds the main stock before the next review, a further order is placed immediately.

15. Material control is an area where the 80–20 relationship is found to operate, that is, normally a relatively small proportion of the total lines in stock in a manufacturing organisation accounts for the greater portion of the stock value.

16. In material/stock control this phenomenon is often called the ABC of stock control. 'A' items, the smallest in number, but of high individual value, can be watched carefully and money spent in strict control of stocks. 'B' items can be re-ordered on the two-bin system, and 'C' items, while numerous, represent a small proportion of the total stock value and can be held in reasonable quantities to avoid shortages.

17. Costs of holding stocks include:
     (a) purchasing costs (the price paid);
     (b) cost of capital invested in stock (especially if the money is borrowed from banks);
     (c) warehousing/storage costs, including depreciation;
     (d) insurances;
     (e) administrative costs and charges;
     (f) price fluctuations (particularly downwards);
     (g) stock-outs.

18. An attempt to make ordering more scientific is the search for a simple formula to identify the optimum re-ordering quantity for any particular line. The economic order quantity (EOQ) can be calculated in various ways according to the assumptions made, but a popular version is:

$$EOQ = \sqrt{\frac{2C_1 Ur}{C_2}}$$

     where EOQ = economic order quantity
           C_1 = ordering/set-up costs
           Ur = usage rate per period (usually one year)
           C_2 = holding cost per item per period

19. Such a formula should be used with other considerations, for example suppliers' minimum order quantity restrictions, quantity discounts, or the possible obsolescence of the item.

20. Stock classification and coding systems (numerical or alpha-numerical) assist in variety reduction and standardisation.

21. In contrast, materials requirements planning (MRP) asserts that ordering policies should as far as possible equate with the needs of production, and the ordering of components follow that of the predicted output from the production function.

22. Stocktaking is (at least) an annual requirement, often six-monthly. Stock can be checked physically (against the records) in two ways:
     (a) *periodically* — the total stock is checked at one time;
     (b) *continuously* — a proportion of stock is checked each working day.
     The latter alternative is to be preferred, as it interferes little with production, and reasonably accurate figures of total stock values can be available *at any time*.

23. Stock can be valued as follows:
     (a) *Lot pricing* — stock is issued and valued at the price originally paid for it. Each lot is identified separately.
     (b) *First in, first out* (FIFO) — similar to (a), but stock is *assumed* to be used up in strict purchase order. Issues are valued at the price paid for the oldest

material in stock and the rest of the stock is valued at the prices paid subsequently.

(c) *Last in, first out* (LIFO) — issues to production are at the latest price paid; stock valuation is, as for FIFO, made using all the prices paid for stock in hand.

(d) *Replacement value* — stock issues are valued at the current market price, as is the total stock at valuation.

(e) *Weighted average* — a continuous average price is maintained, updated with each new receipt of stock.

(f) *Standard prices* — a predetermined unit stock value is used for a complete period (say one year). Both stock issues and total stock valuation are carried out on these figures.

24. In total stock valuation, an overriding rule is 'price at cost', however arrived at, or market (that is, resale) value, whichever is the lower.

Questions

Review questions

15.1 What functions other than the storage of goods come under materials control?

15.2 List the major classifications of materials. What is meant by:
(a) free issue material;
(b) consumable stores;
(c) returnable packages?

15.3 What is meant by the term 'buffer stock'? Why are buffer stocks necessary?

15.4 Why is it important to control the capital (money) spent on materials? List *three* other objectives of a materials control system.

15.5 Distinguish between buying *on contract*, buying *as needed* and buying *on spec*.

15.6 Why should internal purchase requisitions ideally go to the stores before being sent to the purchasing office?

15.7 What is a purchase order? What is its function?

15.8 What is meant by:
(a) overstocking;
(b) understocking?
Describe the effects of each on the organisation.

15.9 What *three* functions (other than the immediate needs of production) should any stock control system take into consideration?

15.10 Compare and contrast the two-bin and the periodic review and order systems of stock control.

15.11 Explain what is meant by the following terms:
(a) bin cards;
(b) multiple stores;
(c) maximum stock level;
(d) re-order level;
(e) minimum stock level;
(f) zero stock level?

15.12 What is meant by the ABC division of stocks? How does this type of classification affect the way in which stocks are managed?

15.13   List the major costs of material and stock control.
15.14   What does EOQ mean? State a formula for establishing it. What other functions need to be taken into account when re-ordering?
15.15   What is MRP? How does it differ from the EOQ approach?
15.16   Distinguish between periodic and continuous stocktaking.
15.17   Explain the difference between the FIFO and standard pricing methods of stock valuation.

Discussion topics

15.18   Either in groups or as a whole class, consider the following list of firms. Decide which are likely to have a large percentage of their capital tied up in stock, and which will have comparatively small stocks.
        (a)   dairy (bottling plant) serving 500 000 customers;
        (b)   jeans factory producing 40 000 pairs per week;
        (c)   goldsmith;
        (d)   jobbing plumber;
        (e)   steel stock-holders.
15.19   Ms Hubbard is stores manager at a local firm. Recently she told colleagues from other firms that she was the most efficient stores manager in the area: 'In seven years with the company, with 12 000 lines to look after, never once have I been out of stock.'
        Ms Hubbard claims to be an efficient stores manager. What does she believe is the major function of the stores? Is she correct?
15.20   Discuss the possible consequences of the following:
        (a)   a car assembly works running out of tyres;
        (b)   a failure to order new supplies of heating oil in mid-winter at the same works;
        (c)   a college delaying ordering textbooks until September;
        (d)   the wrong-sized paper being delivered for use with a firm's computer printout.

Assignments

15.21   In groups, examine the stores and work areas of the college machine shop or other suitable workshop. Classify the materials identified there under the following categories:
        (a)   raw materials;
        (b)   bought-out items;
        (c)   patterns;
        (d)   gauges;
        (e)   part-finished items;
        (f)   tools;
        (g)   consumable items;
        (h)   scrap.
15.22   Examine the purchase order procedure of the college, or any other organisation with which you are familiar. List the documents used (obtaining samples if possible) and chart the flow of information and goods. Note especially both the differences and the similarities between the procedures you examine and those outlined in this chapter.
15.23   By arrangement, visit the stores of a local company. Interview the stores manager about his or her work, and write a short report which should contain the following:
        (a)   the position and responsibilities of the job;

(b)   a comment on the relationship between high-value and low-value stocks —
whether an ABC breakdown or an 80–20 relationship exists;
(c)   the procedures used in ordering and re-ordering stocks;
(d)   how stocktaking is carried out.

Case study

15.24   Mr Ivor Plenty, stores controller of Mastermodel Truck Ltd (manufacturers of model
signals, points, track and line-side items), has become concerned about his stocks of
bought-in models. These models — made by other manufacturers — enable the firm to
offer a wide range of products. However, recent changes in the market — an increasing
demand for kits, rather than 'ready to run' models — have made stock control of these
bought-in, 'ready to run' models more important.
Using figures obtained from the last six months' demand totals from the stock control
cards, Mr Plenty identified the following monthly demand figures for wagons:

GWR 20 brake van	1 780
Perfection 7 plank wagon	1 521
BR hopper (with sand)	469
Timson 5 plank wagon	1 439
LMS brake van	506
Saxa salt	555
Private-owner wagons	819
Freightliner van	409
Cattle wagon	321
Twin silo wagon	50
45-tonne steel carrier	65
Track cleaning coach	631
BR bogie bolster	559
Smiths closed van	400
Other wagons (52 types with less than 20 per month demand)	620
	10 144

(a)   Using the information above, complete the following table, ranking the figures by
demand.

Wagon	Average monthly demand	Percentage of monthly demand	Cumulative percentage of monthly demand	Cumulative percentage of wagon types in stock
GWR brake	1780	17.5	17.5	1.5
Perfection	1521	15.0	32.5	3.0

(b)   Does the ABC rule apply here? What are the figures? Plot them on a graph.
(c)   What action should Mr Plenty take?

16
Quality Control

The aim of this chapter is to provide as direct an approach to quality control as possible, while retaining sufficient groundwork for the more mathematically inclined student. At the same time the authors are aware that the treatment of the subject may be rather wider than suggested by the wording of the BTEC objectives, but feel that it is justified by the importance of quality assurance.

16.1 Role of the quality control department

The word 'quality' can have various meanings, but essentially 'fitness for purpose' describes goods manufactured for sale to discerning customers, of whom there are many types.

The primary objective of any business concern is to make a profit, and, after all, people do not invest their savings in a concern which does not promise a reasonable rate of interest in return.

Here we have the two ends of the scale: the manufacturer needs to produce goods of reasonable quality at minimum cost in order to sell to customers who require satisfactory service from the goods at reasonable cost to themselves. Hence the role of the quality control or quality assurance department is to ensure that the goods produced meet both these needs.

While 'quality assurance' merely implies achieving the desired standard before dispatching to the customer, the term 'quality control' means to actually control the standard during manufacture in order to nullify the probability of sub-standard products. Methods of implementing such control without incurring the very high costs of 100 per cent inspection, in which every dimension or attribute of every component is compared with the required standard, vary from the use of binomial and Poisson distributions in connection with acceptance sampling to the use of normal distribution and standard deviation of observed results in the preparation of quality control charts, the basic tool of the itinerant or patrol inspector. (It should be noted that quality control charts may also be used to good effect by the process operator in order to supplement the work of the quality control department.)

The overall standard to which the department works is laid down initially by management decisions taken at director level: in setting up the company or deciding to manufacture a product, the directors have to assess the minimum quality the customer or the general market requires and set the manufacturing tolerances to meet, or just improve on, this minimum.

In addition, there are the general engineering standards required for 'interchangeability' of mating components in certain assemblies, ensuring correct operating clearances, since too generous or too tight a tolerance may lead to early failure of mechanical products.

It is thus apparent that manufacture to standards approaching 'dimensional' or 'finish' perfection is a very long and exacting series of processes requiring materials, operators and equipment of at least the minimum, but preferably of higher, standard.

The end result of achieving such high standards is that the cost of the goods escalates to the point where customers are no longer interested, preferring to buy a product with a quality standard perhaps lower and more appropriate to their needs, at less expense.

16.2 Internal organisation of a quality control department

There must be a chief inspector or chief quality control engineer to co-ordinate and delegate, and be ultimately responsible for the activities of the department. He or she will be responsible to the board of directors, either directly or indirectly, depending on the nature of the business concerned; for example, in the aircraft industry the former arrangement is a requirement of the approving body.

In general, inspection of products should be impartial, accepting or rejecting goods simply on the basis of comparison with specified standards, without the added influence of production or sales targets. Thus the organisation of the department would be directed towards such achievements, with as little scope for interference as possible. To this end much of the work of the department is concerned more with preventing sub-standard products than with merely rejecting them.

The area in which the department can make a significant contribution to maintenance of a good standard of production is vast, but some specific services, each of which will have a senior inspector or quality control engineer in charge, are the inspection of the following.

Raw materials and bought-out components

Inspection or quality control commences with the arrival of raw materials and bought-out components at the stores, since, irrespective of the origin of these goods, the user becomes responsible for them as far as the customers are concerned. It may be that the suppliers themselves are approved firms, but this does not absolve the user from responsibility for a product which incorporates such materials. It may therefore be necessary for raw materials, etc. to be placed into 'quarantine' until approved for use by the quality control department.

The inspection of raw materials would consist of inspection for damage and corrosion followed by a test schedule carried out on a representative specimen from the batch to establish that its physical properties are satisfactory, and here the services of a metallurgical test laboratory would be enlisted. These safeguards are necessary to prevent abortive work on unsatisfactory materials.

Bought-out finished components would be inspected for dimensional accuracy, correct material, finish and damage in transit; the method of inspection, which would depend on quantities involved, may be 100 per cent inspection for small numbers of highly expensive goods or acceptance sampling for a large number of cheaper items.

When considered satisfactory, the batches of raw material or finished parts would be transferred to their respective stores for general production use.

Standard measuring equipment (metrology)

The maintenance in good condition of all standard measuring equipment used by both the quality control department and the toolroom is obviously a prime need in any manufacturing company, since the quality of the product will be affected by inaccurate dimensions. The standards section function is to check and arrange for correction of such equipment.

Manufacturing tools and fixtures

These aids to production may be bought-out or may be manufactured in the company's own toolroom (in-house manufacture). As with the standard measuring equipment, the accuracy of manufacturing tools and fixtures is of paramount importance, since it is from these that the product will be fashioned, and any error here will lead to costly scrap.

After checking the tools against the jig and tool design drawings, the usual procedure is to manufacture a few items using the tools to ascertain that they are within limits and that the tool functions correctly and does not damage the surface of the material.

In-process work

There are three methods of inspecting such work. The components may be inspected at the completion of an operation on a batch by *100 per cent* inspection (that is, each component is inspected), which is expensive and time-consuming, or they may be inspected on a random sampling basis. If the batch is small the 100 per cent inspection may be feasible; if it is large, inspection by *random sampling method* means choosing an acceptance quality level as a basis for accepting the whole batch and passing some out-of-limit work through to the next operation.

These inspections are usually carried out at a central point or fenced-off inspection area which allows for greater specialisation of staff, concentration of measuring equipment, closer control of inspection standards and an atmosphere which assists staff to concentrate on their exacting task.

Against such conditions must be weighed the fact that when the batch reaches the area, either the components are all within limits or some are not, and these may be scrapped, leaving the batch short for the next operation.

The third method of inspection is *floor inspection*. This method requires a patrol inspector, who will inspect the first-off from a batch process and allow it to run if satisfactory. Such inspectors move around the workshop to a regular timetable, stopping at machines where a batch of components is being dealt with after gaining first-off approval. A sample (perhaps five) of recently machined items from a batch is selected and a particular dimension is checked and averaged; this value and the range of variation across that sample are recorded, with the time, on a quality control chart on which previously calculated control limits have been placed. From the regular time-based plotting of such values the tendency for the process to produce dimensions outside the control limits can be observed and the time of occurrence can be estimated. Thus the process can be halted before the event and reset to keep it under control and avoid the production of scrap components.

One advantage of such a system is that the inspector may be able to identify the reasons why the process is wandering; a second advantage is that the batches do not have to be moved to a central point in order to be inspected, thus avoiding production delays.

A modification to this third method is gaining emphasis in many large companies: encouraging and training operators to check their own work. Such encouragement fosters pride in their work; it also relieves the monotony, develops a 'right first time' attitude which reduces scrap and rectification work, and incidentally cuts down inspection department workloads.

Final inspection

Such an inspection is carried out after the process has been completed, perhaps prior to assembly in the same factory. Since there will have been some kind of quality control on the preceding operations, the final inspection really serves as a check that the quality control system is working correctly. The decision about whether a final inspection is necessary depends on the cost of making it compared with the cost incurred in allowing defective work to pass to the customer. Sometimes 100 per cent inspection is the only answer, since defective work may impair the safety of the assembly of which the component is a part.

Where the component is assembled in the factory, the act of fitting the component and testing the assembly may well be the final inspection, but again this depends on the relative costs.

Another interpretation of final inspection is where the process consists of a sequence of simple operations and intermediate inspections would incur costs out of proportion to throwing away an offending part at final inspection.

16.3 Importance of co-ordination of expertise in the pursuit of 'zero defects' or 'right first time' philosophy

Analysis of Figure 16.1 shows that, however excellent the preventive measures may be, some costs are incurred as a result of any kind of inspection, whether by the operator or by a patrol inspector. As may be anticipated, the less spent on prevention, the more likely is the difficulty of producing components to close tolerances, with attendant scrap (if under size) and rework (if over size). It is true that the figure perhaps shows a pessimistic cost assessment of wide-tolerance working, since some components may be quite acceptable at such standards, but it does indicate the increased inspection care required when equipment, operators or materials are not of first-class quality. On the other hand, close-tolerance working would be impossible without such qualities, since, even in the best quality circumstances, the attainment of 'zero defects' is not easy and depends very much on operator skill and motivation, apart from the advantages inherent in first-class equipment.

The slogans 'zero defects', and 'right first time' may be described as a motivational technique of quality control, based on the premise that defects, like accidents, are

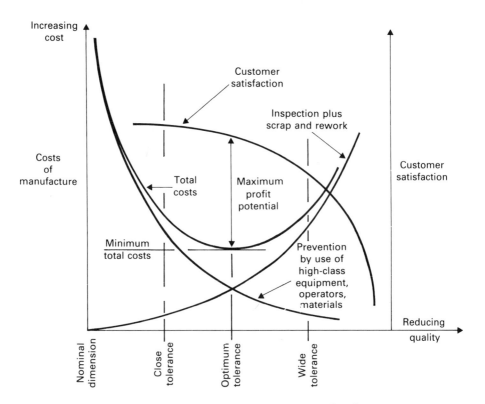

Figure 16.1 *Influence of quality on cost and profit.*

caused, rather than merely occurring at random. Thus elimination of operator error would go some way towards 'no scrap/no rework' ideals, with a lessening of inspection involvement. The implementation of the technique would seem to depend on sufficient mutual confidence between operator and management in order to practise an open-minded approach, and a willingness to co-operate, adopting improvements on the basis of worth rather than origin. It may be that this type of approach would give the best returns in 'semi-skilled operator' processes, since it must be assumed that the highly skilled operator always work to 'zero defects' standards.

However, such an ideal cannot be achieved without the co-operation of the person doing the job. He or she must be motivated towards the standard by the management choice of a satisfactory method of manufacture, provision of equipment and materials capable of the precision required, and provision of detailed and adequate training coupled with clear-cut instructions about operation sequence.

It follows that these requirements are the very least that management should satisfy. In addition the operator must receive some financial reward, as well as the experience of pleasure gained from faultless work, in return for adherence to any cost-reducing procedures.

Obviously the need for inspection is much reduced by the use of a well planned and well executed production system and, the operators having been trained and motivated to a high degree, much advantage would be lost without prompt feedback of information regarding their work from the patrol inspector. Better still, the training of operators to carry out their own inspection, with suitable equipment and time allowances, and paying them to accept such responsibility, would further improve motivation and reduce patrol-inspector involvement, cutting down production time and costs.

There is, however, a drawback to the system in that information about behaviour of the process must be available in the form of feedback to interested parties, such as design, production control, quality control, jig and tool, process planning/work study departments, for updating their knowledge and possibly influencing future work. This means that the operators would have to keep some sort of record of dimensions or percentage defective and tool-resetting operations by means of a quality control chart which would then be available to those who need the information. Again, the operators would have to be allowed the time to record events and inspection results on as simple and straightforward a chart as possible. Such a feedback system would be part of an open-loop control system where the operators, the patrol inspector or representatives of the interested departments may well implement changes or improvements in the process.

Feedback in an automatic process forms part of a closed-loop system in which sensors detect tendencies for 'out-of-tolerance' work to be produced. The signals produced by the sensors, when amplified, may be used to give warning and if necessary to shut down the process or make adjustments in order to maintain the required standard of output.

Some companies are finding that the implementation of production systems with a smaller patrol inspector/operator ratio can result in considerable improvement in both component quality and staff involvement in the company's success. To this end, the introduction of quality circles, in which frank and objective discussion relating to the manufacture of a particular component, involving all contributing parties from designer to operator, in search of the most efficient form, is seen by many engineering businesses as a necessary adjunct to improved product performance, greater customer satisfaction and enhanced sales and profit. The quality circle tends to strengthen the quality assurance of products by virtue of the demolition of the traditional barriers between quality of design and quality of conformance to that design, for in spite of how well made the poor design may be, and the converse, the success of any company depends on customer goodwill.

16.4 Use of acceptance sampling schemes

As indicated in the earlier sections of this chapter, the use of sampling schemes is widespread in the quality assurance function. Although 100 per cent inspection, (i.e. all products inspected) would appear to be a more positive method of ensuring that quality standards are met, this is not necessarily the case, since the method relies on the infallibility of the inspector during repeated and fatiguing checking operations. On the other hand, the use of sampling schemes does not appear to be a sufficiently responsible approach to the business of producing goods to a standard of reliability and fitness for purpose such as to interest existing and, more importantly, new customers.

Basis of a sampling scheme

Perhaps this is most easily understood in connection with bought-out components and the need to ensure that the quality is of the required standard. A sample of the components is removed from the incoming batch and subjected to 100 per cent inspection. On the results of this inspection the whole batch is accepted or rejected. The sample size is critical: if it is too small the results will be misleading; if too large, the expense of checking the sample will be excessive.

   The sampling schemes are based on the binomial distribution for very small sample sizes (n) and on the Poisson distribution for the larger samples. From these distributions can be plotted curves of probability of a certain number of defective components appearing in a sample taken from lots or batches of components containing a range of 'per cent defective' items. These curves are called operating characteristic curves, and are described later.

Types of acceptance sampling scheme

Acceptance sampling may be based on inspection by attributes, which means that each unit of product inspected is classified as either acceptable or defective, and the system does not depend on the degree of acceptability or the degree of defectiveness; or may be based on inspection by variables, which does take degree into account. The former inspection is made by the use of 'go/no go' gauges and is a relatively simple, unskilled inspection method; the latter inspection is usually more elaborate, requiring a high degree of inspection skill (use of micrometer and Vernier scales), and gives more precise information on how well the product is made. Inspection by attributes (BS 6001:1972) is most commonly used in acceptance sampling schemes, all of which are based on an acceptable quality level (AQL), a sample size which itself is based on the lot/batch size and a level of inspection (which merely relates batch and sample sizes). A further safeguard for the user is the availability of three standards of inspection, reduced, normal or tightened, each of which may be applied, depending on the standard of the supplier's 'process average' percentage defective among the incoming goods.

Single sampling.   This consists of taking only one sample from a lot or batch in accordance with Table I (sample size code letters) and one of Tables IIA, B or C (BS 6001:1972), subjecting the sample to 100 per cent inspection and accepting or rejecting the lot or batch as recommended, e.g. AQL = 0.065 per cent, batch size 3500, level of inspection II gives a sample size of 200 for 'normal' inspection (Table IIA) and acceptance if no defectives are found, rejection if one defective or more is found. For 'tightened' inspection (Table IIB) the sample size increases to 315 with the same acceptance/rejection values, while for 'reduced' inspection (Table IIC) the sample size reduces to 80, also with the same acceptance/rejection values; or, if AQL = 1.0 per cent, batch size 3500, level of inspection II, this gives sample size 200 for 'normal' inspection (Table IIA) and acceptance if five defectives or fewer are found, rejection if six or more are found; for 'tightened' inspection (Table IIB) this gives sample size 200 and acceptance if three or fewer defectives are found, rejection if four or more are found; for 'reduced' inspection (Table IIC), this gives sample size 80 and acceptance if two or fewer defectives are found, rejection if three or more are found.

Double sampling.   This is similar to single sampling but the first sample taken is smaller than would be taken for single sampling and if the quality is sufficiently good or bad the batch would be accepted or rejected as appropriate. But if intermediate results are obtained a second sample is taken: e.g. AQL = 1.0 per cent, batch 3500, level of inspection II gives for normal inspection (from Table IIIA) a sample size of 125 for the first sample and acceptance if there are two or fewer defectives, rejection if five or more are defective, and a sample size of 125 for the second sample suggests acceptance if there are six or fewer defectives (sum of both samples) and rejection if there are seven or more defectives (sum of both samples); for tightened inspection (from Table IIIB) this gives a sample size of 125 for the first sample and acceptance if one or fewer is defective, rejection if four or more are defective, and a sample size of 125 for the second sample suggests acceptance if a total of four or fewer are defective (sum of both samples), rejection if five or more are defective (sum of both samples). Reduced inspection values may be obtained from Table IIIC.

Multiple sampling.   This follows the same pattern as double sampling, and tables for up to seven samples are given in BS 6001:1972, Tables 1VA, B and C. Subjecting our example to multiple sampling we find: AQL 1.0 per cent, batch size 3500, level of inspection II, for normal inspection (sample code letter L, from Table I BS 6001:1972), as in Table 16.1.

Table 16.1

Sample	Sample size	Cumulative sample size	Accept quantity	Reject quantity
1	50	50	*a*	4
2	50	100	1	5
3	50	150	2	6
4	50	200	3	7
5	50	250	5	8
6	50	300	7	9
7	50	350	9	10

a Acceptance is not permitted at this sample size. Note also that the accept/reject quantities are totals of defectives in all samples to that point, e.g. 'Accept quantity 5 defectives and reject quantity 8 defectives' applies after five consecutive samples of 50 each, and simply means that, if the total defectives are five or fewer, accept the batch, if total defectives are eight or more, reject the batch, and if total defectives are six or seven, subject another sample of 50 to 100 per cent inspection.

Sequential sampling. This requires no fixed sample size and relies on a continuous sampling process with the results (accept/reject) being summed algebraically and a decision to accept or reject the whole batch being taken upon certain limiting totals being attained.

These totals are derived from a formula:

Score or total = (Handicap + Number of acceptable units) − (Penalty × Number of defectives)

The bases of decision are

(a) accept batch when total = 2 × 'handicap';
(b) reject batch when total = 0 or becomes negative;
(c) if maximum sample size is reached with no basis for a decision then reference should be made to the corresponding 'multiple' plan table to determine acceptance or rejection.

Sequential sampling is not available either for reduced inspection or for AQL values greater than 10 per cent.

Values of H, handicap, and b, penalty, can be found in Tables IA and B of BS 6001:1972.

Example. A batch of components, 5000 in number and of AQL = 0.25 per cent, is subjected to sequential sampling at general inspection level II and tightened inspection, with the following results.

From Table I, sample size code letter for 5000 batch at general inspection level II is L and from Table IB, sequential sampling plans for tightened inspection give maximum sample size 560 components, the handicap value, $H = 216$, and the penalty value, $b = 215$.

The results of inspection by sequential sampling are shown in Table 16.2.

Table 16.2

Component number	Accepted	Rejected	Individual score	Cumulative score
1 – 67	√		216 + 67	283
68		√	−(215 × 1)	68
69 – 253	√		+ 185	253
254		√	−(215 × 1)	38

Since there are only 560 − 254 more sample components to be checked, then the best result possible is 38 + 306 = 344, i.e. less than $2H = 432$, yet rejection cannot be made since the total is not yet zero or negative. Hence, resorting to the 'multiple sampling plan' for this batch, we find from Table IVB that there is no sampling plan for code letter L at AQL = 0.25 per cent and we have to use sampling plan appropriate to code letter M, which gives the results shown in Table 16.3.

Table 16.3

Sample	Sample size	Cumulative sample size	Accept quantity	Reject quantity
1st	80	80	*a*	2
2nd	80	160	*a*	2
3rd	80	240 (254)	0	2
4th	80		0	3
5th	80	320	1	3
6th	80	400	1	3
7th	80	480 560	2	3

a See Table 16.1.

In the sequential sampling inspection we have reached the equivalent of the fourth sample of 80 components in the multiple sampling plan, and at the 14th component our total number of rejects is two. The batch cannot be accepted because we have more than zero defectives, but also it cannot be rejected unless we find one more defective by the time we reach a cumulative sample size of 320, 400, 480 or 560; if we do not have a total of more than two defectives when we reach 560 components, then the batch can be accepted.

The validity of sampling schemes

This depends on what is known as an acceptable quality level, or AQL, defined in BS 4778 (*BSI Handbook 22*, 1981) as the maximum per cent defective (or the maximum number of defects per 100 units) that, for the purposes of acceptance sampling, can be considered satisfactory as a 'process average', that is, the supplier's production process. The following is an extract from BS 4778 entitled 'Concept of acceptable quality level (AQL)':

> when a consumer designates some specific value of AQL for a certain characteristic or group of characteristics, he indicates to the supplier that his (the consumer's) acceptance sampling plan will accept the great majority of the lots the supplier submits, provided that the 'process average' level of per cent defective in these lots is no greater than the designated value of AQL.... It is necessary to refer to the operating characteristic curve of the sampling plan that the consumer will use ... to determine what protection the consumer will have (see BS 6000).

The best AQL is the one which costs the least when all implications have been considered and standard tables are available relating batch size, sample size and number of defects in each sample for acceptance/rejection decision to the chosen AQL.

Choice of an AQL depends on:

(a) the cost of inspection of a sample of an incoming batch of components;
(b) the actual value of the batch to be inspected;
(c) the cost of unsatisfactory or defective items reaching production lines.

From these considerations it follows that minimum overall cost is the overriding factor.

The AQL is therefore a supplier's standard and the supplier must ensure that the 'process average per cent defective' is less than the AQL. However, if it is much less than the AQL then the supplier is producing at too high a quality; if above the AQL, then there is the risk of excessive rejections of the products by the consumer.

The operating characteristic curve.   The curve for the operating characteristic is based on a sample size and the probability of obtaining c defectives in that sample which is taken from a batch containing p per cent defective items.

It may be based on the binomial distribution $(p + q)^n$ but, since the values of n are usually large, the Poisson distribution is used. For example, if the sample size $n = 100$ and $p = 1.0$ per cent, then the probability of finding up to $c = 2$ defectives in the sample is given by the Poisson distribution:

$$e^{-z} + \frac{ze^{-z}}{1!} + \frac{z^2e^{-z}}{2!} \quad \text{etc. where } z = np = \frac{100 \times 1}{100} = 1.0$$

$(P(c) = 0) \; (P(c) = 1) \; (P(c) = 2)$

$\therefore$ Probability of finding up to two defectives $= 0.36787 + 0.36787 + 0.18394$
$$= 0.91967$$
$$= 0.92$$

Similarly, for values of $p = 0$, $p = 0.5$ per cent, $p = 2.0$ per cent, $p = 3.0$ per cent, $p = 4.0$ per cent, $p = 5.0$ per cent, $p = 6.0$ per cent, the probabilities of finding up to two defectives are 1.0, 0.986, 0.677, 0.423, 0.238, 0.125 and 0.062.

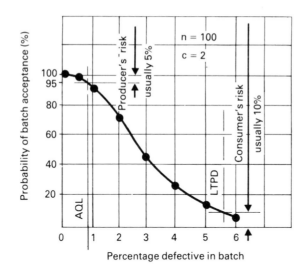

Figure 16.2 *Operating characteristic curve for* n = *100,* c = *2.*

Plotting these probabilities against a base of 'per cent defective in batch' and assuming that up to two defectives constitutes acceptance of the batch, we have an operating characteristic curve for $n = 100$, $c = 2$ (see Figure 16.2).

On analysing the curve we see that the probability of accepting the batch on the basis of discovering up to two defectives in a sample of 100 (rejecting it if more than two are found) diminishes quickly with an increase in the batch per cent defective. The shape of the curve can be varied by changing the value of n or c or both.

It is from such a curve and its variants that values for acceptable quality level (AQL) and lot tolerance per cent defective (LTPD) are decided and, with them, producer's risk and consumer's risk.

AQL is the level of defectives the producer or supplier has implicitly agreed with the customer to be acceptable. This level is often found by using the percentage defective in a batch as given by the 95 per cent probability level on the operating characteristic curve. In this case (for $n = 100$, $c = 2$) the percentage defective in a batch at 95 per cent probability level would be less than 1.0. If this is less than the supplier's 'process average (percentage defective)' then much of the supplier's work may be rejected.

The choice of the 95 per cent probability level implies that the producer is prepared to risk that 5 per cent of satisfactory batches are likely to be returned as unsatisfactory and requiring re-inspection.

The lot tolerance per cent defective (LTPD) is the level of defectives above which the consumer considers the batch to be definitely unsatisfactory. Although a greater number of defectives than the AQL, it is not to be assumed to replace it; the AQL is still the standard that the consumer expects. The LTPD is usually fixed at about the 10 per cent probability level on the operating characteristic curve, and in this case the per cent defective in batch is just over five.

The choice of the 10 per cent level implies that the consumer is prepared to risk that there is a 10 per cent probability that this quantity of per cent defective will reach the production line.

The lot tolerance per cent defective is defined in BS 4778 (*BSI Handbook 22*, 1981) as follows: 'limiting quality: In a sampling plan, the fraction defective that corresponds to a specified and relatively low probability of acceptance' (Note — when expressed as per cent defective, it may be referred to as "lot tolerance per cent defective").

So when the sample size n is very large then the binomial distribution is replaced by the Poisson distribution, or when p in (np), i.e. per cent defective in sample, is very small compared with q.

Average outgoing quality limit (AOQL).   The average outgoing quality (AOQ) is defined in BS 4778 as 'the fraction defective or the number of defects per 100 items of the products obtained after inspection, including not only lots accepted by the sampling plan, but also lots that have been rejected by the plan and have been given 100 per cent inspection and in which all defective items have been replaced by non-defective items'.

The average outgoing quality limit (AOQL) is also defined: 'for a given sampling plan, the maximum value of the average outgoing quality (AOQ) for all possible incoming fractions defective'.

It follows that the AOQL indicates the general standard of supplies the consumer is likely to receive as a result of the sampling plan used, since the ultimate outgoing (to the production line) components are a mixture of those accepted by the plan and those rejected and subsequently given 100 per cent inspection and, apparently, raised to '100 per cent effective' status. The curve of the operating characteristic shows the probability of acceptance of batches with various per cent defective contents and it is from such a curve that the curve of average outgoing quality is plotted and a limiting value computed. However, Tables VA and B of BS 6001:1972 provide factors appropriate to various acceptable quality levels (AQL), sample sizes and batch sizes and these factors are used to find the exact AOQL:

$$\text{AOQL} = \text{Factor from Table VA or B} \times \left(1 - \frac{\text{Sample size}}{\text{Lot or batch size}}\right)$$

For example, consider batch size 3500 with AQL 1.0 per cent, level of inspection II and normal inspection.

From Table I, the sample size code letter is L. Hence from Table VA the sample size is 200 and the AOQL factor is 1.6. Hence the exact AOQL value is:

$$1.6 \left(1 - \frac{200}{3500}\right) = 1.51 \text{ per cent}$$

16.5 Control charts

Control charts for the production of satisfactory goods may be prepared and used either on the basis of the variability of a particular dimension (inspection by variables), discovered by the regular sampling of components in production processes, or on the basis of the number of proportion defective (inspection by attributes), also discovered by regular sampling inspections. Variability of a dimension is ascertained by direct measurement against a scale and is generally preferred, in practice, to segregation by number/proportion defective, achieved by use of a limit gauge, since the former provides evidence of process variability relative to a specification, which is especially useful when seeking to remove a source of rejections from a process.

The procedure of substituting such charts for 100 per cent inspection is known as statistical quality control and has been developed from scientific analysis of the behaviour of manufacturing processes during the reasonably constant conditions prevailing when machines are correctly set up and properly supplied with necessary power, lubrication and, of course, properly trained and competent users.

To construct a chart for the control of a selected process its production characteristics have to be examined. From observations made, the frequency of occurrence over a particular period of time of either the variation in dimension or the number/proportion defective, when plotted against a base of size or number defective, as appropriate, produces a curve which approximates well to what is known as the normal (Gaussian) curve of frequency distribution, a mathematical derivation, as shown in Figure 16.3.

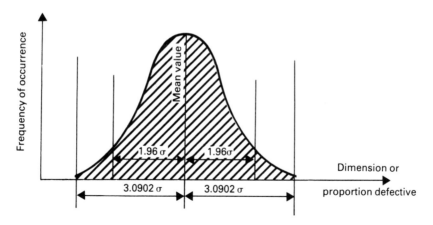

Figure 16.3 *Normal (Gaussian) curve of frequency distribution.*

Analysis of such a curve exposes interesting and useful properties relating to the area between the curve itself and the horizontal axis (shown hatched). This area — either (Frequency of occurrence × Dimensional value) or (Frequency of occurence × Number/proportion defective) — represents the complete sample population and is a good indication of the standard of the whole batch of components. If the standard deviation — the square root of the average of the square of the deviations (from the mean value) of all the observations — is calculated for the sample population and is then plotted on the diagram in multiples of 1.96 standard deviations and 3.0902 standard deviations each side of the mean value, the enclosed areas account for 95 per cent and 99.8 per cent respectively of the sample population.

Figure 16.3 therefore gives us a picture of the 'capability of this particular process' (i.e. process capability) and may be interpreted as being capable of producing goods such that 2.5 per cent will exceed 1.96 standard deviations from the mean value in a positive direction and 2.5 per cent in a negative direction, and similarly 0.1 per cent will exceed 3.0902 standard deviations from the mean value in a positive direction and 0.1 per cent in a negative direction, or more simply,

$$\frac{1}{40} \text{ (i.e. 2.5 per cent) or } \frac{1}{1000} \text{ (i.e. 0.1 per cent) respectively.}$$

We therefore see that, left to its own devices, the process produces 1 component in 40 of size greater or smaller than 1.96 standard deviations from the mean value and 1 component in 1000 of size greater or smaller than 3.0902 standard deviations from the mean value; and in a similar manner the number/proportion defective in each sample will vary.

This information can be plotted on a control chart as the limits of normal operation, and any departure of the process from this normal state becomes apparent with the plotting of results from successive samples. The chart is a continuous record of the process behaviour and must be updated regularly to be of maximum advantage to the user.

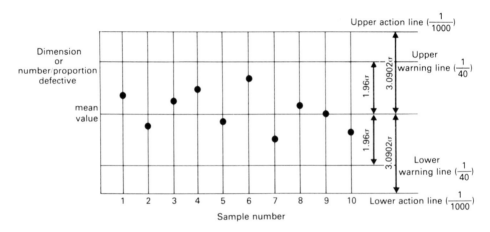

Figure 16.4

Figure 16.4 shows a control chart with the mean value and upper and lower warning and action lines spaced at 1.96 and 3.0902 standard deviations (as obtained from the normal distribution plot for the process) above and below the mean value. Also shown are plots of values obtained from a subsequent use of this process. A sample is usually regarded as being more than one component; often five is the minimum number when dealing with variables and close to 100 when dealing with attributes. The dimension plotted is the mean value of the individuals in the sample when controlling by dimension; when controlling by number/proportion defective, however, the actual number or proportion defective is plotted. It may seem strange to plot number/ proportion defective values less than the mean value, but it could highlight a breakdown in the inspection system which is allowing defectives to slip through.

Calculation of standard deviation (s.d.)

For variables:

$$\text{s.d.} = \sigma = \sqrt{\frac{\Sigma(x - \bar{x})^2}{N}}$$

where x is the individual dimension as measured, $\bar{x}$ is the mean value of all individual dimensions, and N is the total number of individuals measured.

For attributes plotted as 'percentage defective':

$$\text{s.d.} = \sqrt{\frac{\bar{p}(100 - \bar{p})}{n}}$$

where $\bar{p}$ is the mean percentage defective $= \dfrac{\text{Total defective}}{\text{Total inspected}} \times 100$ per cent, and n is the sample size.

For attributes plotted as 'fraction defective':

$$\text{s.d.} = \sqrt{\frac{p(1 - p)}{n}}$$

where p is the mean fraction defective $= \dfrac{\text{Total defective}}{\text{Total inspected}}$ and n is the sample size.

Note that the standard deviation for both percentage defective and fraction defective is obtained by reverting to the binomial distribution, and the *P*-chart, as the control chart for attributes is sometimes styled, retains the classic ± 1.96 (or ± 2) standard deviations for inner control limits and ± 3.0902 (or ± 3) standard deviations for outer control limits, which is a feature of normal or Gaussian distribution.

There is one further form of standard deviation used in calculating control limits for charts dealing with inspection by 'attributes'. The standard deviation of the Poisson distribution is used, again in conjunction with a mean value ± 1.96 and ± 3.0902 standard deviations to delineate inner and outer control limits, for 'number defective' in a sample. These charts are sometimes known as *C*-charts and the standard deviation in this case is given by:

$$\text{s.d.} = \sqrt{C\left(1 - \frac{C}{n}\right)}$$

where $C =$ the mean number defective per sample $= \dfrac{\text{Total defective}}{\text{Total number of samples}}$ and $n =$ constant sample size.

Interpretation of charts generally is such that manufacture may be suspected of being out of control when one point approaches or breaches the outer 'action' lines, or when two points in any consecutive ten approach or breach the inner 'warning' lines; specifically, interpretation should be made by a responsible person. Otherwise the system is operating within its process capability and can be said to be under control.

The foregoing is the basis of control chart construction and use, emanating as it does from process capability and its statistical interpretation based on the normal distribution curve and its characteristics.

However, in practice, we have to manufacture to a specification which usually stipulates tolerances which have to be met to ensure component interchangeability, etc.

Example: 'Percentage defective' control of process capability

Investigation of the capability of a certain process gave the results shown in Table 16.4.

Table 16.4

Sample number	Size of sample	Quantity defective	Percentage defective
1	100	10	10
2	105	9	8.57
3	110	9	8.18
4	98	8	8.16
5	110	11	10
6	112	11	9.82
7	120	11	9.17
8	95	7	7.37
9	99	9	9.09
10	104	10	9.62
11	110	12	10.91
12	96	8	8.33
	1259	115	

Construct a *P*-chart for the process, showing mean percentage defective, percentage defective per sample and inner and outer control limits.

$$\bar{p} = \text{Mean percentage defective} = \frac{\text{Total defective}}{\text{Total inspected}} \times 100 \text{ per cent}$$

$$= \frac{115 \times 100}{1259} = 9.134 \text{ per cent}$$

$$n = \text{Average sample size} = \frac{1259}{12} = 104.917$$

$\therefore$ Standard deviation = $\sqrt{\dfrac{9.134\ (100 - 9.134)}{104.917}}$ = 2.81 per cent

$\therefore$ Inner limit lines occur at $9.134 \pm 1.96 \times 2.81\% = 14.64\%$ and 3.63%

Outer limit lines occur at $9.134 \pm 3.0902 \times 2.81\% = 17.82\%$ and 0.45%

This is shown in Figure 16.5.

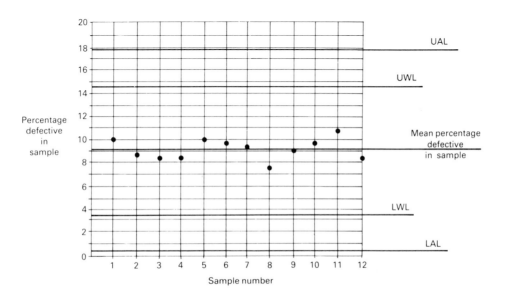

Figure 16.5 *Percentage defective: control of process capability.*

Example: 'number defective' control of process capability

The following results were obtained when a certain process was examined with a view to constructing a control chart for the number defective per sample of 100 components. Calculate and plot control limits and mean number defective per sample and also number defective per sample.

Sample number:	1	2	3	4	5	6	7	8	9	10
Quantity defective:	9	8	10	11	8	8	9	8	9	8

$$\text{Mean number defective per sample} = C = \frac{\text{Total number defective}}{\text{Total number of samples}}$$

$$= \frac{88}{10} = 8.8$$

$$\therefore \quad \text{Standard deviation} = \sqrt{8.8 \left(1 - \frac{8.8}{100}\right)} = 2.83$$

$$\therefore \quad \text{Inner control limits} = 8.8 \pm 1.96 \times 2.83 = 14.35 \text{ and } 3.25$$

$$\text{Outer control limits} = 8.8 \pm 3.0902 \times 2.83 = 17.54 \text{ and } 0.06$$

This is shown in Figure 16.6.

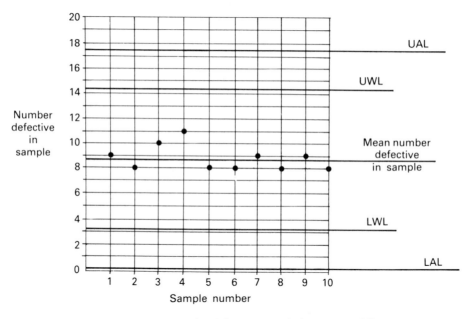

Figure 16.6 *Number defective: control of process capability.*

Control charts for variables (quantitative data) ($\bar{x}$ and w charts) when manufacturing to a specification

The capability of the process for which the control chart is required is investigated by making regular visits and selecting and measuring, for example, the last five items made just previous to the visit. Such items will provide evidence of the minimum variability to be expected in the batch. About ten such samples should be taken.

A recommended procedure is to record only the difference between the measurement taken and the lower drawing specification for that dimension.

From these measurements the average ($\bar{x}$), which is the sum of the readings taken divided by the number of readings, and also the range (w), the difference between the extreme readings, are calculated for each sample.

The ten values of sample average and range are then used to calculate the grand average ($\bar{X}$) and the mean range ($\bar{w}$).

Control charts both for sample average and range could now be drawn and control limits superimposed on them. However, before the control chart for sample average is drawn, the range chart should be constructed to ascertain that the range is under control. There are standard tables for the calculation of control chart limits for range (w) (Table 16.5).

Table 16.5

Sample size	For lower limits		For upper limits		For standard deviation
	$D'0.001$	$D'0.025$	$D'0.975$	$D'0.999$	d_n
2	0.00	0.04	2.81	4.12	1.13
3	0.04	0.18	2.17	2.99	1.69
4	0.10	0.29	1.93	2.58	2.06
5	0.16	0.37	1.81	2.36	2.33
6	0.21	0.42	1.72	2.22	2.53

To obtain limits for the range control chart, multiply $\bar{w}$ by the appropriate value of D'. To estimate standard deviation σ, divide $\bar{w}$ by the appropriate value of d_n.

Quite often the lower limits are not used.

If the addition of limits to the range chart shows tht one or more readings fall outside the uppermost limit, then the process is out of control and the calculation of limits for the sample average chart should be deferred until the process is brought under control.

The limits for the 'sample average' control chart are influenced by the relative precision index (RPI), which is the ratio:

$$\frac{\text{Total specification tolerance}}{\text{Average range}}$$

which relates the specification requirements and the process capability. There are three groups: low, medium and high (Table 16.6).

Table 16.6 *Relative precision index.*

Sample size	Low	Medium	High
2	< 6.0	6.0 to 7.0	> 7.0
3	< 4.0	4.0 to 5.0	> 5.0
4	< 3.0	3.0 to 4.0	> 4.0
5 and 6	< 2.5	2.5 to 3.5	> 3.5

For low and medium values of RPI the control chart limits of sample averages are set outwards from, usually, the dimension mid-way between the drawing limits, or perhaps the grand average ($\bar{X}$) of the process capability, if it permits production within the drawing limits, by amounts derived from multiplying the mean range ($\bar{w}$) by:

Sample size	Inner limit	Outer limit
2	1.23	1.94
3	0.67	1.05
4	0.48	0.75
5	0.38	0.59
6	0.32	0.50

For high values of RPI the control chart limits of sample averages are set inwards from the drawing limits by amounts derived from multiplying the average range ($\bar{w}$) by:

Sample size	Inner limit	Outer limit
2	1.51	0.80
3	1.16	0.77
4	1.02	0.75
5	0.95	0.73
6	0.90	0.71

The control chart limits are found by adding the amounts to the lower specification limit and subtracting from the upper specification limit.

Example (control charts for variables to a specification). Ten samples, each of five components, taken from a continuous process yielded the following dimensions (in millimetres):

Sample number						Range (w)	Sample average ($\bar{x}$)	Sample total
1	9.76	9.75	9.76	9.78	9.75	0.03	9.76	48.80
2	9.75	9.76	9.76	9.77	9.76	0.02	9.76	48.80
3	9.77	9.78	9.77	9.78	9.78	0.01	9.775	48.88
4	9.77	9.78	9.79	9.79	9.80	0.03	9.785	48.93
5	9.75	9.75	9.77	9.76	9.79	0.04	9.764	48.82
6	9.81	9.80	9.79	9.81	9.79	0.02	9.80	49.00
7	9.80	9.80	9.81	9.79	9.80	0.02	9.80	49.00
8	9.75	9.76	9.78	9.77	8.78	0.03	9.768	48.84
9	9.77	9.80	9.79	9.78	9.79	0.03	9.794	48.97
10	9.78	9.81	9.79	9.80	9.81	0.02	9.798	48.99
				Totals		0.25		489.03

Mean range $\bar{w} = 0.025$ mm
Grand average $\bar{X} = 9.7806$ mm

If the drawing limits are 9.78 ± 0.05 mm, construct sample average and range charts and on them plot inner and outer control limits to suit this drawing specification, the grand average ($\bar{X}$) and the samples mean ($\bar{x}$) for each sample (Figure 16.7).

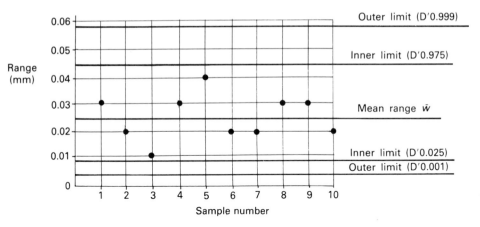

Figure 16.7 *Range chart.*

Sample size $n = 5$:

$$D'0.001 = 0.16 \times 0.025 = 0.004; \quad D'0.975 = 1.81 \times 0.025 = 0.04525$$
$$D'0.025 = 0.37 \times 0.025 = 0.00925; \quad D'0.999 = 2.36 \times 0.025 = 0.059$$

The range chart indicates that the process is under control; therefore the average chart can be drawn, taking account of the relative precision index:

$$\text{RPI} = \frac{\text{Total specification tolerance}}{\text{Average range}} = \frac{0.100 \text{ mm}}{0.025 \text{ mm}} = 4.0$$

Consulting the table we see that this value of RPI for $n = 5$ is regarded as a high value and so the control limits for the average chart are 'set in' from the upper and lower specification limits by:

$$\bar{w} \times 0.95 = 0.025 \times 0.95 = 0.02375 \text{ for inner limits}$$
$$\bar{w} \times 0.73 = 0.025 \times 0.73 = 0.01825 \text{ for outer limits}$$

Therefore control limits would be set at:

$$9.78 + 0.05 - 0.01825 = 9.81175 \text{ mm UAL}$$
$$9.78 + 0.05 - 0.02375 = 9.80625 \text{ mm UWL}$$
$$9.78 - 0.05 + 0.02375 = 9.75375 \text{ mm LWL}$$
$$9.78 - 0.05 + 0.01825 = 9.74825 \text{ mm LAL}$$

Therefore the average chart is as shown in Figure 16.8.

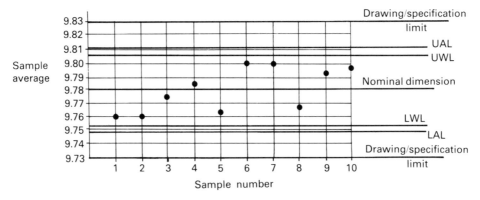

Figure 16.8

Note that the 'sample average' control limits are well within the drawing specification limits, which are for individual 'in bulk' components, and that this reserve should ensure satisfactory bulk production. The following is the result of treating the above example as individual readings and calculating the standard deviation (although not really an alternative treatment, since the 50 components should be spaced at regular intervals instead of being in ten regular samples of five each; however, it will give the student a grasp of the relationship between inherent process 'capability' controls and 'specification' controls).

$$\sigma = \sqrt{\frac{\Sigma(x - \bar{x})^2}{n}} \qquad \text{where } \bar{x} = 9.7806$$

Sample number	Values of $x - \bar{x}$				
1	−0.0206	−0.0306	−0.0206	−0.0006	−0.0306
2	−0.0306	−0.0206	−0.0206	−0.0106	−0.0206
3	−0.0106	−0.0006	−0.0106	−0.0006	−0.0006
4	−0.0106	−0.0006	+0.0094	+0.0094	+0.0194

5	−0.0306	−0.0306	−0.0106	−0.0206	+0.0094
6	+0.0294	+0.0194	+0.0094	+0.0294	+0.0094
7	+0.0194	+0.0194	+0.0294	+0.0094	+0.0194
8	−0.0306	−0.0206	−0.0006	−0.0106	−0.0006
9	−0.0106	+0.0194	+0.0094	−0.0006	+0.0094
10	−0.0206	+0.0294	+0.0094	+0.0194	+0.0294

Sample number			*Values of* $(x - \bar{x})^2$		
1	+0.00042436	+0.00093636	+0.00042436	+0.00000036	+0.00093636
2	+0.00093636	+0.00042436	+0.00042436	+0.00011236	+0.00042436
3	+0.00011236	+0.00000036	+0.00011236	+0.00000036	+0.00000036
4	+0.00011236	+0.00000036	+0.00008836	+0.00008836	+0.00037636
5	+0.00093636	+0.00093636	+0.00011236	+0.00042436	+0.00008836
6	+0.00086436	+0.00037636	+0.00008836	+0.00086436	+0.00008836
7	+0.00037636	+0.00037636	+0.00086436	+0.00008836	+0.00037636
8	+0.00093636	+0.00042436	+0.00000036	+0.00011236	+0.00000036
9	+0.00011236	+0.00037636	+0.00008836	+0.00000036	+0.00008836
10	+0.00042436	+0.00086436	+0.00008836	+0.00037636	+0.00086436
	+0.0052356	+0.0047156	+0.0022916	+0.0020676	+0.0032436

$$(x - \bar{x})^2 = 0.017554$$

$$\therefore \sigma = \sqrt{\frac{0.017554}{50}}$$

$$= 0.018737$$

$$1.96\,\sigma = 0.036724$$
$$3.0902\,\sigma = 0.057901$$
$$\text{IWL} = 9.7806 \pm 0.036724$$
$$\text{OAL} = 9.7806 \pm 0.057901$$

Therefore process capability control limits should be set at:

$$\text{UAL } 9.7806 + 0.057901 = 9.838501$$
$$\text{UWL } 9.7806 + 0.036724 = 9.817324$$
$$\text{LWL } 9.7806 - 0.036724 = 9.743876$$
$$\text{LAL } 9.7806 - 0.057901 = 9.722699$$

Control charts for attributes (qualitative data) when manufacturing to a specification

It is not usual for a specification to make an allowance for defectives in a batch of components, since the customer expects zero defects in the goods supplied. However, the manufacturer is aware that the processes used do not produce 100 per cent effective components continuously, and therefore strives to ensure that the proportion of defectives is kept within reasonable limits, weighing the cost of a few defectives against the cost of precise systems to prevent their production.

P-charts and *C*-charts are all very well in ensuring that the system is running normally, that it is in 'statistical control', but in order to make such charts defectives must be produced and, at best, such charts only indicate when there is a possibility that more defectives than usual are likely to be produced.

A method of artificially producing defectives, as opposed to rejects, is advocated in BS 2564:1955. This is achieved by reducing the tolerances on the limit gauges in order to produce a control chart which gives an early indication of impending increase in the number of 'defectives' relative to the tighter tolerance; however, this system is designed to ensure that such 'defectives' would not qualify as scrap or rejects.

Summary

1. 'Quality' basically means 'fitness for purpose'. Manufacturers need to produce goods of reasonable quality at lowest cost: customers require satisfactory service from goods at a reasonable cost to themselves.
2. The role of the quality control department is to ensure that goods meet both these requirements.
3. 'Quality assurance' implies just achieving a desired standard of product: 'quality control' means a positive effort to control quality throughout manufacture.
4. Final quality standards adopted are laid down by management, also taking into account generally accepted engineering standards and tolerances. Ideally, any standard should be just a little above that acceptable to customers: to make a product to a very high quality standard could price it out of the market.
5. A chief inspector or chief quality control engineer must co-ordinate, delegate and be in charge of quality control. Responsible ultimately to the board of directors, the executive in charge should aim for *impartial inspection* and *prevention* of the making of sub-standard products, rather than merely rejecting those made.
6. The quality control department will be responsible for inspecting:
   (a) raw materials and bought-out components;
   (b) standard measuring equipment;
   (c) manufacturing tools and fixtures;
   (d) work in progress, by 100 per cent inspection, or by a random sampling method, or floor inspection of 'first-offs' (workers are often encouraged to check their own work);
   (e) finished goods.
7. Inspection incurs costs, which increase when equipment, operators or materials are not of high quality. Even with high expenditure on prevention, and an excellent and co-operative workforce, the attainment of a 'zero defect' standard is difficult.
8. The motivation of the workforce, especially if they are not highly skilled, is an essential factor in zero defect/right first time. In addition to proper equipment

and adequate training, precise working instructions and some monetary award are essential in gaining workers' co-operation.

9. Whatever quality control system is adopted, it must include a facility for the controller (worker/supervisor/inspector) to report back to all interested parties — design, production control, quality control, process planning and work study as applicable — on any event which could affect quality and output.

10. Operators will need to keep records on dimensions, defect percentages, etc. by raising a quality control chart, and a time allowance for such recording will need to be made.

11. The introduction of quality circles, in which *all* those involved in production, from designer to operator, can participate, is seen as a way of improving quality, satisfying customers and thereby attracting increased profitable business.

12. The use of sampling schemes in quality control is widespread; 100 per cent inspection is repetitive and greatly demanding on inspectors, who are required to be infallible.

13. Such sampling schemes are based on either the binomial distribution (a very small sample size) or the Poisson distribution, from which can be plotted curves of probability — operating characteristic curves.

14. Sampling as a method of accepting production (acceptance sampling) can be based on considering *attributes* (e.g. a particular shape, size, thickness or colour) possessed or not possessed by a product. Typically such inspection is done with 'go/no go' gauges — a relatively simple, unskilled method. Alternative sampling can be related to the inspection of *variables* (characteristics based on a continuous scale, for example temperature or weight), a more sophisticated activity requiring a high degree of inspection skill.

15. Inspection by attributes is commonly used in acceptance sampling schemes; this is based on the idea of the acceptable quality level (AQL), that is, the greatest percentage of defective items which can be tolerated in a sample before a batch is rejected.

16. Three standards of inspection can be applied: reduced, normal or tightened.

17. *Single sampling* consists of taking one sample from a lot or batch, giving it 100 per cent inspection, and, by applying appropriate statistical guidance mentioned in British Standards, accepting or rejecting the lot or batch. *Double sampling* is similar, but where the first sample is near the borderline between accepting and rejecting, a second sample is taken.

18. *Multiple sampling* enlarges on double sampling, but emphasis is placed on the size of the *cumulative sample size*: the larger this becomes, the narrower the gap between acceptable and unacceptable quantities of defectives in a sample, thus the *area of indecision narrows*.

19. *Sequential sampling* is a continuous sampling process. Decisions to accept/reject a batch are taken on certain limiting totals being attained.

20. The choice of an AQL depends on inspection costs, the value of the batch inspected, and the costs of allowing unsatisfactory products to move further along the production process.

21. *Operating characteristic curves* can be drawn for each sampling plan. The possibilities of batch acceptance (*x* axis) are plotted against the percentage per batch found defective (*y* axis). The probability of a batch being accepted declines rapidly with increases in the percentage defective per batch. Such curves allow

AQL's to be extracted, as well as the lot tolerance per cent defective (LTPD) — the level of defectives above which the consumer considers the batch to be wholly unsatisfactory.

22. The *average outgoing quality limit* (AOQL) indicates the general standard of supplies a customer is likely to receive as a result of the sampling plan used.

$$\text{AOQL} = \text{Factor for BSS Table V, A or B} \times \left(1 - \frac{\text{Sample size}}{\text{Lot or batch size}}\right)$$

23. *Control charts* can be prepared for both variable and attribute inspection by sample. The procedure for substituting such charts for 100 per cent inspection is known as *statistical quality control* (SQC). The production characteristics of a selected process or machine, when plotted on a graph (x axis = frequency of variations of dimensions over a period of time from the mean; y axis the size or number defective), produce a curve similar to that known as normal or Gaussian. The diagram is a picture of the process capability.

24. The control chart can be built up with upper and lower limits (based on 1.96 and 3.0902 standard deviations). Departures from the average state become apparent with the continuous plotting of results.

25. For inspection by attributes, control charts based on the standard deviation of the Poisson distribution are used. When manufacturing to a specification a very tight set of tolerances can be used, to increase the number of 'defectives', which however would probably not all be rejected. It enables a fine degree of control to be exercised.

Questions

Review questions

16.1 What is meant by quality? What is the role of the quality control department?
16.2 What are final quality standards? Who lays them down?
16.3 Explain the role of the chief executive in the quality control department, and the responsibilities of the department.
16.4 How can a workforce be motivated to take part in 'zero defect' programmes?
16.5 What is meant by, and what is the purpose of, quality circles?
16.6 Why are 100 per cent inspection schemes not always used? What type of inspection schemes are used instead?
16.7 Distinguish between the inspection of attributes and the inspection of variables. What degree of skill is required by inspection teams involved in such inspections?
16.8 Explain the differences between single, double, multiple and sequential sampling.
16.9 What are the essential features and uses of operating characteristic curves?
16.10 What are AQL, AOQL and LTPD?
16.11 Describe a control chart. How is it constructed and used?

Discussion topics

16.12 Quality control can be expensive. Discuss the need for it when customers' complaints can be used both to identify quality deficiencies and to ascertain their frequency.

16.13 What is reliability? Discuss this in relation to a car, a dictionary, a set of mathematical tables, a skilled operator, a television set, a manned space probe.

Assignments

16.14 Investigate (using library and similar sources) the history and background of quality circles. In a short report indicate any difficulties the introduction of QCs into a company might bring.

16.15 Visit the quality control department of a production organisation. Write a report on the problems faced by the department and the inspection methods used, and try to obtain copies of the forms used to record results.

16.16 Construct a control chart for assignments or place tests undertaken by members of your course over the year. Plot the work of the class on the chart, and compare your own results with those of the class as a whole. (Note: test failures will of course equal defects, but warning-zone entries will also be important to note.)

Case study

16.17 Curdby Dairies Ltd is a modern dairy involved in the processing and packaging of liquid milk into bottles and cartons, with some milk sent out in churns, and about 5 per cent in special packs used in dispensing machines. The dairy also sells creams and yogurts wholesale.

The production system is essentially a flow process, with a throughput of over 30 000 litres per day, relying heavily on a computerised, automatic process to ensure quick and efficient handling of materials used. The quality control department are aware that if milk is not produced and processed under carefully controlled conditions, at best it will be rejected as sour, and at worst it will be a public health hazard.

As well as Milk Marketing Board central testing schemes, incoming milk is checked (samples taken from bulk tankers) for water content, sediments, fats and solids, and antibiotics, and producers are advised of milk below acceptable standards.

Samples are taken all along the production lines every day to get an indication of where problems might originate. Special attention is given to the cleanness of bottles and churns, and the amount of detergent getting into the finished milk. Water used in the dairy (from the mains) is checked regularly.

Cream samples are also tested regularly. Quality reports are prepared for management each month, and some customers also get copies.

(a) What are the major problems and constraints for the quality control department in their routine work?

(b) What are the possible implications of: (i) rejecting a large producer's milk; (ii) rejecting production samples; (iii) allowing production to send milk out for sale with a high water content?

(c) What differences are there (if any) between the quality control needs at the dairy, and, for example, an engineering company making components for the aircraft industry?

Index

Guidance to students

1. Entries in this index are in strict alphabetical order.
2. Where a theme or topic is referred to more than once, the references are in strict numerical page sequence, and separated by commas. The only exceptions to this rule are when a reference extends over two or more pages, in which case the inclusive page numbers are separated by a dash, e.g. 50–55, and when a figure (or figures) is/are involved, in which case(s) the figure(s) is/are separated by a semi-colon.
3. Subsidiary topics are listed under major themes, again in strict alphabetical order, though more significant topics can also be found listed separately in the general index.
4. All references relate solely to the material in chapter texts. Subsequent mentions in summaries, assignments or case studies are not included.